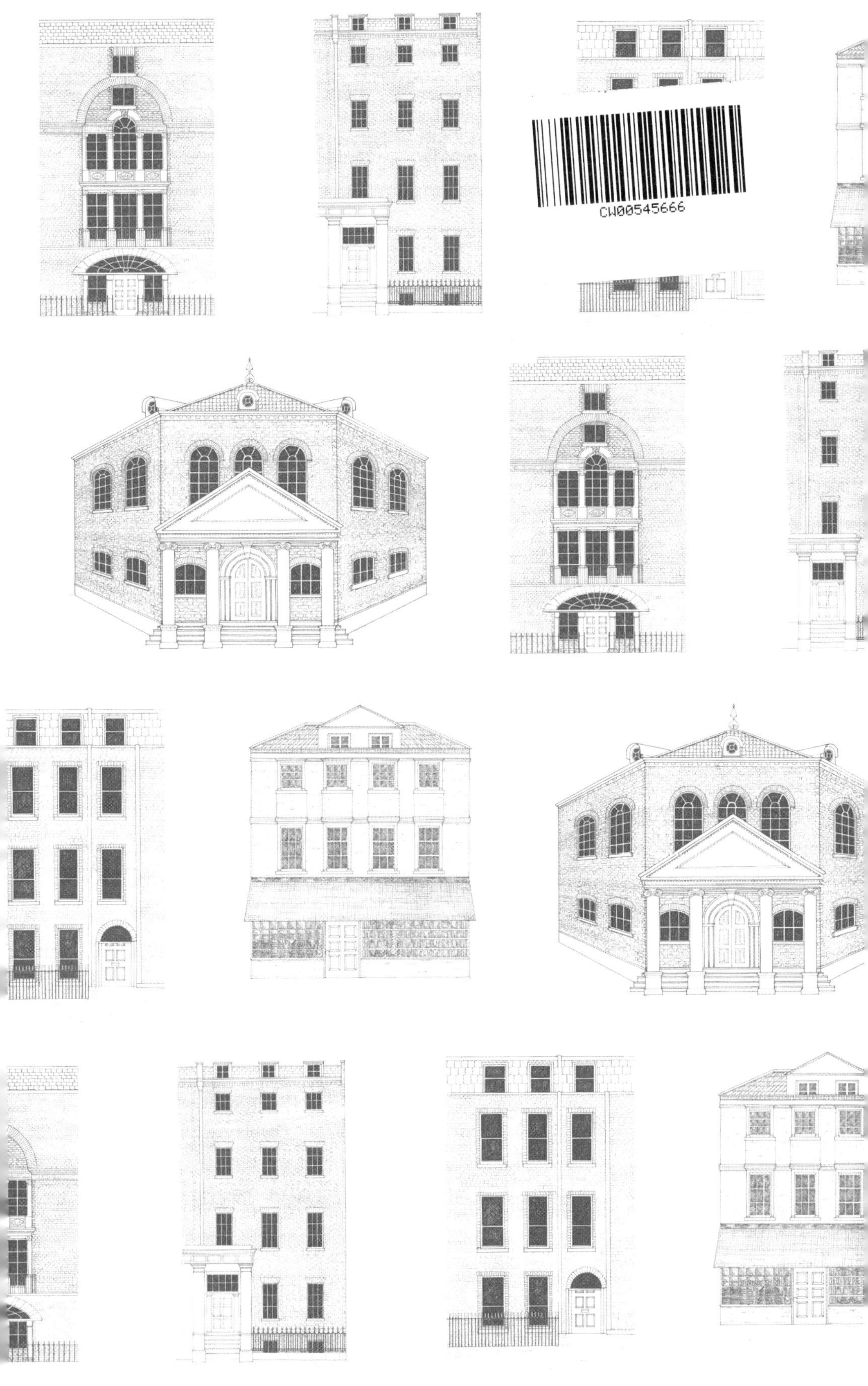

The LORD TREASURER *of* Botany

Sir James Edward Smith and the Linnaean Collections

Tom Kennett

The LORD TREASURER of Botany

Sir James Edward Smith and the Linnaean Collections

First published by The Linnean Society of London in 2016

The Linnean Society of London identifies Tom Kennett as the author of this work. Tom Kennett asserts his moral rights.

ISBN 978-0-9935510-0-0

British Library Cataloguing-in-Publication data:
A catalogue record for this book is available from the British Library.

Typesetting, indexing: Brian Clarke
Editing and production: Leonie Berwick
Cover Design: Heather Oliver
Original Illustrations: Helen Cowdy
Typeface: Book Antiqua *System*: QuarkXpress

Printed and bound in Italy by Graphicom
Printed on GardaMatt Art paper, age resistant, ECF and acid free.
Cartiere del Garda, an ISO 14001 certified and EMAS registered company, uses only cellulose coming from certified or well-managed forests and plantations.

The Linnean Society of London
Burlington House, Piccadilly
London W1J 0BF UK
www.linnean.org Charity Reference No. 220509

For Michael

CONTENTS

		Page
	Preface	ix
	Prologue	3
	Cast of Characters	9
	Timeline	13
Chapter One	Roots: The Early Life of James Edward Smith	19
Chapter Two	London: The Sale of the Century	53
Chapter Three	The Grand Tour	77
Chapter Four	Foundation of the Linnean Society	109
Chaper Five	Establishing Smith	131
Chapter Six	Academic Success	151
Chapter Seven	The Botanical Radical	173
Chapter Eight	The Bereaved and Betrothed	203
Chapter Nine	The *Floras*	229
Chaper Ten	Smith vs. Salisbury	251
Chapter Eleven	The Lord Treasurer of Botany	275
	Epilogue	307
	Notes	315
	Bibliography	351
	Acknowledgements	361
	Picture Credits	362
	Index	363

Illustrations

(Between pages 102 and 103)

Fig. 1 James Smith by Thomas Worlidge, c. 1764
Fig. 2 Frances Smith by Thomas Worlidge, c. 1764
Fig. 3 Norwich Market Place in 1788, by Thomas Rowlandson
Fig. 4 Medal awarded to Smith by Dr John Hope in 1782
Fig. 5 French fashions, c. 1792
Fig. 6 Sir Joseph Banks by Thomas Phillips, 1809
Fig. 7 James Edward Smith by A. L. Lane, c. 1789
Figs. 8 & 9 Linnaean collections
Fig. 10 *Smithia sensitiva* (Sensitive Smithia) from Richard Salisbury's *Paradisus Londinensis* (1805–1808)
Fig. 11 *Tradescantia discolor* (a synonym of *T. spathacea* Sw., or Boat lily) from Smith's *Icones Pictæ* (1790–1793)
Fig. 12 *Lathyrus palustris* L. (Marsh pea) from Smith & James Sowerby's *English Botany* (1790–1814)
Fig. 13 Smith's drawing of *Geum rivale* L. (Water avens)

(Between pages 262 and 263)

Fig. 14 'The Pantheon the morning after the fire' by JMW Turner, 1792
Fig. 15 'Gypsy' portrait of Pleasance Smith by John Opie
Fig. 16 James Edward Smith by John Rising, 1793
Fig. 17 Hafod, Cardiganshire, by John 'Warwick' Smith, 1810
Fig. 18 Ornate marginalia in a copy of Smith's *Flora Britannica* (1800–1804), held in the Society's collections
Fig. 19 Letter to Smith from Mariamne Johnes, 12 April 1796
Fig. 20 *Urbanus proteus* (Long-tailed skipper) and *Clitoria mariana* L. (Atlantic pigeonwings) from Smith and Abbot's *The Rarer Lepidopterous Insects of Georgia* (1797)
Fig. 21 Frontispiece of volume six of John Sibthorp's *Flora Græca* (1806–1837)
Fig. 22 *Dianthus fruticosus* L. (Wild carnation) from *Flora Græca* (1806–1837)
Fig. 23 *Passiflora indet.* (Passionflower) from Smith's herbarium (LINN-HS 1488.50)
Fig. 24 *Viola tricolor* L. (Heartsease) from Smith's herbarium (LINN-HS 1380.54.2)
Fig. 25 Bust of James Edward Smith by Francis Leggatt Chantrey, 1828
Fig. 26 Meeting Room of the Linnean Society, Burlington House

Preface

What a pleasure to see this biography of James Edward Smith, the founder and first president of the Linnean Society of London. And what an extraordinary person Smith was! As a young man, he became one of the most influential botanists in the British Isles by purchasing the world-renowned botanical collections of the great Swedish scholar Carl Linnaeus. Once these collections were transferred to England in 1784, not without some controversy, Smith used Linnaeus's herbarium and library to catapult himself onto the world's botanical stage. The countless herbarium specimens, books, manuscripts, and many of the other objects carefully accumulated by Linnaeus during his lifetime—all these left Sweden and came into Smith's personal possession. Smith was evidently very astute—or lucky—for at that point it was not at all certain that Linnaeus would become as famous as he eventually did, even though the Linnaean classification system had already proven to be useful and was deeply entwined with the continuing success of naturalists accompanying the great global explorations of the 18th century.

Perhaps some of Linnaeus's rise to lasting fame can be laid at Smith's door, for as Linnaeus's celebrity grew, so did Smith's. Linnaeus would become known to later generations of taxonomists as the founder of modern scientific nomenclature and to the wider public as the author of the "sexual" system of classification. By the end of his life Smith was one of the architects of an astonishing renaissance of botanical knowledge in Europe, knighted in 1814 by the Prince Regent (later George IV), the author of important botanical catalogues, a cosmopolitan traveller, entrepreneur, and an authoritative scientific expert at the centre of a remarkable network of botanical correspondents, and the gatekeeper to the treasures of Linnaeus. He founded the Linnean Society of London in 1788, becoming its first President, a post he held until his death. To me, there seems something in this energetic life story that parallels the life of that other great botanist of the era, Sir Joseph Banks, also the owner of vast collections of herbarium specimens, who became a scientific patron of exceptional power, vision, and talent. Smith was 16 years younger than Banks and outlasted him by eight years.

And yet Smith's achievement is relatively unknown. How could a young botanist aged only 25 purchase these significant collections and construct his future life around them? Tom Kennett's fascinating book maps all this and more. He gives us the first truly comprehensive study of Smith—one destined to update and replace the memoir by Smith's devoted wife, Pleasance, published in 1832, and significantly expand on Margot Walker's short treatment in 1988. This book tells Smith's story—and much of the story of botany in Britain at the end of the 18th century.

Janet Browne
Aramont Professor of the History of Science, Harvard University

The Lord Treasurer of Botany

A Note on Conventions

- Original punctuation and spelling have been retained, and all emphases are the correspondent's own.
- Sums of money have not been converted to modern equivalents.
- Plant names as used by Smith and his contemporaries have been retained, with current names, if superseded, placed in parentheses.

Prologue

On 10 January 1778, a shy, slight 18-year-old boy by the name of James Edward Smith could be found deep in the ditches of Norwich Castle, led astray by a book on botany. The day before he had acquired a copy of the second volume of *Outlines of the Natural History of Great Britain and Ireland* (1770), "a systematic arrangement and concise description of all the Animals, Vegetables, and Fossils" to be found in the British Isles. The second volume covered the plant kingdom. Written by John Berkenhout, a physician and naturalist, the work was designed for the "young Botanist" as "a pocket-companion in his botanical excursions", and was arranged according to the principles of the great Swedish physician and naturalist Carl Linnaeus.[1] Overnight, this small volume had inflamed Smith's childhood interest in plants into a desire for scientific knowledge and understanding of the plant kingdom. Impatient for the arrival of spring, he now made his way to the Castle to see what had survived the ravages of winter.

This young man was to become one of the most influential botanists in the British Isles. Only six years after that chilly day, in 1784, Smith outwitted and outbid the scientific community of Europe and Catherine the Great of Russia in the race to purchase the world-renowned collections of Carl Linnaeus. Twenty-six cases, stuffed to the brim with thousands of specimens of plants, insects, fish, books, manuscripts and letters, the result of a lifetime of pioneering study, left the University at Uppsala and came to London. While friends and natural historians from across the country congratulated him on the extraordinary acquisition, Smith devoted himself to study. He considered himself a trustee to the public, holding the "treasures only for the purpose of making them useful to the world and natural history in general", a promise he realised when, in 1788, he founded a new scientific society, devoted to the study of natural history in all its branches—the Linnean Society of London. Based in Smith's home in London, the Linnean Society became a centre of learning, with papers presented and published, specimens collected and a library formed, and at their heart, Linnaeus's collections, "a never failing resource [...] in every difficulty, as well as a fund of information not easily to be exhausted".[2] As Linnaeus's scientific ideas continued to spread across Britain and Europe, bolstered by the dynamism of the Society named in his honour, so Smith's own botanical renown increased. By the end of his life Smith had come to preside over a period of flourishing botanical endeavour, the author of many important scientific publications, an entrepreneur,

Carl Linnaeus (1707–1788), 'Prince of Botanists'.

cosmopolitan traveller and authoritative scientific expert, knighted by the Prince Regent and courted by botanists from as far away as America.

The story begins with Carl Linnaeus. Linnaeus was born in 1707 in Råshult, Sweden, the eldest son of a pastor. He trained as a physician, but his real passion was for plants. An exacting and systematic mind had led the young Swede to question the contemporary methods for plant classification, and in his publication *Systema Naturæ* (1735) he fully introduced his own scheme, which, because of its basis on the reproductive organs of plants, became known as the sexual system of classification.[3] Linnaeus divided the vegetable kingdom into 24 Classes, based on the number and arrangement of the stamens (the male organ), with each class then subdivided into Orders based on the number and arrangement of the pistils (the female organ). The 24th class was reserved for plants without visible flowers or seeds, such as mosses, ferns and lichens. Linnaeus had a vivid imagination, and to ease the understanding of his system anthropomorphised plant sexuality, characterising the stamens, styles and stigmas as husbands and wives, so plants in the *Monandria* Class were described as having "one husband in a marriage", *Diandria* as "two husbands in the same marriage", and so on, up to *Polyandria*, in which there were "twenty males or more in the same bed with the female".

Linnaeus was also committed to standardising the terminology and naming schemes used in botany. In 1751 with the publication of *Philosophia Botanica*, "the first textbook of descriptive systematic botany and botanical Latin", Linnaeus began to establish a style of technical descriptions with the intention of describing each part of a plant in a set order, in which precision and consistency were key. He refined this system over the course of his career, introducing terms such as *petalum*, *stamen*, *filamentum* and *anthera*.[4] In 1753, in his work *Species Plantarum*, he presented his new scheme for nomenclature—the binomial system, in which each plant has a unique Latin name formed of two parts, the genus and species. Prior to this, no set method existed for naming plants, and species were differentiated within their genera with short descriptive Latin phrases, known as polynomials. However, as further specimens were discovered, the descriptions grew in length, incorporating more and more identifying characteristics, making them difficult to remember and use in the field. Linnaeus evolved the idea of using genera with a unique single identifier; in essence, the species name. Thus the hoary plantain, formerly known as *Plantago foliis ovato-lanceolatus pubescentibus, spica cylindrica, scapo tereti* ('Plantain with pubescent ovate-lanceolate leaves, a cylindric spike and a terete scape'), became, in 1753, *Plantago media*.[5] Linnaeus is now regarded as the father of modern taxonomy and classification; of all of his innovations, his binomial system and his standardisation of language and terminology are his defining legacies.

The taxonomic simplicity and aesthetic appeal of Linnaeus's innovations led to them being widely adopted across Europe throughout the latter half of the 18th century. His methods were filtering through to the scientific community in Britain by the end of the 1750s. Philip Miller, superintendent of the Chelsea Physic Garden, was one of the first to implement the binomial system in the 1759 edition of his highly influential *Gardener's Dictionary*. The first English translations appeared around the same time, with Benjamin Stillingfleet's *Miscellaneous Tracts relating to Natural History, Husbandry, and Physick* (1759) and James Lee's *Introduction to Botany* (1760), though it was William Hudson's *Flora Anglica* (1762) that marked "the establishment of Linnaean principles of botany in England".[6] The same year saw its first introduction at British universities, with professors Thomas Martyn and John Hope teaching it at Cambridge and Edinburgh, respectively. There was a corresponding popular surge of interest in natural history, particularly botany, fed by a huge number of botanical and horticultural books that were published in the latter part of the 18th century, including herbals, floras, books on medical botany, letters on botany, gardening books, long poems on botanical themes and botanical drawing books.[7] It is estimated that from 1763 to 1800, in the years following the publication of *Flora Anglica*, about two and a half times as many floras appeared as from 1700 to 1762, a fact borne out in *The Critical Review*'s comment of 1763 that "Natural History, is now, by a kind of national establishment, become the favourite study of the time". Indeed, for a brief period following the accession of King George III in 1760, British society was headed by three enthusiastic botanists: Queen Charlotte, who received the gift of a herbarium from the King; Princess Augusta, mother of the King and *de facto* founder of the botanical gardens at Kew, and John Stuart, 3rd Earl of Bute, the King's chief minister, a botanical patron and important collector in his own right.[8]

After several years of declining health, Linnaeus died in Uppsala on 10 January 1778. By a curious coincidence, this was the very same day that James Edward Smith decided to scramble down into the castle ditches in search of plants. He soon spied a sprig of *Ulex europæus* (common gorse), his eyes drawn by the vivid yellow flowers already in bloom despite the winter chill. His examination, with "infinite delight", of this solitary specimen induced something of an epiphany, as Berkenhout's explanation of Linnaeus's system of classification blossomed in front of his eyes. In a flash of clarity, Smith "first comprehended the nature of systematic arrangement and the Linnaean principles".[9] The specimen was carefully collected and pressed, becoming one of the very first plants entered into a herbarium that would eventually grow to contain over 27,000 specimens. It is one of the few specimens to have a full date and location given.[10] It is curious to note that this plant also had a special association for Linnaeus, who, on visiting England in 1736 and seeing the banks of flowering gorse, was reported "to have fallen on his knees in a rapture of admiration at [...] the spectacle. He always lamented that he could hardly preserve the Furze alive through a Swedish winter, even in a green-house".[11]

Writing after Smith's death, his widow, Pleasance, commented on that fateful January day: "In an age of astrologic faith, such a coincidence would have excited superstitious reflections, and the polar star of the great northern philosopher might have been supposed to shed its dying influence on his young disciple".[12] Though he would not have heard of Linnaeus's death until many weeks, if not months, later, something had happened to Smith as he gazed at the gorse flower, ineluctably changing the course of his life. Initially destined to join his father in the textile industry, Smith instead resolved to commit his life to the study and dissemination of botany, guided by his "polar star" Linnaeus. An astute communicator and observer, even without the purchase of the collections it is likely that Smith would have achieved notice in the annals of botany; with the collections, however, he was able to accomplish something extraordinary, both in his publications—amongst which were the first illustrated works on the Australian flora and American insects—and the institution he founded, the Linnean Society of London, now the world's oldest biological society. Smith became one of the most eminent and successful botanists of his generation, playing an instrumental role in broadening the appeal of, and access to, the science. There were also many battles, not least to establish himself as a professional botanist at a time when scientific careers were almost non-existent outside of privileged circles. He remained committed to his principles, even at the cost of royal favour and academic honour. Never particularly modest, Linnaeus had styled himself 'Prince of Botanists'. In 1821, James Edward Smith received his own epithet from a German admirer, perfectly encapsulating this engaging figure who stood at the helm of Linnaean botany for over 40 years: "The Lord Treasurer of Botany".[13]

Cast of Characters

Johan Gustaf Acrel (1741–1801)	Swedish physician and the Linnaeus family's agent for the sale of the Linnaean collections in 1783–1784.
Sir Joseph Banks (1743–1820)	President of the Royal Society (1778–1820). Circumnavigated the globe with Captain Cook (1768–1771); his home at 32 Soho Square was an epicentre of British botany for over 40 years.
Robert Batty (1762–1849)	Smith's confidant and best friend from his time at the University of Edinburgh.
Francesco Borone (1769–1794)	'The Milanese lad'; engaged as Smith's valet during his 1786–1787 tour of Europe and accompanying him back to Britain.
Robert Brown (1773–1858)	Premier British botanist of 'the natural system'; appointed Linnean Society Librarian in 1805 and Sir Joseph Banks's librarian in 1810; discovered what was later named 'Brownian motion' in 1828.
Thomas William Coke (1754–1842)	Agricultural improver and MP for Norfolk for 25 years; a close friend of Smith's later life. Became 1st Earl of Leicester in 1837.
Edmund Davall (1763–1798)	English born botanist resident in Orbe, Switzerland; enjoyed a productive and intense correspondence with Smith.
Jonas Dryander (1748–1810)	Swedish student of Carl Linnaeus; became Sir Joseph Banks's librarian in 1782 and the first Linnean Society Librarian in 1788.

Samuel Goodenough (1743–1827)	Classical tutor, clergyman and botanist; co-founder of the Linnean Society in 1788 and first Treasurer. Became Dean of Rochester in 1802 and Bishop of Carlisle in 1808.
John Hope (1725–1786)	Professor of Botany at the University of Edinburgh from 1761; along with Thomas Martyn credited with being one of the first teachers of Linnaeus's system in the British Isles.
Thomas Johnes (1748–1816)	MP and agriculturalist; Smith was a frequent visitor to his 'picturesque' estate at Hafod in Cardiganshire, where he treated the spinal problems of Johnes's daughter, **Mariamne** (1784–1811), a precocious and gifted young naturalist.
Aylmer Bourke Lambert (1761–1842)	Gentleman botanist; an early Fellow of the Linnean Society, he was appointed vice-president in 1796.
Alexander Macleay (1767–1848)	Civil servant and entomologist; he was Secretary of the Linnean Society from 1798 to 1825, when he emigrated to New South Wales, Australia.
Thomas Marsham (1748–1819)	Civil servant and entomologist and co-founder of the Linnean Society in 1788, becoming the first Secretary before being appointed Treasurer in 1798.
Thomas Martyn (1735–1825)	Professor of Botany at Cambridge from 1762; along with John Hope credited with being one of the first teachers of Linnaeus's system in the British Isles.
William Roscoe (1753–1831)	MP, abolitionist, historian and patron of the arts; became a close friend of Smith's following their meeting in 1803.

Richard Salisbury [*formerly* Markham] (1761–1829)
Gentleman botanist and Edinburgh friend of Smith's; they later became inveterate enemies.

John Sibthorp (1758–1796)
Professor of Botany at Oxford from 1784; undertook two tours of the Levant in preparation for the monumental *Flora Græca* but died before completion.

James Smith (1727–1795)
A Norwich draper, and **Frances Smith** (1731–1820) [*née* Kindersley]; parents of James Edward Smith and seven other children.

Sir James Edward Smith (1759–1828)
Botanist; purchased the Linnaean Collections (1784); founded of the Linnean Society of London (1788); knighted (1814). In 1796 married **Pleasance Smith** [*née* Reeve] (1773–1877).

James Sowerby (1757–1822)
Natural history artist, botanist and mineralogist; collaborated with Smith on numerous botanical works from 1789 onwards.

Dawson Turner (1775–1858)
Banker and botanist living at Yarmouth; became a close friend of Smith's following his return to Norwich in 1796.

Mary Watson-Wentworth (c. 1735–1804)
Widow of Charles Watson-Wentworth, 2nd Marquess of Rockingham and twice Prime Minister, she developed extensive gardens at her home in Hillingdon in Middlesex and became a patron of Smith's.

Thomas Woodward (1744–1820)
Suffolk botanist and magistrate and one of Smith's early mentors; they maintained a close friendship for many years.

Timeline

23 May 1707: Carl Linnaeus born in Råshult, Sweden

1735: Publication of Carl Linnaeus's *Systema Naturæ* (introduction of sexual system of plant classification)

1751: Publication of Carl Linnaeus's *Philosophia Botanica* (the first textbook of descriptive systematic botany and botanical Latin)

1753: Publication of Carl Linnaeus's *Species Plantarum* (introduction of binomial nomenclature; now considered the starting point of modern botanical nomenclature)

1754: Joseph Black discovers carbon dioxide

1758: Publication of the 10th edition of Carl Linnaeus's *Systema Naturæ* (now considered the starting point of modern zoological nomenclature)

2 December 1759: James Edward Smith born in Norwich, England, eldest of eight children

1762: Publication of William Hudson's *Flora Anglica* (the first English flora arranged according to Linnaean principles)

1769–1771: Voyage of HMS *Endeavour* to observe the transit of Venus at Tahiti, captained by James Cook. The botanists for the expedition were Sir Joseph Banks and Daniel Solander

1771: Joseph Priestley isolates oxygen

1775: James Watt develops the first efficient steam engine

10 January 1778: Carl Linnaeus dies in Uppsala, Sweden

1781: William Herschel discovers the planet Uranus

1781–1783: Smith studies medicine at the University of Edinburgh

1783: Smith moves to London to continue his medical studies at William Hunter's anatomy school at Great Windmill Street and St Bartholomew's Hospital

1783–1784: Negotiations for Smith's purchase of the Linnaean collections; they arrive in London in October 1784

1785: Smith elected a Fellow of the Royal Society

1786–1787: Smith travels to Europe to gain an MD from Leiden University and follows this with a 'Grand Tour' of the continent, visiting France, Italy and Switzerland

1787: 'The First Fleet' sets sail for Australia to establish a penal colony at Botany Bay, under the advice of Sir Joseph Banks

18 March 1788: Smith founds the Linnean Society of London with Samuel Goodenough and Thomas Marsham. Smith is elected first President, and the Society is based at his home 12 Great Marlborough Street, London

1789: The French Revolution begins

1789: Smith begins lecturing in natural history from Great Marlborough Street

1789: Publication of Antoine Laurent de Jussieu's *Genera Plantarum* (successfully introduces a natural system of plant classification)

1789–1791: Smith publishes *Plantarum Icones Hactenus Ineditæ*, his first collaboration with James Sowerby

1790–1793: Smith publishes *Icones Pictæ Plantarum Rariorum*, the figures by James Sowerby

1790–1814: James Sowerby publishes *English Botany; or, Coloured Figures of British Plants*, the text by Smith

1791: First volume of *Transactions of the Linnean Society of London* published

1792: Smith publishes a new edition of Linnaeus's *Flora Lapponica*, using materials from the Linnaean Collection

1793: Smith publishes *A Specimen of the Botany of New Holland*, the first illustrated flora of Australia, the figures by James Sowerby

1793: Smith publishes *A Sketch of a Tour of the Continent, in the years 1786 and 1787*

1794–1797: Smith lectures on botany at Guy's Hospital, London

1795: Smith moves to Hammersmith; the Linnean Society moves to new premises at 10 Panton Square, London

1796: Edward Jenner develops the smallpox vaccine

1 March 1796: **Smith marries Pleasance Reeve of Lowestoft; the Linnaean minerals are auctioned in London on the same day. Smith and Pleasance move back to Norwich in November, taking up residence at 29 Surrey Street**

1797: **Smith publishes *The Natural History of the Rarer Lepidopterous Insects of Georgia*, based on drawings and materials provided by John Abbot, the first illustrated work on American insects**

1799: Foundation of the Royal Institution, London **(Smith later holds an annual course of lectures here)**

1799: William Smith produces the first geological map

1799–1828: **Smith commences work on John Sibthorp's *Flora Græca***

1802: **The Linnean Society receives its Royal Charter**

1800–1804: **Smith publishes the three-volume *Flora Britannica***

1805: **The Linnean Society moves to new premises at 9 Gerrard Street, London**

1807: **Smith publishes *An Introduction to Physiological and Systematical Botany*; the most popular of Smith's works, it went through eight editions**

1808–1819: **Smith contributes 3,291 botanical articles and 57 biographies of botanists to Abraham Rees's *Cyclopædia***

1813–1819: **Smith's ill-fated campaign to become Professor of Botany at Cambridge**

1814: James Edward Smith knighted by the Prince Regent

19 June 1820: Sir Joseph Banks dies at Spring Grove, Isleworth

1821: The Linnean Society moves into Sir Joseph Banks's old home at 32 Soho Square, London

1821: Smith publishes *A Grammar of Botany*

1827: Robert Brown observes what will later be named 'Brownian motion'

1824–1828: Smith publishes the four-volume *The English Flora*

17 March 1828: Sir James Edward Smith dies in Norwich

1829: Charles Lyell publishes *Principles of Geology*

1831: Robert Brown discovers the cell nucleus

1831–1836: Charles Darwin sails on HMS *Beagle*

1857: The Linnean Society moves to Burlington House, Piccadilly, London

1 July 1858: Joint presentation of Charles Darwin's and Alfred Russel Wallace's papers *On the Tendency of Species to form Varieties; and on the Perpetuation of Varieties and Species by Natural Means of Selection* read at a meeting of the Linnean Society of London, the first announcement of the theory of evolution by natural selection

1873: The Linnean Society moves across the courtyard to its current location in Burlington House, Piccadilly, London

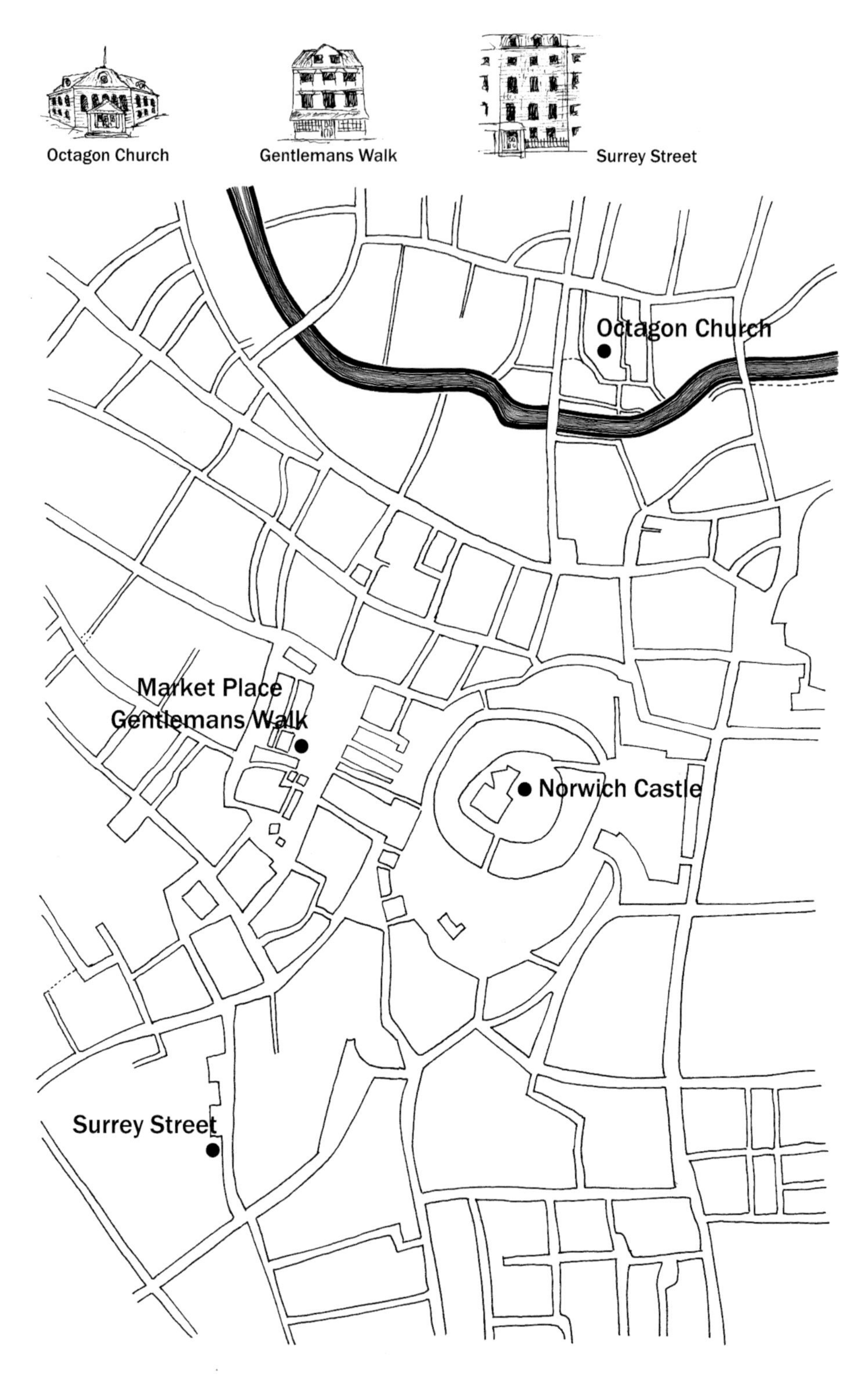

Map of Smith's Norwich.

CHAPTER ONE

Roots: The Early Life of James Edward Smith

James Edward Smith was born in Norwich, Norfolk, England, on 2 December 1759, the first of the eight children of James and Frances Smith.[1] James Edward's father (referred to hereafter as James Snr) was born in 1727, the only son of James and Esther Smith. Esther was 16 years older than her husband and already had two daughters, Hannah and Esther, from her previous marriage to Thomas Withers, which had ended with his death. She gave birth to James Snr at the age of 40, and died in 1757, two years before the birth of her first grandson. A seemingly prosperous family, James Snr's father was elected one of Norwich's two sheriffs for the year 1745.

Frances was born in 1731, the daughter of John Kindersley, an Anglican priest and domestic chaplain to the Countess of Leicester at Holkham Hall, Norfolk, and Sarah, *née* Raining, the daughter of a wealthy Dutch merchant, an elegant woman "considerably more accomplished than ladies of her day usually were".[2] Frances's grandfather, Nathaniel Kindersley, was a civil engineer who lost the family fortune overseeing projects to improve the navigation of the River Dee near Chester and drain the fens near King's Lynn, whilst his father, Geoffrey, was a close friend of writer Daniel Defoe and once sheltered him after an unfavourable reaction to one of his political writings.

By the time of his marriage to Frances in February 1759, James Snr had established himself as a successful woollen draper, operating in partnership with a William Smith (of no identified relation), at 37 Gentleman's Walk, located on the south side of Norwich's market place. James Edward

James Edward Smith (1759–1828), aged 3 years and 8 months.

followed 10 months later, and was baptised in the Presbyterian Octagon Chapel in Colegate, Norwich, on 13 December. For his first five years, he was the Smiths' only child, which, combined with his delicate health, forged a close and protective bond between parents and child. An etching of James Edward aged three years and eight months portrays a small, serious boy wearing a huge bow-topped hat. The original drawing, now lost, by Thomas Worlidge, was made around the same time as Worlidge's matching portraits of James and Frances Smith in 17th-century costume. James Snr looks directly at the viewer, his large brown eyes and strong nose giving an indication of his independent spirit, whilst Frances inclines her head away, the better to show her slender shoulders and long neck. The house at Gentleman's Walk was full of artwork, including a Virgin with the Infant Jesus and St John, which Smith later described as hanging "disgracefully on the staircase" – at one point James Edward believed it was an original by Raphael (its true provenance is unknown).[3]

In August 1764, a younger brother, Francis, joined James Edward, and the Smiths went on to have six more children: John Frederick in 1765;

Frances in 1767 (died 1775); Richard in 1768; Sarah Maria in 1770; Esther Anne in 1773; and Frances Julia in 1777.

The growing brood of Smith children grew up in an industrious and cultured household. James Snr had learnt French at a young age, which would have assisted in his dealings with foreign markets, and also read widely in both French and English for pleasure, working his way through around 20 books a year. According to his eldest son, James Snr was a "man of strong understanding" who possessed "inflexible integrity in all his mercantile transactions, and of moderation blended with generosity in his domestic regulations". Smith inherited a love of history from his father, and at the age of 11 he wrote a fictional history of Scotland, unfortunately now lost, in which two races of kings, along with their fashions, language and furniture, were described. James Edward's mother was a successful cultivator of flowers and it was through her that his interest in plants first developed. Many years later, Smith vividly recalled "tugging ineffectually with all my infant strength at the tough stalks of the Wild Succory [*Cichorium intybus*, chicory] on the chalky hillocks about Norwich, [since which time] I have found the study of Nature an increasing source of unalloyed pleasure".[4]

Life in Late 18th-Century Norwich

Norwich at this time was enjoying what became known as its 'gilded era', a century of prosperity beginning in the 1680s and brought to an end only by the crippling effect of the French Revolutionary and Napoleonic wars (1793–1815) on the city's textile exports. Though it had been surpassed as England's second city by Bristol in 1750, there was still enormous confidence and civic pride, particularly in its textiles, the staple industry and principal employer. From 1565, the city authorities had begun inviting Protestant refugees from the Spanish Netherlands to settle in the city, bringing with them their superior knowledge of weaving. These 'New Draperies' revitalised the industry in the 16th century, and by the late 17th century the principal production had in turn evolved into 'Norwich stuffs', making the city famous across Britain and Europe for the variety and quality of its worsteds. The city's population grew from 28,881 in 1693 to 36,169 in 1752. By 1783 it was claimed from the number of looms in the city that the industry employed 100,000 people in Norwich and beyond, including those who spun the yarn, trading to the value of £200,000 per annum. Indeed, as the author of the 1783 Norwich Directory stated, the "inhabitants are generally so employed in their manufactures within doors, that [Norwich] appears a melancholy place, except on Sundays and public days, when the streets swarm with them".[5] Norwich's prosperity was reflected in an impressive array of new public buildings that were constructed from the 1750s onwards, including the Octagon Chapel, a new Methodist Meeting House, Assembly Rooms, Theatre Royal and Artillery Barracks. The Norfolk and Norwich Hospital was built by public subscription in 1772.

The Smith family lived above James Snr's shop at 37 Gentleman's Walk, in what was one of the most prominent commercial streets in Norwich, lying on the eastern side of the market place. On market days it became:

> A space of parade-like appearance [...] thronged with a collection of very interesting characters; the merchant, the manufacturer, the magistrate, the provincial yeoman, the militia officer, the affluent landlord, the thrifty and thriving tenant, the independent farmer, the recruiting officer, the clergy, faculty, barristers, and all the various characters of polished and professional society [...], [a] proud scene of bustle and business, health and wealth, prosperity and pleasure.[6]

The market place was the stage for Norwich's civic life, the natural venue of choice for large political meetings and protests, public celebrations and illuminations, and the location of the polling booths for the city and county elections. Compared to other large cities like Bristol and Exeter, Norwich had a relatively open civic structure and a large electorate, formed of freeholders and freemen, admittance to the latter obtainable by birth right, apprenticeship or purchase. At some points in the 18th century, up to a third of the adult male population was able to vote. In 1701, it became the first city outside London to publish its own newspaper, the *Norwich Post*. By the middle of the 18th century there were nine booksellers in the city, and it is estimated that about three-quarters of men in some parishes

No. 37 Gentleman's Walk, Norwich; James Smith Snr's business and family home.

were literate. The citizens had a national reputation for being "assertive and disputatious".[7]

Along with their looms, the Dutch (and later, French) refugees also brought their churches, the privileges of which were enshrined and protected by the city. These differing creeds found a welcome home in Norwich, which had long been a centre of nonconformity: Lollards had been burnt just outside the city in 1428. By 1783, in addition to the 36 Anglican parish churches, the city boasted meetings for the Methodists, the Independents, Anabaptists, old Presbyterians, new Presbyterians, Quakers and a Roman Catholic chapel. Despite the repressive Test and Corporation Acts (which sought to limit public office to Anglicans), the dissenters of Norwich were able to wield considerable political influence by occasionally 'conforming' to the Church of England. Between 1740 and 1760 half of the city's mayors came from nonconformist backgrounds.

James Snr and his family worshipped at the Octagon Chapel in Colegate, which followed the Presbyterian creed, albeit with Unitarian leanings that became more pronounced towards the end of the century. Built in 1756 at a cost of £5,000, the Octagon Chapel was a potent symbol of the congregation's cultural and economic clout in Norwich, despite the Presbyterians being the smallest of the city's dissenting groups. John Wesley, one of the founders of Methodism, visited in 1757, and thought it "perhaps the most elegant [meeting house] in Europe", though this was hardly a compliment—he had significant reservations about the interior, which was "finished in the highest taste and is as clean as any nobleman's saloon. [...] How can it be thought that the old, coarse Gospel should find admission here?".[8] The last remark was most likely a swipe at the Unitarian leanings of Dr John Taylor, the Chapel's first minister. The Octagon Chapel developed a reputation for intellectually rigorous sermons, and it was not uncommon to see members of other chapels and even Anglican clergymen in the congregation.

Many of Norwich's leading lights were members of the Octagon congregation, including Philip Meadows Martineau, a renowned lithotomist (a surgeon specialising in the removal of bladder stones), who founded Norwich's first public subscription library in 1784; James Alderson, a minister at the chapel who later became Recorder of Norwich and a respected doctor; Robert Alderson, the father of Amelia Opie, author and poet; and William Taylor, a key translator of German literature into English in the 1790s. By the 1790s, most of the leading Whig families were in attendance. James Snr sat comfortably amongst the dissenting and economic elites of Norwich; even the book club he frequented included figures like Martineau and Alderson, and many members of the club served as a Sheriff of Norwich and a few became Mayor.

The Young Smith

The young James Edward was an extremely timid child; he suffered from a "diffidence amounting to a degree often painfully embarrassing", and would be thrown into despair if he feared he had said or entertained a wrong word or thought.[9] His father was strongly influenced by his reading of John Locke's *Some Thoughts Concerning Education* (1693), in which he noted that Locke recommended "a private education, because [...] the greatest object of education is virtue and goodness. In reading his observations, 'tis impossible not to reflect how very different is the mode of education in the great schools from that he thinks proper".[10] Smith was educated entirely at home, though Norwich was possessed of the King Edward VI Grammar School, one of the oldest schools in the country. Smith learnt Latin, French, and Italian, becoming proficient in the latter two, and mathematics. His evenings were given over to reading and conversation with his parents; his father encouraged him "not to follow any received opinion blindly and implicitly, but dare to think for himself and stand alone".[11]

Smith found refuge from the bustle of Norwich by indulging his interest in plants, of which the area had a great variety. Despite its prosperity and rapidly expanding population, development was still largely confined to within the city walls, so that wild flowers grew up to the city gates. Within the walls, the city abounded with many orchards and gardens. Smith would later remark how "Norwich had long [...] been conspicuous in its love of plants", crediting the Dutch refugees with introducing a taste for the cultivation of flowers.[12] By the 1630s an annual florists' Feast was celebrated in the city, culminating in a flower show and play. A Natural History Society was founded in 1747, and in 1779 plans to establish a botanical garden were put forward, though nothing ever came of the proposals. However, the numbers of botanists were "always very inconsiderable compared with the cultivators of fine flowers, who among the journeyman weavers, and other persons employed in the manufacture, [were] very numerous". Smith would later recall his youthful interests in the gardens:

> The taste for horticulture [...] sometimes extended itself, from the flowery parterre, and the well-arranged rows of tulips, hyacinths, carnations, and auriculas, into no less formal labyrinths [...] Greenhouses of exotic plants, except oranges and myrtles, were at this time scarcely known, and the writer well collects having seen, with wonder and admiration, one of the first African geraniums [*Pelargonium* spp.] that ever bloomed in Norwich. [13]

Though his lessons and other concerns had always prevented him from snatching "but a few moments for [his] favourite object", Smith maintained his interest in plants throughout his childhood.[14]

Planting the Botanical Seed

Very little is known of Smith's adolescence. His domestic education continued to develop his confidence and self-assurance but he never quite lost his delicacy and tenderness. This enabled him to form particularly close and lasting friendships, but it also left him vulnerable to the disappointment of misplaced regards. He wrote in 1783 that his "heart was formed for social enjoyments; but how often have its warmest affections been torn asunder when just most fully developed!".[15]

A letter written as a young man to one of his earliest and most constant friends, his cousin, Nathaniel Edward Kindersley, gives a glimpse of Smith as a youth. Nathaniel Edward was the only son of Frances's brother, Nathaniel Kindersley. The Kindersleys lived at Yarmouth, just a short ride away from Norwich, so the cousins would have seen each other regularly, and a shared sensibility allowed for a free exchange of thoughts and emotions:

> How often do I think of the days of our childhood, when we have so often by sympathy retired from the social scene [...] to communicate our little discontents and joys, our childish observations, and our innocent merriment; but chiefly to indulge that sympathy of soul which appeared so early, and which may Heaven still cherish![16]

As Smith approached the age of 18, with his home education now concluded, the question of his future profession became more pressing. James Snr had always intended to train Smith in the family concern, specialising in the importation of raw silk, an idea Smith apparently resisted. His indulgent parent allowed the plan to be dropped, even though Smith had offered no alternative profession. Uncertain of how to proceed, Smith sank into an uncharacteristic despondency that was only dispelled on his serious application, beginning in 1778, to the science that was to define his life: botany.

Smith had made a few exploratory botanical efforts in 1777, when he was 17 years old. There are several plants extant in his herbarium recorded as being collected from St Vincent's Rocks, Bristol, on a family visit to the springs at Hotwells that year, including *Geranium columbinum*, *Galium saxatile* and *Chlora perfoliata*. Smith himself dated the start of his botanical education to 9 January 1778, the day he received the second volume, covering the plants, of John Berkenhout's three-volume *Outlines of the Natural History of Great Britain and Ireland* (1770). This book became his principal collecting guide for several years: the many crosses against the plant names in his copy correspond with specimens in his herbarium collected during this period.[17] It was on the next day that Smith descended into the ditches of Norwich Castle, unaware that, just as he was examining the gorse flowers, "the world was losing the great genius [Linnaeus] who was to be my future guide".

Smith was propitiously placed to begin his botanical education. In addition to Norwich's abundant flora, the city was also in possession of one the earliest translators of Linnaeus into English, the apothecary Hugh Rose. It was in Norwich that the merits of the Linnaean system were much earlier "studied and appreciated than in any other part of Britain". Two of the earliest known students of Linnaeus in Norwich were Rose and the Revd Henry Bryant, a mathematician and assistant at St Peter Mancroft, Norwich. Rose was already a knowledgeable botanist from having studied the botanical systems of Tournefort and John Ray. In about 1764 the pair came across Linnaeus's *Philosophia Botanica* (1751), and at first "scarcely knew what opinion to form of it". Rose, loyal to John Ray, was initially suspicious of "lurking heresies and unfounded novelties", but Bryant was impressed with its "mathematical precision" and was soon a committed Linnaean. Rose followed shortly thereafter. Rose and Bryant attracted other amateur Norwich botanists to the Linnaean system, including Henry's brother, Charles Bryant, Beadle of the Court of Guardians of the City of Norwich; John Pitchford, a Roman Catholic surgeon and apothecary, who specialised in mints; and James Crowe, a somewhat cantankerous surgeon who lived just outside the city at Lakenham, interested in mosses, fungi and willows. Also part of the group was Thomas Jenkinson Woodward, a wealthy gentleman who lived at Bungay, Suffolk, who was particularly interested in fungi and seaweeds.

In 1775, with Bryant's assistance, Rose published a translation of *Philosophia Botanica* as *Elements of Botany*, which also included an appendix listing newly discovered plants in Norfolk and Suffolk. Along with Erasmus (grandfather to Charles) Darwin's *Phytologia* (1800), Rose's book was one of the only introductory botanical works with which Smith could find no faults, and in 1804 stated that the "principal part of [the] work [was] still highly valuable, full of solid information, and not superseded by any other English publication".[18]

In addition to Berkenhout, Smith also acquired James Lee's *Introduction to Botany* (1760), Rose's *Elements of Botany* (1775), and Benjamin Stillingfleet's *Miscellaneous Tracts* (1759). Smith compared the initial theory of his botanical education to "the necessary drudgery of a grammar-school; it trains the mind to labour, it fixes principles and facts and terms and names, never to be forgotten".[19] Using these texts to gain a better understanding of the basics of botany, he began putting his new learning into practice on further botanical expeditions, though he soon felt the need for a tutor. Fortunately, Hugh Rose offered his services to young and curious men as a botanical and classical tutor. In the summer of 1778, with his copy of Berkenhout and a parcel of wild flowers in hand, Smith started attending botanical lessons at Rose's home at 8 Tombland, Norwich.

It was here that Smith had his first introduction to the unabridged, unadulterated works of Linnaeus, which was as much, if not more, of a revelation as his encounter with the gorse:

> I was shown the works of Linnaeus; nor shall I ever forget the feelings of wonder excited by finding his whole system of animals, vegetables and minerals, comprised in three octavo volumes. [...] I expected to find the systematical works of Linnaeus constituting a whole library; but they proved almost capable of being put, like the *Iliad*, into a nutshell. Hence a new world was opened to me.[20]

This was probably the 12th edition of Linnaeus's *Systema Naturæ* (1767–1768), the last to be published in Linnaeus's lifetime and first to be printed in just three volumes. Smith's astonishment at its compact size shows the popular appeal of Linnaeus's concise system. Smith equated them to "the indexes to things. His works are a clue to the learning of all former writers, whose labours he quotes, & whose information he brings to practical use, for he gives the stamp which makes their bullion current coin".[21] From this point on, Smith was fully committed to Linnaeus's scientific principles.

Quickly showing his proficiency, Smith soon became the youngest member of the loose collective of Norwich Linnaeans. The group encouraged and provided opportunities for one another. On Pitchford's introduction, Rose established lifelong correspondences with William Hudson, and John Lightfoot, author of *Flora Scotica* (1777). When Rose lost his sight in 1779 he gave his idea for a popular work on the uses of plants to Charles Bryant, published as *Flora Dietetica* in 1783 and dedicated to James Crowe. Smith would later dedicate his own *Tracts Relating to Natural History* (1798) to Crowe, in which he recollected "how much of [his] earliest progress [was] to be attributed to [him]".[22]

Smith now began earnestly collecting and drying plants for his herbarium. The herbarium was an essential and invaluable tool for any serious botanist in the 18th century, aiding plant identification and allowing specimens to be exchanged and compared with specimens belonging to other botanists. He collected extensively in and around Norwich, including the nearby village of Thorpe, with its species-rich meadows and hedges. Later in 1778 Smith joined his family on a journey to Yorkshire, Derbyshire, and Lancashire, his first opportunity to botanise outside East Anglia. Though he had visited the area several times before in his youth, he now "felt like a man born blind, who first walked abroad to look about him. The wild moors, the mossy rocks, the mountainous woods, to me were 'opening Paradise'".[23]

Smith added some 800 plants to his herbarium in the period 1777–1781; of these he personally collected at least 650. The others he received as gifts or exchanges from friends and fellow botanists, including Crowe, Woodward, Pitchford and Henry Bryant. Smith's herbarium at this point was formed almost exclusively of the native flora, though he also had a few exotics from the greenhouse of Alderman Jeremiah Ives.

In 1779, encouraged by his parents, Smith began developing the garden at College Farm, a cottage Smith's father had rented in order to "air the young folks and wash the linnen". It has not been possible to identify its exact location but it would likely have been within a short ride of Norwich. During the period 1779–1781 about 100 plants were added to the herbarium from the "Cottage Garden", as it was referred to by Smith. He was active in adding new plants, growing *Festuca ovina* from a root brought from St Faith's Bogs, near Norwich, and *Geranium sanguineum* from seed gathered at St Vincent's Rocks, Bristol. Smith assiduously compared these cultivated specimens against their wild counterparts, and his parents quickly recognised the benefits that gardening and frequent botanical excursions had on the "health & amusement" of their delicate son.[24]

Smith's pursuit of botany was also sociable. He quickly ingratiated himself with the Norwich botanists, thanks to his botanical ardour and his warm personality. Lessons, visits to gardens, botanical excursions, discussion of new discoveries and identifications were all opportunities for an exchange of shared sensibilities. Smith loved the "tranquillity of the country, the sight of gardens, the unpacking even of dried specimens", all of which engendered "a flow of happy spirits, never overbearing, a ready wit, an enjoyment which communicated its happiness to all about him, not a solitary pleasure, exclusive of society, but which made society itself more welcome". The study of nature offered an almost redemptive consolation to Smith, strengthening his timid nature and giving him confidence. It also enabled communication with like-minded individuals, and Smith would always view natural history as an "unerring clue to intercourse with the best minds [...] [bringing] those together who are connected by a most commendable, disinterested and delightful tie; it brings forth the best of every character".[25] Likewise, Smith was able to find pretexts for indulging his favourite activity on almost any occasion. A letter sent in 1800 from his old friend Humphry Repton, who had since found fame as a landscape gardener, reminded Smith of when bad weather had forced them to seek shelter under a tree in a bog, incredulously recounting "while the most tremendous thunderstorm drench'd us to the skin – you found an unexpected source of comfort in the most perfect specimen of *Helvella acaulis* [*Stereum hirsutum*, a bracket fungus]".[26]

Within a few years Smith had gone from only a basic understanding of botany to being able to debate the identification and classification of difficult plants with men many years his senior. In the first half of 1781, Smith paid a visit to London. With a pocketful of introductions from the Norwich Linnaeans, he visited the gardens at Kew, Chelsea Physic Garden and William Curtis's London Botanic Garden, taking specimens from each. Smith also made the acquaintance of James Dickson, a nurseryman and seed salesman based in Covent Garden. Dickson was particularly interested in fungi, a group of organisms poorly understood at the time. He warned Smith that no author on fungi, particularly William Hudson, was "to be depended upon".[27] Dickson supplied Smith with his *desiderata* (list of wanted plant specimens) and they began a botanical correspondence following Smith's return to Norwich in July. The first package from Smith contained a 16-page letter and 13 specimens, with detailed notes on their locations and appearances, and instructions for moistening the fungi.[28]

Smith acted as an intermediary between this new London contact and his Norwich friends, initiating a correspondence between Dickson and James Crowe, who also went on to exchange specimens.[29] In return, Dickson enabled exchanges between Smith and Curtis. Smith was eager to assist Dickson and requested his full *desiderata*, surmising that Dickson was not of "that miserable class of botanist who know not the pleasure of giving as well as receiving".[30] Smith's correspondence with Dickson is amongst the earliest surviving and represents the beginning of his botanical correspondence.

Botany had become his ruling passion, and he was determined for it to form an integral part of his future life. His father realised this, and in 1780 recommended his son take up medicine, as at the time it was only possible to attend lectures on botany as part of a medical course. Probably of equal, if not greater importance, for James Snr at least, was the fact that in sending his son to train as a physician, Smith would be able to advance himself considerably in society. Physicians were regarded as gentlemen, and if established in a good practice could earn significant sums. Botany was considered "entirely subservient to physic", developing from the need to identify the medicinal plants used in curing diseases.[31] The botanical gardens at Padua and Pisa in Italy were founded in the mid-16th century for the purpose of growing those plants considered essential in the treatment of disease, and a sound knowledge of plants and their properties was essential for any 18th-century physician or apothecary.

Smith began receiving tuition from the physicians Dr Manning and Robert Alderson, in order to prepare him for his new course of studies. Because he was not a member of the Church of England, Smith was barred from attending either the universities at Oxford and Cambridge. Instead, he opted for Edinburgh, which did not discriminate on the grounds of religion, with the intention of beginning his education in the autumn of 1781. Happily for Smith, since the 1760s Edinburgh had been considered one the most progressive centres for medical education in Europe, so much so that it provided the model for medical schools in the American colonies. The Royal Infirmary enabled practical, hospital-based teaching, ensuring an excellent clinical reputation and allowing for real medical advances to occur. Edinburgh attracted ground-breaking teachers, such as William Cullen—who organised a system for the classification of disease—and Joseph Black, from more reactionary schools such as the University of Glasgow, whose Calvinistic heritage made it view medical advances as dangerous. The Edinburgh course was also much shorter, generally requiring three years' study, compared to the seven years needed for a BA, followed by four years for the MD, at Oxford, Cambridge, and Dublin.

On 14 October 1781, aged 21, Smith set out on the long journey to Edinburgh, accompanied as far as Wansford, a small village on the Cambridgeshire-Northamptonshire border, by his father and second youngest brother, John Frederick. It was an emotional experience for the family, and for James Snr it was to leave him with "some of the tenderest ideas my mind is possessed of".[32] For Smith, it would be the first time he had been entirely separated from his family, though he went in earnest hopes of being of "more use to [Dickson], & to the rest of [his] friends, who had lent [Smith] their assistance in the Botanical way", by collecting and sending

Scottish plants.[33] Enjoying a last breakfast together at Wansford, the final parting left James Snr distraught. He wrote to Smith a couple of weeks later how "the separation and the rest of that day was cutting & as much as I could well bear, but every reflection on the prospects that attend you is a balm to heal the wounds that absence gives the mind".[34]

Edinburgh: Keys to the Doors of Science

Smith arrived in Edinburgh around the 22 October 1781. Before leaving Norwich, Smith had engaged lodgings in Crichton Street, close to the university. Unlike Oxford and Cambridge, Edinburgh did not provide college accommodation; unsurprisingly this sometimes caused tension between the local and student populations. Smith explained to his father, there were "many young men who make themselves contemptible by their rioting and debaucheries, and unhappily these are the most conspicuous to the people at large, who can know nothing of the numbers who sit quietly at home".[35]

Smith shared his lodgings with John Henry Engelhart, son of the King of Sweden's physician and "a most accomplished and agreeable young gentleman", and another Norwich youth, Richard Lubbock (Smith and Lubbock were apparently unknown to one another before Edinburgh).[36] The most vivid personality in Crichton Street though, was their landlady, Mrs Beveridge. She was "so furious in her attachment to the old Ministry", that after the fall of Lord Frederick North's Tory government in March 1782, she often railed against the new Whig administration led by the Marquess of Rockingham, "and all who favour them".[37] "Cool argument" would bring her to reason on such occasions, but their conversations were more commonly on other subjects—Smith wrote that she was "a very sensible woman, and knows a great deal of the world".[38]

The medical school offered eight courses: Anatomy and Surgery, Chemistry, Medical Practice, Medical Theory, Clinical Lectures, Midwifery, Materia Medica (a subject roughly corresponding with modern pharmacology), and Botany. Students were expected to have attended each, bar Midwifery, before sitting for their MD. The year was split into two sessions: 'winter', which ran from November to April, and 'summer', from May to July. All courses were available in the winter session, except

Botany, available only in the summer, along with a continuation of Clinical Lectures. The courses ran five days a week and were timetabled at separate hours, so it was possible for particularly diligent students to attend all courses in one year.

Unlike at other universities, students paid their fees, 3 guineas per course, directly to the professor. A small matriculation fee was paid to the university, which was put towards purchasing books for the library. The professors received no stipend, or if they did it was nominal, so they had a strong imperative to keep the quality of their courses high so as to attract as many students as possible. Lectures could be extremely crowded, with the Anatomy and Surgery course attracting up to 400 students per session, and Chemistry over 250. As well as ensuring quality, this system also often resulted in innovation. Professors during Smith's time at Edinburgh included Alexander Monro the second, Professor of Anatomy, "without a doubt the most influential anatomist of his time"[39]; Joseph Black, Professor of Chemistry, a proponent of the 'New Chemistry' who made significant discoveries regarding latent and specific heat, and carbon dioxide; and Dr John Hope, Professor of Botany, one of the first to teach the Linnaean system in Britain.

Smith reported that botany was considered a very necessary qualification at Edinburgh, "the advantage of it is strongly enforced by the professors in their introductory lectures". However, as a subject it was considered "so laborious, where there is no taste, that most people will always be content with a small portion".[40] Analysis of attendance rates for each course shows that Botany attracted only 25 per cent of the students in each cohort in the period of 1760 to 1826, compared to 65 per cent for Anatomy and 75 per cent for Chemistry. However, as the Botany course only took place in the summer session the true attendance figures may have been under-reported.[41] Yet, considering that Smith had only notionally taken up the study of medicine for the botanical aspects, he showed surprisingly little enthusiasm for Dr Hope's upcoming course. He had to attend in order to graduate, but expected this part of his study "to cost me but little pains" and assured his father there was no danger of it engrossing his attention too much.[42]

Of all his new acquaintances, Smith expected to derive the "most comfort and advantage" from Dr Hope:

> He has the highest character for abilities, and real goodness of heart, and is a man of the first consequence in this place. His behaviour was at first (as it generally is) a little reserved, but botanical subjects opening the way, he became perfectly affable, and treats me with almost paternal tenderness, having found that I am quite a novice in the study of medicine: he talked the whole over with me.[43]

Hope advised Smith to improve his Latin, the weakest of his languages, and recommended a tutor. Though the teaching at Edinburgh was conducted in English, a good knowledge of Latin was needed for most of the standard textbooks, not to mention the MD thesis and examination. Hope also offered practical advice, suggesting that even with the utmost economy Smith could not spend less than £120 a year. This was more than Smith was expecting, particularly as the Latin tutor was to cost an additional eight guineas a year. Indeed, after paying his course fees and first quarter's rent, Smith found himself drawing upon money much sooner than he expected. Smith, anxious to justify the additional expense of the Latin tutor, promised his father "frugality in every case, where I can save money, without missing anything of real importance".[44] Though James Snr was suspicious of the true value of the classics, believing there was "a great deal in the parade of them besides the use", he recognised that they were the "Keys to the Doors of Science" and reassured his son regarding the additional expense.

Dr Hope recommended that for his first winter session Smith only take Anatomy and Surgery and Chemistry, and that he not start attending the Clinical Lectures, held in the Infirmary, until the summer. Smith's father was happy to concede to Dr Hope's judgement, though after learning that the fee for the Clinical Lectures would cover his attendance for the duration of his MD he tried to convince his son to begin attending straight away, "so you may begin early and pay no more".[45] Smith resisted, reasoning that with his limited medical knowledge he would struggle. His squeamishness may also have influenced his decision. Visiting the Infirmary soon after his arrival, he found his "apprehensions and disgust much less than expected" and hoped to completely conquer them after a week's attendance, now conveniently deferred for six months. After attending the professors' introductory lectures he also decided to take Materia Medica, reckoning that as it came so easy to him it made sense to get it out of the way.

Though a little homesick, Smith enthusiastically threw himself into his new life, and was "as happy as [he] could be anywhere removed from [his] friends". Of his new subjects he favoured Anatomy, "a most entertaining and interesting study", though by the end of November Dr Monro was still on "the dry bones" and tended to hold very long lectures.[46]

A further advantage of Smith's studying in Edinburgh was that he would "experience the advantage of travelling", from which he could "reap the benefit of forming [his] own manners".[47] Patients were genuinely concerned that their physician would prescribe unnecessary treatment in order to boost their fees; so new practitioners strived to appear that they were gentlemen of fortune with no financial interest in the illness.[48] As Smith's childhood friend Humphry Repton observed, "more physicians have owed their eminence to fashion or accident than to their skill— […] the multitude are more easily dazzled with a bright conceit or a brilliant hypothesis, though a false one."[49]

Repton explained further:

> The great school for this kind of learning is the company of ladies—women have a knack at giving a lively turn to the simplest subjects and if you have free access to those polite circles where cards allow a few moments conversation, never omit going to attend the lecture. You know the professor's fee on this occasion and I need not tell you that <u>delicate flattery</u> such as <u>truth</u> with very little straining […], will be quite sufficient without parting with your freedom or disturbing your peace.[50]

Soon after his arrival, Smith had fallen in with "a great many young ladies", particularly the Misses Riddel, whom he considered his "privy counsellors in all matters of etiquette, as I can say anything to them, and they are quite unreserved and familiar with me".[51] James Snr was certain they would enliven his son's "temper and spirits, polish [his] manners and wear away the mauvaise honte [bashfulness] which more or less always stick to a home education". He was also careful to remind him, should "any favourite one [...] take possession of your affections and destroy your peace of mind", that "Scotch girls [...] have very small fortunes".[52]

His favourite social pastime was dancing. In the early part of 1782 he and Lubbock regularly attended a subscription ball held every Friday night in Edinburgh's New Town. Another new, and useful, friend was Lady Gordon, "who always finds me a partner, when I am at a loss for one". It was reported that "if you are known to be a Gentleman, you will meet with every civility and attention [...] otherwise you will find the young ladies very much on the reserve".[53]

Real advancement came through conversation with eminent and influential men. During an evening at Dr Hope's he met James Burnett, Lord Monboddo, judge, philosopher and proto-evolutionist. Smith described to his father in detail Monboddo's dress and conversation, which included "the great decline of classical learning at Edinburgh, [and] the Norfolk husbandry, which he said he had adopted".[54] James Snr replied that "a superficial view of singular and great characters is entertaining and an acquaintance with them honourable and useful".[55] At another party Smith met Drs Hutton and Black, who were curious to know the exact recipe for a Norfolk dumpling. Smith quickly wrote to his mother for the recipe, hoping that it would help cement his connection with Dr Black.[56]

Smith also indulged in gentler, less socially advantageous pleasures. Smith always enjoyed the company of children, and he wrote to his mother that he had "met with a number of young play-fellows, as you said I should". He was often with the family of a Dr Adam, whose daughter told her mother that Smith was "a bonny man", to which the girl's brother added "ay, and a good man too!"[57] Smith's parents were relieved to hear Smith took socialising seriously, fearing he "might suffer in [his] health from too intense study". They were also pleased to hear that had grown "fat".[58]

Smith and his family wrote to each other regularly, generally allowing no more than three weeks to pass between letters. Smith's parents received his missives with a "pleasure equal to transport", and in return he received care packages containing dried apples and pears, black silk stockings, then much in vogue in Edinburgh, letters from his siblings, and all the Norwich gossip. Smith was close to both his parents, but his closeness with his father is illustrated particularly vividly in the correspondence. Reams of advice, both moral and practical, flowed from James Snr's pen, admonishing his son not to make any hasty, ill-considered friendships, nor "to press your stomach against the table but write with your body as upright as you can". Aware of how overbearing he could sometimes be, he begged Smith to "make allowance for a father's tenderness, for indeed Jammy I love you as much any father ever did a son, and I have the joy of supposing you will allow me to shew it to the last, I will take care it shall not be ridiculous fondness if I can, but fondness I must be indulged in".[59]

He was particularly pleased with the account of Smith's fellow lodger Engelhart, who seemed both "entertaining and useful", and recommended cultivating the relationship. Lubbock met with less approbation, and after hearing of his anguish at the departure of the friends who had accompanied

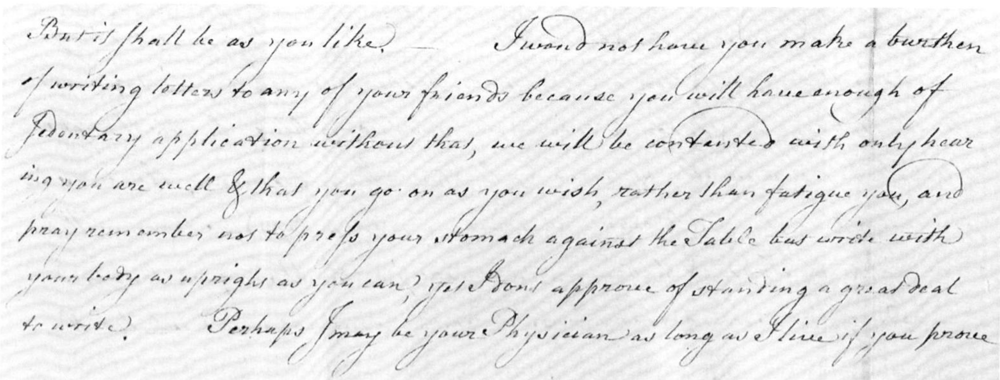
But it shall be as you like. — I would not have you make a burthen
of writing letters to any of your friends because you will have enough of
sedentary application without that, we will be contented with only hear
ing you are well & that you go on as you wish, rather than fatigue you, and
pray remember not to press your stomach against the Table but write with
your body as upright as you can, yet I don't approve of standing a great deal
to write. Perhaps I may be your Physician as long as I live if you prove

"And pray remember not to press your stomach against the Table": Smith Snr to his son, 12 November 1781.

him to Edinburgh, James Snr forbade his son from forming a closer friendship, lest Lubbock's possible "indiscretions" have an impact on his own son's good reputation.[60]

In any case, Smith's relationship with his fellow lodgers had cooled by the end of November. Despite Lubbock's good heart and "quick parts", he lacked judgement and had been "very dissolute".[61] The "universally beloved and admired" Engelhart fared better, though he was "now and then guilty of some excesses". Engelhart had charmed Smith by confessing the worst and elucidating all "their disadvantages". Well aware of the value of potentially influential foreigners, James Snr continued to encourage the friendship, it being "impossible to say how useful they will happen to be in every walk in life".[62] This was prescient advice; just two years later Engelhart would go on to play a crucial role in Smith's purchase of the collections of Carl Linnaeus.

Late in December 1781, Engelhart introduced Smith to Edinburgh's Royal Medical Society (established 1737). Unable to become a member until the next academic year, Smith regularly attended as a visitor instead, and it was here, at a meeting on 2 March 1782, that he first engaged in public speaking. He spoke twice, once on worms in horses, and again during a discussion on the analogy of animal and human diseases and how far treatments were interchangeable. Utilising his botanical knowledge, Smith ventured "to represent the danger [...], considering that many plants which are poisonous to some animals, [are] wholesome to others". He quickly ascertained that the Society was "wonderfully ignorant of natural history", and anticipated his knowledge in this field giving him an advantage over his contemporaries. Proud of his contribution, he hoped his parents would view this public speaking as evidence of his growing confidence.[63]

Smith's growing social and academic confidence at this time can be attributed to his aptitude in natural history. Smith freely acknowledged that without this he "might have drudged [...] for a couple of years" before making any kind of impact in Edinburgh's scientific community. As it was, the Revd Dr John Walker, Edinburgh's professor of natural history, was so impressed by the breadth of Smith's knowledge that he gave the young man a free ticket for his natural history course.[64]

For months, if not years, James Snr had been entertaining great hopes that his son's accomplishments would "procure [him] the esteem and veneration of the world".[65] The whole family indulged in a peculiar manifest destiny of sorts regarding Smith's medical prospects. He was the only one of his brothers to be sent to university, and whilst Smith was gossiping with the Misses Riddel, his next two younger brothers were embarking on their first arduous journeys selling textiles in the Norfolk countryside. Of his son's success James Snr exclaimed "O my dear son! How much gratitude we think is due to your great Creator from us, who are so inexpressibly concerned for your temporal and eternal happiness, that your mind is so naturally formed for Virtue".[66] Smith went so far as to agree that his prospects appeared to be "peculiarly directed by the Almighty".[67]

That True Union of Hearts and Minds

Possessed of "those amiable qualities that gained and fixed [him] so many friends" in Norwich, Smith quickly drew a small circle of like-minded associates about him.[68] They included Richard Markham (later Salisbury), a "young man of large fortune" studying physic for amusement, and by Smith's consideration an excellent botanist, and William Thomson. Thomson, the son of a Worcester physician, had already graduated with a BA from Oxford and studied in London before coming to Edinburgh. With a "taste for the fine arts and a good judgement, [...] [and] all the small talk of learning, as well as a good stock of its solid part", Smith was frequently in his company.[69]

Smith's greatest friend at Edinburgh, however, was Robert Batty. Four years his junior, Batty had already spent five years training under a surgeon in his native Kirby Lonsdale, Westmorland, in the north of England. Seeing his "amiable modesty and diffidence", Smith actively sought out his friendship, recognising that it was "better worth my cultivating than that of the forward or splendid". Together they "enjoyed that true union of hearts and minds that is the essence of friendship", bonding over natural history and music: Batty sang and played the flute, and was interested in zoology.[70]

Smith and his friends met regularly to discuss their latest natural history acquisitions and discoveries. The idea of formalising these meetings within the structure of a society developed gradually, and on 31 March 1782 the first meeting of the *Societas Naturæ Studiosorum Edinburgena* (generally referred to as the Natural History Society) met. The founding members included Smith, Richard Markham and William Thomson. Though he was not the originator, Smith can be credited as the catalyst that "galvanised the ditherers".[71] Dr Walker immediately offered his museum as a meeting place, which included the use of his books and specimens, and, at the next meeting was admitted an ordinary member, along with Batty, Lubbock, and another of Smith's intimates, Francis Buchanan (later Hamilton). Drs Hope and Black were made Honorary Members.

Smith's first paper for the Society, "An Essay on Collecting and Preserving Specimens of Plants", was read on 19 April 1782. A beginner's guide to creating a herbarium, Smith detailed everything, from the best time of day to gather plants, to their final arrangement and storage. For botanical expeditions, he recommended that the botanist should be:

> Clothed in the lightest manner, [...] and to have as much Pocket Room as possible: [...] furnished with a convenient knife, a simple pocket Microscope, a dissecting needle, and in rocky countries, a Hammer and Chisel to get the crustaceous lichens, an instrument proper to take up the roots of plants, [...] a Tin Box to receive specimens and a small book of blotting paper for the more delicate and minute plants.[72]

The paper was a success, debated for three hours after reading, and receiving commendation from both Hope and Walker.

By the end of its first year the Society had grown so much (26 ordinary and four honorary members) that it became necessary to draw up a formal constitution. Seeking to instil discipline and commitment, a long series of rules and regulations was created, many of which had subscriptions and fines attached to them. Absence from the roll call at the start of a meeting warranted a sixpenny fine, as did leaving before the final half hour. Non-production of a paper at the required time resulted in a one guinea fine. This was in addition to the initial three guinea entrance subscription and the half-guinea annual contribution. The role of President was also formalised, with the appointment of four annual presidents instead of rotating at each meeting. Smith was named the first president on 16 January 1783.[73] His father was ecstatic: "these distinctions I flatter myself are prognostics of the eminent rank you will by and by stand in, and the use you will be of to yourself, your friends, and to mankind".[74]

The Society also attracted attention from outside the student body. James Bolton of Halifax, a self-taught mycologist and botanical illustrator of humble background became an Honorary Member. From the opposite end of the social spectrum, shortly after its foundation, three "young Noblemen of fine parts and great fortunes", the Earls of Glasgow and Ancram, and Lord Daer, son to the Earl of Selkirk, had all petitioned to be admitted as ordinary members. In the following session, Lord Buchan wrote requesting to be admitted; Smith sent a copy of this letter to his father, explaining that Buchan was "a man of parade and wishes to be thought learned, and a patron of science".[75] This noble patronage was an important indicator of the scientific credibility of the new Society, at a time when such recognition was derived not only through practice but also from where the practitioner stood on the social ladder. The premier scientific society of the time, the Royal Society, had emerged along similar lines. The Natural History Society continued to prosper for another 30 years, before being subsumed into the Royal Physical Society of Edinburgh in 1812.[76] In recognition of his contribution, Smith was later listed as a "Benefactor of the Society", alongside other early members Walker, Thomson and Buchanan.

The first winter session of Smith's time in Edinburgh drew to a close at the end of April 1782. "Besides being really sorry that the lectures were over", it made Smith "vapourish to see so many students going away and all the places which used to be so cheerful and busy, quite vacant and gloomy".[77] Worst of all, Smith's "delicate, scrupulous" friend Batty had been suddenly called home to Kirby Lonsdale and was not expected to return until the following winter.[78]

With the start of the summer session in May, Smith began attending the clinical lectures at the Infirmary (having "quite got over the disagreeable feelings I had at first going there") and Dr Hope's botanical lectures, held in the Leith Walk botanic garden. In 1763 Hope had secured permanent government funding to transfer the two existing, inferior gardens, the Royal Abbey Garden and the Town Garden at Trinity Hospital, to a new site in Leith Walk, just outside the city. The 33 plots on the five-acre site were named after prominent botanists both past and present, and a Society for the Importation of Foreign Seeds and Plants was founded in order to acquire exotic new stock from North America. Hope also used his connections with past pupils to acquire plants and seeds from the West Indies and India.

Dr Hope's course was the one of the most progressive of its day, thanks to its emphasis on physiology and the prominent coverage his own plant experiments received. Individual topics covered included the "restoration of vitiated air" by plants in light; the motion of sap; sex and hybridisation; and natural classification. The final part of the course aimed to show living examples of plants and phenomena discussed earlier in the course. The course was spread across 60 to 65 lectures from May through to July.

Smith admired Dr Hope's botanical lectures, finding his delivery "agreeable, with as many 'behoves' as Dr Walker; [and] his politeness and condescension unparalleled".[79] Other students were less admiring. In order to graduate as MD, students had to attend the botany course, but as it was only offered in the summer session many resented having to pay both rent and the three guinea fee to look at plants, which, in the words of a contemporary, "may be done cheaper at home". One student, Job Harrison, writing to his father in 1775, was particularly unimpressed:

> Edinburgh is now more filthy and disagreeable than in winter, particularly at night after eleven o clock, when the inhabitants discharge their daily excrement thro' the windows, and in the morning before the scavengers have cleaned the streets. I am obliged to go quite thro' the town every morning to the Botanical Garden, and whenever the morning is hot, and at the same time free from wind, the stench is intolerable.[80]

Despite his admiration for Hope, Smith did not anticipate learning a great deal of new information, and felt no guilt at missing several lectures to travel to Sheffield in early June in order to see his father and brother Francis, who were visiting on business. Two further incentives were to be the company, as far as Kendal, of a newly-made acquaintance, Dr Pierre Marie Auguste Broussonet, "an agreeable and ingenious Frenchman, […] and an eminent naturalist intimate with Sir Joseph Banks", and an invitation to visit Robert Batty in Kirby Lonsdale.[81]

Smith left Edinburgh on 11 June, and after spending some time in Carlisle with Broussonet, arrived in Kirby Lonsdale three days later. It rained throughout his two-day stay, so he was unable to see the country, but he was charmed by Batty's family; in particular his sister, who—to Smith's mother's relief—was married. They insisted he visit again on the return journey so he could see the area's "natural curiosities". James Snr, Francis and Smith spent two weeks together in Yorkshire, and Smith's father could not find words to describe the "pleasure and comfort" he received from seeing his son again. James Snr was certain that Smith would become one of the "main props" of his and Frances's old age, and knowing his other children would have "such a friend and support" made them "both more ready to quit this world at the call of Heaven".[82] There was evidently much discussion about Smith's future. In a letter (now unfortunately obscured in part) sent to Thomas Woodward shortly after his return to Edinburgh, it appears that, after completing the next winter session, Smith intended to spend the summer of 1783 at Norwich, the following winter and summer studying in London, and the next two years back at Edinburgh, in order to graduate in the summer of 1786.[83]

In October 1782, some months after their parting in Yorkshire, James Snr wrote to his son, fearing that plans of another sort may be underway. Over the course of the Smith family's semi-regular trips to Yorkshire, it appears as though Smith and an unnamed lady had made a romantic connection. James Snr was now anxious to know whether the recent visit to Sheffield had "produced or discovered anything more intimate", and urged him not to make any decisions without first consulting his parents. He appealed to Smith's reason, reminding him he did not yet know "what fortune may throw in your way of Merit, Beauty and Fortune", and to keep his "heart at liberty" for a while longer.[84]

Smith had, in fact, already bound his heart, like "an inestimable jewel", to another. Not to the unworthy Yorkshire girl feared by his father, but rather Robert Batty.[85] Smith and Batty corresponded throughout the latter's absence from Edinburgh, and from the few surviving examples it is clear their feelings for each other went beyond the bounds of ordinary friendship. He reassured Batty that "nothing would be too much to serve the friend I really loved", and confessed that he was "capable of very strong attachments [...]. I offer you, my Batty, a warm, an honest heart". Like a forlorn lover, whenever Smith walked to his botanical lectures, he found that "something unavoidably takes me down Robinson's Close, and I cannot help looking at that gloomy dwelling which I have so often visited with a cheerful step when it contained my friend". Batty was his brother in virtue, and Smith hoped they would assist each other in "avoiding the snares of the profligate, and the still more dangerous solicitations of the good-natured but inconsiderate". Smith's widow Pleasance would later destroy all of Smith and Batty's correspondence, with only two letters printed in the *Memoir* acting as witness to their friendship. This invites speculation on the true nature of the relationship, but Smith's sense of morality rules out anything but the most platonic, though intense, of relationships. Smith was aware his friendship had stepped into a romantic ideal, but he doggedly vouched for his too full heart, and Batty's place in it, against the discouragement of those who told him "that his ideas of friendship, love, honour, [were] merely romantic" — he believed that there was "more virtue in the world than we are generally told of".[86]

Botanical Expedition

After his summer travels, Smith returned to Edinburgh on 2 August 1782. A new academic year also brought with it new lodgings, with Smith and Lubbock moving to Mrs Beveridge's newly acquired house on Patrick Street. John Henry Engelhart did not join them, having left Crichton Street under a cloud some months prior. According to Smith he had become "a perfect debauchee, [...] neglect[ful of] his studies and [...] perpetually engaging in drunken frolics", several of which had occurred at Crichton Street. Smith had remained the model of virtue throughout, even at Engelhart's outrageous parties, where he kept "constantly to two glasses only, [...] a great thing to do, when all the company besides were drunk". Smith's consistency earned him Engelhart's respect, to the point that Smith once heard him "speak very much in [his] praise to some of his gay companions". Lubbock, too, had repented of his former indolence, but on discovering that Lubbock had been "gay formerly", Engelhart railed at his hypocrisy and became his "secret enemy".[87]

Including Smith and Lubbock, five lodged in the new house, with another seven joining them for dinner, most of them of Smith's "particular acquaintance". They formed "a very happy party", though they did not get "drunk together"—indeed, Smith had not seen "two bottles of wine drank since [they] came into the house".[88] Mrs Beveridge remained a forceful personality. James Snr, upon witnessing his son's witty repartee in a letter to the wife of a friend, found that he had "a better knack at la Badinage" than he had realised.[89] Smith revealed that he had "abundant opportunities of exercising [himself] at 'la Badinage', and could not possibly be in better hands than Mrs Beveridge's for that purpose". Evidently, a slightly flirtatious relationship existed between the delicate young man and his experienced landlady.[90]

In May 1782, in honour of the new Natural History Society, Dr Hope revived his botanical medal, which had been in abeyance for some years. Hope had first offered an annual gold medal to his students for the best Scottish herbarium in 1763, to encourage them, and to spur the formation of a dried Flora Scotica. For the revival, only members of the Society would be allowed to compete. Smith felt that, with a little effort, he was in with a chance, reckoning that "such an honour is surely worth taking some pains for". He began planning a three-week botanical expedition to Loch Lomond, largely at the instigation of Hope, who wanted his son, 16-year-old Thomas Charles, to be of the party. His other companions were to be Thomas Hardy, a member of the Society, and Richard Lubbock.[91]

On 20 August, with the encouraging news from Dr Hope that the botanical medal was "all in my own hands", Smith and his cohorts set out for Loch Lomond.[92] They established a base at an inn in Luss, some 80 miles distant from Edinburgh, where they met the Revd John Stuart, a "first rate naturalist" who had accompanied the naturalist Thomas Pennant on his 1772 tour of Scotland. Smith had previously met Stuart in Edinburgh and successfully recommended him as an honorary member of the Natural History Society, and he now joined the party on their ascent of Ben Lomond (height 3,196 feet), a distinctive peak in the Scottish Highlands.

On 23 August they took a boat across the loch to the base of the mountain, accompanied by two men to carry the provisions. Assisted to "great advantage" by the "3 wine glasses" of rum he imbibed along the way, Smith reached the summit with little difficulty. They "stood as on an island in a sea of clouds". Smith was impressed by the wildness; from time to time they had "transient views of the country below as if by enchantment, on one side Loch Lomond chequered with islands, on the other a sweet valley with the Forth winding thro' it in the most fantastic manner".[93] They began their descent at 6 o'clock, reaching Luss before 9. The main purpose of their trip was well rewarded with a great number of rare plants.[94]

Over the next few days it rained so hard that they could barely leave the inn, and seeing no prospect of the weather clearing they abandoned the rest of the trip. They took coaches all the way back to Edinburgh, arriving on 26 August, less than a week after setting out. Receiving much ribaldry from Dr Hope and their friends on hearing what had become of their "walking expedition", Smith claimed that the exertion of "walking up and down Ben Lomond will atone a little for some riding in coaches".[95] However, once in receipt of a few specimens promised from Stuart's garden, Smith's competition herbarium would contain examples of almost all the then known rare Scottish plants.[96] As it turned out, Smith's was the only herbarium submitted. It was still examined, and on being awarded the medal in December 1782, was told that it was "thought very worthy; indeed Dr Hope paid me very high compliments upon it, and it exceeds in number that of Dr [John] Parsons which was the last successful one [awarded 1766]".[97]

Smith continued his conquest of Edinburgh's scientific scene with his election, on 23 November, to the Royal Medical Society, though it was a close run thing. Of the 35 petitioners, 17 were rejected. Names were balloted as they were pulled from a hat, with two "triangles" sufficient to reject a candidate. Those that came toward the end were almost all rejected, but though Smith's name was the last but one it received only one triangle, "so think I came off very well".[98]

For his second year, Smith continued to take the Anatomy and Surgery course, in addition to Medical Theory and Medical Practice and Dr Walker's natural history course. He had an extremely full day:

> I rise about half past seven. Attend Dr Gregory from 8 to 9. Cullen from 9 to 10, after which I come home and get a very comfortable breakfast with Mr Lubbock, (the others breakfasting earlier), then from 11 to 12 on Mondays, Wednesdays and Fridays I attend Dr Walker, from 12 to 1 is the Infirmary hour, from 1 to after 2 is Monro's, at 3 we dine, from dinner till 5 I either go to the Infirmary, or chat by Mrs Beveridge's fireside, or shall now often lounge in the Library of the Medical Society, from 5 to 6 twice a week I attend the Clinical Lectures on the cases in the Infirmary and 3 times a week Dr Duncan's on the Theory of Medicine, at 6 I drink tea either abroad or at home and afterwards read or write till 9, we generally go to bed rather before 11.[99]

On 19 December his second paper for the Natural History Society was read, "On the Phenomena of Vegetable Odours", which was well received.[100] It is clear Smith had been carrying out his own investigations and experiments in addition to researching the available literature on the subject. He explored the possible origin of the "odorous matter of plants", surmising that it must consist either of "a resinous substance, an essential oil, or which I take to be almost always the case, of a substance partaking more or less of the nature of both". He also discussed the habit of certain plants to release odours only at certain times of day, noting that the flowers of *Asperula odorata* [*Galium odoratum*, woodruff] "have a very sweet smell [...] rarely to be perceived; for although I have repeatedly examined the plant at all hours and in various kinds of weather, I never experienced it but once which was on a fine summer's evening".[101] By the time he departed Edinburgh, Smith had made about 50 additions to Lightfoot's *Flora Scotica*, mostly in the cryptogamic class (plants without visible flowers, such as ferns, mosses and liverworts), and in early 1784 he presented 20 of them to the Natural History Society in a paper, "On the Flora Scoticae Supplementum".[102]

The summer session of 1782 also saw Smith regularly attending the Infirmary, which he did "with much pleasure, there is so much room for observation and reasoning, and I have got over the disgust".[103] Because of his confessed lack of medical knowledge at the start of his time in Edinburgh, Smith engaged in few medical discussions in his correspondence, though this changed as he progressed. On 2 January 1783, Smith attended the funeral of an acquaintance, the son of Dr Thomas Reid, "author of a celebrated work on the human mind". It was Reid's first winter in Edinburgh, and his death was a shock to Smith as they had already become friendly. Reid was the last of a numerous family who had all died about the same age, and Smith was greatly affected by the dignified behaviour of Reid's father, comparing him to a "venerable oak that has bowed before many a blast, and been stripped by degrees of its leafy honours; but that now has nothing to lose, and braves the fury of the storm inflexible". Smith reported that many young men had fevers but all recovered; Reid differed in developing tympanitis at the fever's crisis. Smith explained this to his father: "a collection of air on the outside of the intestines in the cavity of the abdomen; none of the Professors ever saw it before, the hole in the intestine thro' which it passed was so small as to be found with difficulty on dissection". Though there were no bad fevers in the Infirmary to which those of the students could be attributed, Reid's sudden death alarmed Smith's parents.[104] His mother Frances even forbade her son from attending any further funerals. Smith meekly agreed, but argued that the danger from attending a funeral was very small "compared to what every medical man must often be exposed to". Smith explained his own theory of infection, believing that "every living person is every day exposed to abundant sources of infection, only their constitutions are seldom in a state to receive it so as to produce a fever, but this is only entre nous".

As per his intentions, having completed his second session of winter courses, Smith left Edinburgh for Norwich in the middle of May 1783. As he travelled through Cumberland he was taken seriously ill with pleurisy (an inflammation of the pleura, the lining surrounding the lungs) and was forced to stop at Kirby Lonsdale with the Battys until recovered. Smith had probably suffered such attacks more than once in his youth, though this was the only serious indisposition he suffered during his two years in Edinburgh. Nevertheless, his weak lungs would plague him his whole life. Smith was confined to Kirby Lonsdale for several weeks. This crisis, delaying as it did Smith's much anticipated return home, greatly alarmed his parents. James Snr expressly forbade Smith running any sort of risk on the remainder of his journey, "nor suffer any temptation to botanise, to see the lakes, mountains, or any other natural curiosity, but come home as soon as you can safely, and bless your dear affectionate mother and me with a sight of you".[105] It was not until mid-September that his recovery was complete. Refusing to let it delay any of his plans, he was soon departing the family home once again, this time bound for London, where events were to take an unexpected and significant turn.

CHAPTER TWO

London: The Sale of the Century

Smith arrived in London on 25 September 1783, shortly preceded by Robert Batty, with whom he was to share lodgings for the year at 10 Great Windmill Street. They were in London to enhance their medical education by taking advantage of the city's flourishing private anatomy schools. Just a few doors down the street, at number 16, stood William Hunter's school, one of the earliest founded (1746) after the United Company of Barber-Surgeons lost their monopoly on teaching anatomy and surgery in 1745.

The new provision of private anatomy schools was entirely unregulated, free from the control of governors, universities and medical guilds, so Hunter's course was able to reflect the most up-to-date thinking. Whilst students remained spectators at the Company of Surgeons (the Barber-Surgeons split at the same time as losing their monopoly), Hunter was advertising courses at which "Gentlemen may have the opportunity of learning the Art of Dissecting [...] in the same manner as in Paris".[1] The adoption of the 'Paris method', by which each student had a corpse to dissect and study with his own hands, was a major advance in the teaching of medicine in Britain. This reflected a growing trend towards "anatomico-clinical" medicine, in which objective practice and observation were encouraged.[2] During his second year at Edinburgh, Smith had become increasingly exasperated by some of the outmoded teaching methods, and believed medicine to be in:

> The most barbarous condition of any science, and only just emerging from the greatest darkness and absurdity. It is com-

> monly declared by all practitioners that Theory is nonsense, and that experience, that is empiricism, is everything.[3]

In addition to developing a comprehensive system of anatomy and physiology, Hunter also assembled an unrivalled museum of specimens to aid his teaching and demonstrations. His school offered the opportunity to "break from the narrow introduction to medicine secured through apprenticeship or the English universities". As proof of its success and influence, it acted as a "nursery for other private medical schools and established London as a centre for medical education".[4]

Though the location of Smith and Batty's lodgings suggests that they were in London to study at the Great Windmill Street school, other establishments soon distracted them. Hunter had died on 30 March 1783, just a few months before their arrival, and management of the school had passed to his nephew, Matthew Baillie. While he successfully maintained the quality of the course, he was no Hunter. Fortunately, there was another Hunter in London: John, the younger brother of William, who had that very year set up his own anatomy school in Castle Street (off Leicester Square, now underneath the present Charing Cross Road). Smith and Batty were "charmed" with John Hunter, stating "he alone is worth coming to live in London for".[5] There was just one problem: Smith had never convincingly conquered his fear of dissection. In direct contravention of the proven benefits of the 'Paris method', he confessed to his father shortly after arrival that on "seeing the dissecting-room, which is abominable and horrid beyond conception, I found it very easy to persuade myself that I could do without being anything more than a spectator there".[6]

In October, after "mature consideration", he instead enrolled as a physician-pupil at St Bartholomew's Hospital. Though the fee was high, between 21 and 25 guineas, it gave "all the privileges of a surgeon's pupil" without having to "dissect with my own hands but only attend the dissecting-room". He promised his father that he would "occasionally handle the knife myself": whether he ever summoned the courage to do so is unknown.[7] Smith's teacher at St Bartholomew's was Dr David Pitcairn, the hospital's physician. Pitcairn was a skilled practitioner, gentle and dignified in manner, honest in his opinions, and frank in acknowledging what he considered the limitations of medicine. Through his employment as physician in the country's largest hospital he became acquainted with the great and the good, as well as the abject and low. Pitcairn was an inspirational figure for Smith; a successful, respected physician, who could move easily in society and, away from the wards, could indulge his extracurricular scientific interests.

The Immortal Banks

As in Edinburgh, James Snr encouraged his son to make the most of the social advantages before him. He even increased his allowance, trusting that his son would "not go beyond the bounds of prudence and moderation". London had enough fops, "fribbles" (a frivolous person—and a favourite insult of James Snr's) and questionable characters to concern any parent, but James Snr was content to leave his son "without control, at a critical time of life; situated in the midst of all the fascinating pleasures, and the most alluring temptations, that the most sumptuous, most luxurious, and most vicious and corrupt capital in Europe, or perhaps the whole world, can produce".[8]

Smith's Edinburgh friends, on the other hand, were concerned, not so much for Smith's morals but his not having "an opportunity of indulging [his] botanical inclination". Thomas Charles Hope, the son of Dr Hope, was convinced that Smith would be stranded in a botanical desert unless he could access "some of the famous horti sicci [herbarium collections] which I dare say are numerous".[9] This was a fairly accurate appraisal: aside from a few trips to the gardens of Kew and Chelsea, Smith does not appear to have collected many specimens during his time in London. What he lacked in new plants, however, he more than made up for with his acquisition of the friendship of the influential Sir Joseph Banks, president of the Royal Society and the most famous British botanist of his day.

Banks, like Smith, possessed a childhood interest in plants that developed into an adolescent ardour for botany. Fabulously wealthy, he dedicated his income of £6,000 a year to enthusiastically pursuing his interest in natural history. In 1768 he joined Captain James Cook's *Endeavour* voyage to observe the 1769 transit of Venus as the expedition's botanist, using his own money to recruit a scientific team including the botanist Daniel Solander—one of Linnaeus's 'Apostles'—two artists, a scientific secretary and two servants. They returned to Britain in 1771 having mapped the coast of New Zealand, 'discovered' and mapped the coast of eastern Australia and collected thousands of new specimens. On their return Banks and Solander became the talk of London, so much so that King George III received Banks even before Cook, and quickly became a lasting friend. From 1772 he was advising on the management of the royal gardens at Kew and sending plant collectors around the world. Elevated to baronetcy in 1781, he joined the Privy Council in 1797 and was described by a contemporary as "His Majesty's Ministre des Affaires Philosophiques".[10]

Banks soon rose to prominence in scientific circles, too. In 1778, aged 35, and 10 years younger than most of his predecessors, he was elected President of the Royal Society. An avowed naturalist in a Society where the "presiding deity [...] was Newton", he went on to become the longest ever serving President.[11] Linnaeus addressed him in a letter as "the immortal Banks", and the old Swede regretted that he would likely never see Banks's Australian discoveries published. In reality, not even the youngest of Banks's contemporaries lived to see this. Despite paying, at great expense, for the engraving of the *Endeavour* plates, they were not fully published until the late 20th century as *Banks's Florilegium* (1980–1990). However, what he lacked in publications he more than made up for through his skills as a scientific facilitator, administrator and promoter. In 1777 he bought 32 Soho Square, which, through a combination of Banks's outstanding collections and open hospitality, quickly became the chief meeting place for London's scientists and natural historians. One of his first foreign visitors, the Swedish Linnaean 'Apostle' Carl Peter Thunberg, rated Soho Square "an Academy of Natural History".[12] The only requirements for entry were scientific skill and enthusiasm: age, rank, wealth or nationality bore no consequence.

Smith made his first appearance at Soho Square on 28 September 1783, just three days after moving to London. His introduction probably came

No. 32 Soho Square, London; Sir Joseph Banks's home and the centre of British botany for over 40 years.

via Dr Hope, although the French botanist Pierre Broussonet and the Norwich botanists were also likely conduits. In any case, Banks was already aware of Smith's botanical skills, for John Pitchford had been communicating his finds for some time; in April 1782 Banks and his librarian, Daniel Solander, had identified Smith's *Lichen miniatus* as *Lichen deustus*.[13]

Any first time visitor to Banks's house usually had to submit to the ordeal of the weigh-in. From 1778 to 1814, Banks faithfully recorded the weights of his visitors in a special book. On that first visit, Smith weighed 9st 3lb 8oz (almost 59 kilograms), showing how slight he had remained; he is the lightest adult male recorded in the book. The Banks family, comprising Banks, his wife, Dorothea, and sister, Sarah Sophia Banks, by contrast, dominated the scales. They weighed themselves regularly, and from a modest beginning of 13st 10lb for Sir Joseph, 8st 12lb for Lady Banks and 11st 8lb for Miss Banks, they steadily ballooned in weight to reach, respectively, 16st 3lb, 13st 12lb, and 14st 3lb. Some blame may be laid at the door of Mary Esam, the cook, who, in 1780, weighed in at 18st.[14]

The Sale of the Century

Smith made a favourable impression at Soho Square and was soon in regular attendance, including at Banks's famous breakfast parties. It was at one of these, on the morning of 23 December 1783, that the course of Smith's life was to change forever.

On the death of Carl Linnaeus in 1778, Banks had offered his heirs between £1,050 and £1,200 for his scientifically invaluable herbarium. Linnaeus's only son and successor as professor of medicine and botany, also Carl (hereafter Linnaeus the Younger), rejected this as a "cruel offer" and kept the herbarium for his own use. However, on 1 November 1783, Linnaeus the Younger unexpectedly died, and the collections reverted to the elder Linnaeus's widow and daughters, who sought to realise the financial value. No longer just the herbarium, the sale now included the entirety of the elder and younger Linnaeus's natural history and medicine collections, "an immense hortus siccus, with duplicates, insects, shells, corals, materia medica [papers and materials relating to the teaching of medicine], fossils, a very fine library, [and] all the unpublished manuscripts".[15] The family engaged Johan Gustaf Acrel, a physician and former pupil of Linnaeus, as their agent for selling the collections, fixed at 1,000 guineas. Considering that Banks had previously offered up to £1,200 for just the herbarium of Linnaeus the elder, this was an extremely competitive price for what amounted to one of the most important natural history collections ever assembled. There was certainly pressure to settle the business as quickly as possible, and theories have been offered that they feared that King Gustav III, a great admirer of Linnaeus, who happened to be outside the country at the time, would oblige them to be sold to the University of Uppsala at an even cheaper rate.[16] Knowing that Banks was the last to enquire, and that he would presumably have ready money, Acrel immediately sent two letters to his London contacts. The first was to Dr John Henry Engelhart, the son of the physician to the Swedish King and Smith's formerly dissolute roommate, to offer the collection directly to Banks. The second was to Jonas Carlsson Dryander, another pupil of Linnaeus and Daniel Solander's successor as Banks's librarian, to press Banks for a decision.

Banks received Engelhart's forwarded letter at Soho Square on the morning of 23 December. On reading the offer, Banks announced that he intended to decline it and instead handed the letter to Smith, urging him to make the purchase "as a thing suitable to [his] taste, and which would do [him] honour".[17] Smith met with Engelhart that same day and they both wrote to Acrel; Engelhart to endorse Smith, and Smith to request a full catalogue and the promise that if it met with his expectations he would purchase at the proposed price.

It is unclear why Banks declined the collections for himself. Various theories have been offered, including that the American War of Independence had significantly reduced his income; that he was daunted by the idea of housing such a vast collection; or that Banks was no longer as interested in botany as he had been when younger, now more administrator than naturalist. Recognising Smith's botanical talents and personal charms, Banks may also have been selflessly giving Smith the chance of a lifetime. Banks knew the possibilities and opportunities opened by possession of a unique collection, and Smith had the knowledge and patience to fully exploit them for the benefit of not just himself but also the scientific community. More selfishly, there could be great advantage in having a young and impressionable friend absorb the expense of purchasing and housing such a collection, and who would presumably grant privileged access to the noble patron that enabled the acquisition.

Though he was now 24 years old, Smith was still financially dependent on his father, and it was to him he now turned for the not inconsiderable sum of 1,000 guineas (at this time, a successful draper like Smith's father could hope to earn up to £500 a year). He wrote the next day, 24 December, carefully phrasing the proposal so as to present the acquisition of the collection as a potentially advantageous part of his future career: "I am so ambitious as to wish to possess this treasure, with a view to settling as a physician in London, and read lectures on natural history". He attempted to hurry his father to a decision by stating that, "there is no time to be lost, for the affair is now talked of in all companies, and a number of people wish to be purchasers". He appealed to the merchant in his father by emphasising the collection's monetary potential, including its "invaluable" manuscripts and letters, particularly the dissertations of which only small part had been previously published in *Amœnitates Academicæ* (1763). He added that Sir Joseph Banks and Dr Pitcairn, as well as many of his other friends, approved "highly" of his intention.

Though his father's reply has not survived, it was sufficiently discouraging to "produce great uneasiness and alarm", and was followed by another, advising great caution.[18] Behind the scenes, Banks encouraged Smith to continue with his appeals and subtly exerted his own influence by asking Dryander to submit a report on the collections as he had seen them *in situ*, in Sweden. Smith's persistence paid off, and on 12 January 1784 he received a letter from his father giving tentative approval for the purchase. The momentary denial of his son's wishes had occasioned James Snr much pain: "had I but you I had not hesitated one moment, every shilling of my specie [money in the form of coins rather than notes] should be at your devotion". As it was, he had 6 other children to clothe and feed, as well as continuing to fund Smith's London lifestyle. He still had many reservations, chief of all being the collections' sheer bulk. Dryander's report was in fact counterproductive, as James Snr was now concerned it would require "no small nor inelegant house to place so capital a collection and library in a commodious manner". Neither could he believe that Sweden would let such a magnificent collection leave the country for such a comparatively small sum, or that the sellers would suffer any compunction in satisfying a higher bidder. He warned his son not to fixate on it with "the enthusiasm of a lover, or the heat of an ambitious man", lest the purchase should fail.[19]

In early April, Smith received two letters from Acrel in short succession, opening negotiations between London and Uppsala. The first contained the requested catalogue, at which point Smith and Banks realised that the collections had been somewhat undersold, and were in fact much more comprehensive than either of them anticipated: 19,000 sheets of pressed plants, 3,198 insects, 1,564 shells, plus a further 200 uncatalogued specimens, between 700 and 800 pieces of coral, 2,424 minerals, 45 birds, 158 fish, 3,000 books, numerous manuscripts, and the collected correspondence of the elder Linnaeus, amounting to around 3,000 letters. Many of the books were rare or valuable, as he hastened to inform his father, including:

> The King of Denmark's book of shells, like that at Cambridge; Sloane's *Jamaica*, worth ten or twelve guineas; and many others worth from five to ten pounds; besides a complete collection of the most useful books in natural history, and many medical books. [...] There are also a few books which from their extreme scarcity sell for an exorbitant price.[20]

The second letter was less encouraging, announcing that a small herbarium collected by Linnaeus the Younger following his father's death was to be given to Baron Clas Alströmer to satisfy a debt of 200 Swedish riksdaler (about £55 in Smith's time). Unwilling to split the collections, the executors had offered everything to Baron Alströmer for the same price Smith was offering, 1,000 guineas. Rejecting Alströmer's offer of 2,200 riksdaler (£462 10s), the small herbarium had gone to the Baron after all, and Smith was offered a hundred guinea discount. Smith was frustrated by this unexpected alteration, but replied to say he accepted the new terms: 900 guineas for the remaining collections, with 450 guineas to be paid as soon as the bargain was concluded and the rest following six months later.[21]

As James Snr had feared, elements of the Swedish scientific community were also mounting an attempt to retain this "state jewel" in the country. Carl Peter Thunberg, Uppsala's Professor of Botany and Medicine, convinced the Secretary of State to write to the King, who was still absent in southern Europe, to intervene, but it appears the communication was never received. Thunberg also wrote to Jonas Dryander, before hearing of Smith's involvement, to try and discourage Banks from purchasing the collection, or at the very least leave the collection of English plants in Sweden. After his own offer was rejected, Baron Alströmer motioned for the University of Uppsala to purchase them, but they were unable to match Smith's offer. Anders Dahl, a former student of Linnaeus, also made a bid with the support of a Gothenburg merchant, though this was apparently too vague against the certainty of Smith's offer. Interest was also being received from further afield, including unlimited offers from a Russian nobleman reportedly acting on behalf of Catherine the Great, enquiries from John Sibthorp, the Professor of Botany at Oxford, currently in Göttingen, Saxony, on a

Radcliffe travelling scholarship, as well as unspecified interest from parties in Paris. Fortunately for Smith, the honourable Acrel had committed the Linnaeus family to the offer from London until either the sale completed or he relinquished his interest. Having received final approval from his father in a letter of 12 April, Smith committed to buying the collections a few days later in a letter of his own to Acrel.

After confirming with Acrel, Smith lost little time in informing his Norwich friends, writing to them personally to ensure they heard the news first-hand. Smith took great pride in the manner in which the purchase had been achieved. Informing Thomas Woodward of those whom he had "cut out" in the race, he exclaimed "is not this a good piece of Generalship?". He also acknowledged the significant role Dr Engelhart had played, their friendship allowing him "to conclude the bargain whilst the rest of the world [was] beginning to enquire if the Collection [were] to be sold or not". Woodward congratulated Smith on the acquisition, "undoubtedly the most valuable that could come into the hands of any naturalist", and was soon offering his advice on its management. He presumed that Smith would be interested in just the herbarium, and recommended selling the valuable, scarcer books, which "probably have no very great attraction except their rarity", the shells, which "would probably fetch a very good price", and the fish and insects "on account of their very perishable nature".[22] John Pitchford commented on the great boon the arrival of this treasure afforded to British botanists, who would "now have an opportunity of knowing what natives of his own country are in the *Sp. Pl.* [*Species Plantarum*, first published by Linnaeus in 1753, listed every species of plant known at the time]".[23]

Now began the long wait, as James Snr gathered the first 450 guineas and drew up a bill of exchange, to be sent to Acrel via a trading house in Amsterdam. In the meantime, father and son made enquiries so as to limit their exposure to any custom-house dues on receipt of the collections. On 31 August 1784, Smith wrote to his father with some delight, informing him that thanks to Sir John Jervis, naval hero, MP for Yarmouth and later Earl of St Vincent, "an order had come from the treasury, that every thing except the books should be admitted [...] without duty, or any charges whatever". The duty on the books came to £98 15s. Just over a week later, Smith received news that Acrel had received the first 450 guineas and had duly dispatched the collections, which were to travel from Uppsala to London via Stockholm. Here they waited six weeks in a warehouse till they could be loaded onto the English brig *Appearance*, the first suitable ship bound for England, which embarked on the 17 September.[24]

With such a fortuitous sale, Acrel soon began to incur the displeasure of his scientific colleagues.[25] Smith always defended Acrel, and went on record when he gave an account of the purchase to Joseph Trapp, the translator of Dietrich Stoever's *Life of Linnaeus* (1794):

> All sorts of false reports have been raised against [Acrel], such as, I bribed him with 100 guineas, which however is so far from being the case, that he never had a present from me, except a few English books out of the Linnaean library, (worth about 6 or 8 guineas), which he desired to purchase of me, as he could not get them in Sweden, and which I prevailed on him with some difficulty to accept. I thought this a very small and inadequate return for the trouble he had on my account, and it could surely not be considered a bribe.[26]

Smith privately agreed with Acrel that it was "certainly a disgrace to the University [of Uppsala] that they suffered such a treasure to leave them, but that is not your fault or mine, and if those who ought most to have loved and protected the immortal name of Linné failed in their duty, he shall not want a friend or an asylum while I live, or have any power, though ever so small, to do him honour".[27]

Anders Dahl had made the greatest effort of any Swede to retain the collections in their native country. Such was his resistance to a foreign sale that he was still maintaining that the King should be "graciously moved" to reclaim the collections, "not only whilst they were in Stockholm, but even while on board ship ready to start". Linnaeus's herbarium, in his own words "the greatest collection the world has ever seen", had been a working collection: the descriptions of plants in his publications were taken from his own specimens. However, the descriptions were often so succinct that without an engraving it was impossible to identify the plants, so it was essential to refer to the original specimens used in the composition of the work in order to ascertain those names. Dahl feared that "foreigners would always taunt the Swedes for their inability to retain such precious collections; that the possessor would become a Dictator in Science, and lovers of it would be obliged to impart their discoveries to him". In the years following the purchase an apocryphal story arose that the Gustav III returned just as the *Appearance* departed, dispatching, unsuccessfully, a warship to bring the collections back. Smith had no knowledge of this story three years after the acquisition, "though afterwards spoke of and believed it". The story was further perpetuated in 1800 when Robert Thornton depicted the chase under a portrait of Smith in his *New Illustration of the Sexual System of Linnaeus*.[28]

Evidence relating to this period of Smith's life, other than in connection to the collections, is scarce, but it is clear that Smith did not remain idle. His medical training continued, as he informed Woodward that the purchase was "not to interrupt my going to Edinburgh next winter". However, he was now planning to spend just one further year there, rather than the initially planned two years, before returning to London in the autumn of 1785 to "form a plan for my final situation". For the time being he wished "to have it believed that [he] still [meant] to fix in Norwich" after the conclusion of his studies.[29]

Smith's introduction to the botanical community had also continued. In February 1784, thanks to an introduction from his Edinburgh cohort Jonathan Stokes, Smith began correcting and commenting on the proofs of the second edition of William Withering's *The Botanical Arrangement of All the Vegetables Naturally Growing in Britain* (1787–1792), the first edition of which, published in 1776, had quickly become a standard botanical text. In May, Withering thanked Smith "most sincerely for the very judicious and liberal criticisms" he made, and appears to have taken Smith's advice over the accenting of the generic and trivial names, "as most people seemed to concur with your opinion". Withering, in complete innocence, wrote to Smith of some tentative plans to compare specimens with

Linnaeus's son before his death, "but we hear the whole collection is coming to England, though ignorant into whose hands it has fallen".[30]

On 9 February 1784, Smith was elected a member of the Society for the Promotion of Natural History (SPNH). The SPNH had been founded only a little over a year before, on 13 October 1782, the inspiration of William Forsyth, superintendent of Chelsea Physic Garden, and his friend, George Prince, its object "Natural History in all its branches". Smith had been proposed by Forsyth and seconded by Isaac Swainson, a medical botanist who had used the profits of a dubious patent medicine known as Velnos' Vegetable Syrup to develop an extensive botanical garden at his home at Heath Lane Lodge, Twickenham. The SPNH met once a month at the Black Bear Inn in Piccadilly, with members encouraged to bring "the most curious and rare specimens in natural history, which he can possibly obtain" for examination and discussion.[31] Papers were also submitted. The SPNH filled a need, though it was not without problems. Despite the presence of Banks as President, there was little scope for the natural historical sciences at the Royal Society. From the early days of the Royal Society, when it was formed "of all sorts of men, of the Gown, of the Sword, of the Shop, of the Field, of the Court, of the Sea; all mutually assisting each other", it had become increasingly exclusive.[32] By the mid-18th century it could be said: "men of high social status joined easily, those of middling status less so, and those of low social class not at all".[33] In fact, the Society had been in something of a decline since the death of Sir Isaac Newton in 1727, with grumblings about the abandonment of pure mathematics and a springing up of rival organisations. These ranged from informal groups congregating in the coffee houses based around the Royal Exchange in the City, to the establishment of the Society of Arts in 1745, "concerned with manufactures in a way which the Royal Society was not".[34] Tellingly, none of the SPNH's five founding members were Fellows of the Royal Society (FRS). The SPNH was much cheaper, with an entrance fee of 10s 6d, and a quarterly fee of 2s 6d (compared to the Royal Society's 5 guinea entrance fee and £2 12s annual subscription). The only prerequisite for becoming a member of the SPNH was to be "a known lover of natural history", and recommendation by two existing members. It was also socially equalising.

At the SPNH, gardeners, surveyors and other tradesmen were able to mix as equals with famous FRS like John Hunter, David Pitcairn and Josiah Wedgwood.

Smith was quickly disappointed by the SPNH, and after joining attended only sporadically. Its objects were not clearly defined, to the point where members were not even sure what exhibits were appropriate. One such instance occurred when William Thomson showed an unusual specimen of glass, which a member objected to as "not being a part of Natural History". A motion was raised, whether "such specimens as are the result of Artificial Chemical operations shall be considered as a part of Natural History", which a humiliated Thomson seconded; the result was in the negative. There was also a preponderance of mineral and fossil specimens, to the point that agricultural writer Edmund Rack accidently addressed a paper to "the President and Members of the Fossil Society in London". Despite these frustrations, the SPNH performed a useful function in initiating connections between members. It was at the SPNH that Smith met or developed his friendships with Samuel Goodenough and Thomas Marsham, amongst others, both of whom were to play a significant role in the other great achievement of his young adult life: the establishment of the Linnean Society of London.

The Arrival of the Linnaean Collections

In anticipation of the delivery of the Swedish cargo, on 13 September 1784 Smith moved from Great Windmill Street to 14 Paradise Row, Chelsea. He was still planning to return to Edinburgh in October: on 23 September he informed his physician friend Jonathan Stokes that he was waiting until the summer of 1785 "to examine the whole, and hope then to be able to make it of use to the scientific world".[35] As the time for departing approached there was still no word of the *Appearance*'s arrival and Smith's resolve began to slip. By mid-October he had decided to stay in London another year, in order to safely receive and conduct a first examination of the collections. Smith's Edinburgh friends were disappointed at the postponement; Thomas Charles Hope wrote how his expectations of seeing Smith "are now blasted and have ended in nothing", but neither he nor

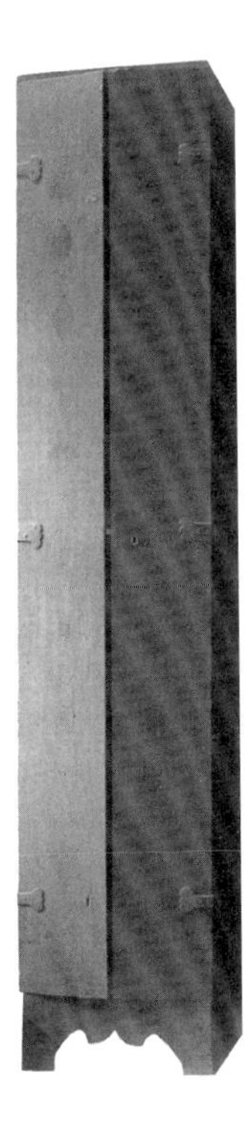

One of Linnaeus's original herbarium cabinets, used to transport part of the collections to England.

his father, Dr Hope, were surprised, "knowing that you so fond of natural history would not be satisfied with a transient glance of the noble Linnaean museum". According to Hope, William Younge, who succeeded Smith as President of the Natural History Society back in Edinburgh, "storms and rages at the alteration of your plans, which have proved a great disappointment to him".[36]

The *Appearance* finally arrived in London on the 26 October. Jonas Dryander received a letter from Claes Grill, a Swedish importer based at Dunster Court, Mincing Lane, informing him that "26 boxes marked IES containing the collection of the late Linaus" had arrived from Stockholm, and needed to be collected within the week.[37] Smith paid £80 for the freight and £5 to the captain, a price he considered "too much by half", but which he willingly gave over, keen as he was "to avoid all delay".[38] However, on 8 November, Smith's father, in London for the occasion, informed a friend that they had not yet been able to examine "the Museum" as some of it was still on the ship, almost a week after Grill's injunction.[39] The total cost of the collections, including freight and charges, came to £1088 5s.

Smith continued to receive congratulations on his acquisition. The ornithologist John Latham wrote to Robert Batty for an introduction to Smith, and asked if he could visit when next in London "in order to treat myself with what I never expected it would fall to the lot of an Englishman to possess".[40] John Sibthorp begrudgingly offered his congratulations from Göttingen, enlightening Smith on how fortunate he had been to close the deal with Acrel "a short time before he received a letter from me offering 1,000 guineas". However, the disappointment he felt was "in great measure alleviated by the kind opportunity you offer me of consulting upon my return to England".[41] There was a peculiar national pride in Smith having brought the collections to England. The Revd Samuel Goodenough, a headmaster in Ealing and member of the SPNH, informed Smith that his "noble purchase of the Linnaean cabinet most decidedly sets Britain above all other nations in the Botanical empire".[42] Stokes had similar sentiments, revealing his joy "in finding that one of his countrymen, animated by a love of science, has had the spirit to make the purchase, and import into his own country so valuable a collection".[43] From France, Broussonet and Charles Louis L'Héritier de Brutelle also sent their felicitations. In his very first letter to Smith, the latter informed him: "had the death of the younger Linnaeus occurred six months later, I should perhaps have competed with you for them". L'Héritier also offered to buy the whole at purchase cost, including freight and duties. More seriously, he also offered to purchase any plant duplicates at Smith's price.[44] Smith received much interest in other parts of the collection, including from Sibthorp, who requested first refusal should Smith choose to dispose of any of the component parts.[45] Smith offered Woodward first refusal on any duplicate books.[46]

James Snr, knowing that his son would carefully consider anything recommended by his Norwich friends, was anxious for Smith to seek their advice as to the management of the collections. Pitchford, whilst conceding that Smith must "unavoidably be much engrossed by the variety and pleasingness of the many objects about you", strongly recommended getting everything in order and taking a complete catalogue before considering whether to dispose of any of it. Pitchford also advised caution over any publication of the manuscripts, considering the amount of time required to verify any alterations made in the herbarium. Instead he suggested an original work, "which I am sure you have in your power to publish yourself and you only, provided you could have possession of Ray's plants, viz a *Flora Britannica*, the most correct that can appear in the Linnaean dress".[47] Woodward also recommended publication of such a work.[48] Sir Joseph Banks and Jonas Dryander offered their advice in person.

Shortly after arrival, and for the next seven months, Smith, Banks and Dryander carefully arranged and sorted the collections, focusing on the herbarium. Smith used a copy of the 14th edition of Linnaeus's *Systema Vegetabilium* (1784, preserved in the Linnean Society Library), a gift from Banks, as his guide to the herbarium, making extensive annotations; he ticked those species that the three men agreed were the specimens described by Linnaeus. According to a later statement by Smith, the Banksian herbarium was compared with the Linnaean "throughout, to their mutual advantage, by a copious interchange, not only of information, but of specimens".[49] Smith quickly established his ownership of the collections: there is evidence that the herbarium was rearranged to reflect the arrangement in his edition of *Systema Vegetabilium*, and on the title-page of every publication Smith inscribed "E. Bibl. propr. Linn. 1784". Smith also outright gifted Banks 83 specimens from the herbarium in January 1785, largely exotics first given to Linnaeus by the Spanish botanist José Celestino Mutis. Smith did not consider this a mutilation; the gifting of duplicates and fragments (and sometimes originals!) allowed Smith to curry favour and influence and to exercise his newfound privileges as the possessor of an internationally significant collection.

Though Paradise Row could never rival Soho Square, Smith became a new focal point for the botanical community. The Linnaean collections were still in disorder at the end of January 1785, particularly those of Linnaeus the Younger, when Smith began receiving visitors.[50] Thomas Woodward and Robert Stone, another Norfolk botanist, were early visitors, the former being particularly excited having heard that the Linnaean mosses had thrown the British mosses into "entire confusion".[51] Margaret Cavendish Bentinck, the Duchess of Portland, one of the great natural history collectors of her day, visited in May, just three months before her death, taking some small memorials of Linnaeus with her. Her chaplain, the Revd John Lightfoot, author of *Flora Scotica*, thanked Smith for the sight of the "magnificent collection", which had afforded "the mightiest gratification to the Duchess [...] and the little presents you made her obliged her extremely".[52]

On 17 February 1785, Smith's nomination for election to the Royal Society was submitted and received wide support: George Fordyce, chemist and teacher at St Thomas' Hospital; John Lightfoot; William Hudson; John Whitehurst, scientific instrument maker; Alexander Garden, botanist and physician; Sir John Cullum, 6th baronet and antiquary; Charles Combe, apothecary; Richard Price, a dissenting preacher and intimate friend of Benjamin Franklin and Joseph Priestley; David Pitcairn; and John Hunter—all signed his nomination form.[53] Smith also had the approval of President Sir Joseph Banks. Smith told his father he "thinks I have no fear of being rejected; at least, he says, I shall have him on my side". Smith's impressive list of supporters shows how adeptly he moved within London's social and scientific circles. Smith was duly elected on 26 May, "without a single black ball", as he informed his father, which he found "very flattering, and I believe gave my good friend the President great pleasure". James Snr acknowledged the honour Smith's unopposed election to the Royal Society conferred, but as he rose to greater and greater prominence advised caution in his interactions: "I would only wish to guard you against either the flatteries or circumventions of pretended friends, and men who may be interested in misleading your conduct with respect to it".[54]

Smith was also receiving much advice on his own potential publications. As already identified by Pitchford and Woodward, there was a pressing need for a *Flora Britannica*. In May 1785 Smith informed Acrel that he had already been labouring on such a project for several years, "which the Linnaean Herbarium will now enable me to make perfect".[55] James Snr was anxious for any publication to be delayed until the completion of his son's medical studies, but Woodward thought that Smith "ought to strike whilst the iron was hot" and that "publishing your name as proprietor, may be of more use to you in your profession, than the delay can be".[56] John Lightfoot "freely and unsolicited promised me his assistance, and the

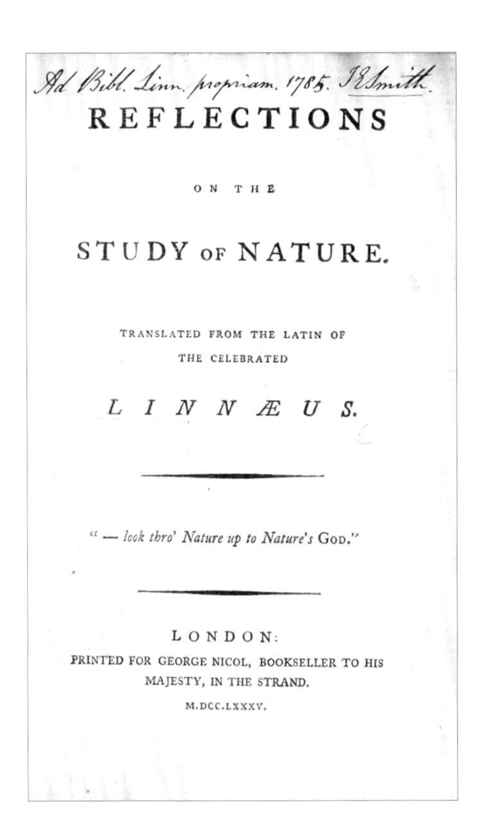

Ad Bibl. Linn. propriam. 1785. JE Smith.

REFLECTIONS

ON THE

STUDY OF NATURE.

TRANSLATED FROM THE LATIN OF
THE CELEBRATED

L I N N Æ U S.

"— *look thro' Nature up to Nature's* GOD."

LONDON:
PRINTED FOR GEORGE NICOL, BOOKSELLER TO HIS
MAJESTY, IN THE STRAND.
M.DCC.LXXXV.

Smith's first publication, *Reflections on the Study of Nature* (1785).

use of all the notes he has made", and a request to utilise the herbarium of Sir Joseph Banks "of course was granted".[57] On hearing this, Woodward changed tack and now reasoned that no one would dare supersede Smith in publication. It was now incumbent on Smith "to take care that the promised work should be as perfect as possible, and consequently more enlarged in its plan than what I at first proposed".[58] Smith had still bigger plans in store. He informed Acrel that he would "at my leisure publish all the works of Linnaeus that are proper, but this will take time".[59]

In the interim, Smith made his first appearance as a published author, albeit anonymously, publishing in June a pamphlet entitled *Reflections on the Study of Nature*. This was a translation of Linnaeus's preface to *Museum Regis Adolphi Friderici* (1754), a catalogue of the King of Sweden's natural history museum. However, it was only notional anonymity: in the preface he identifies the translator as having recently come into possession of the Linnaean library. Smith used his own preface to expound on his beliefs regarding the sanctity of natural history. As described, Linnaeus's preface "begins by showing that this study leads to a proper knowledge of the Deity, then takes a comprehensive view of the economy of nature, and ends with a number of curious and striking facts in the history of a number of animals".[60] Linnaeus's treatise was intended for "the more sensible and ingenuous", not the "triflers in philosophy, who mistake whim and affectation for genius", nor the "pretenders to science [who] affect universal knowledge. What these people cannot attain they treat with contempt; they pollute the holy fountain of truth with their crude and often malicious effusions". His greatest displeasure, though, was reserved for the "men of real learning and skill in particular branches, treating the scientific pursuits of others with contempt". One imagines he had particular individuals in mind, perhaps those at the Royal Society dismissive of the merits of natural history:

> How much soever such men may excel in their own science, and how lofty and important soever that science may be, they can neither be esteemed true philosophers, nor friends of mankind.[61]

Despite his initial promise that the arrival of the Linnaean collections would not alter his plans for a career as a physician, Smith was finding it increasingly difficult to tear himself from the herbarium sheets to attend the dissecting-room. However, he still needed to make a living. John Pitchford acknowledged the dilemma on first hearing that Smith was the purchaser of the Linnaean collections: "the cultivation of natural history cannot be pursued with vigour but by persons of independent fortunes; for others it must only be an amusement, or relaxation from other studies".[62] There was a dearth of salaried posts for naturalists in 18th-century England. Chairs of Botany existed at Oxford and Cambridge, but for the majority of the century they were occupied by father-son successions, who unwittingly competed with each other on the number of years between lectures.[63] A scattering of other positions existed at the British Museum, in the keepership of gardens such as the Chelsea Physic Garden and Kensington Palace, or as a clerk or secretary to the Royal Society. This was in stark contrast to continental Europe, where examples such as Peter

Simon Pallas, salaried by the Imperial Society of St Petersburg, or Carl Linnaeus, producing some of his greatest work whilst professor of medicine and botany at Uppsala University, showed "how effectively the higher educational patronage of *ancien régime* Europe could serve the cause of the advancement of science". In lieu of either a fortune or a salary, the only options remaining for many naturalists of the period was either medicine or the Church. The reasons were obvious: for the former, a knowledge of medicinal plants was an essential for the treatment of disease, whilst for clergymen, the "ascent 'through nature up to nature's God' remained canonical throughout the period".[64]

Impatient to begin, in the summer of 1785 Smith abandoned his plans to return to Edinburgh for the next winter session, and now resolved to obtain a medical degree from the University of Leiden, in Holland. Here a degree could be acquired at any time of year, without the obligation of having to attend a single lecture. Leiden would be followed with a brief foray to Paris to "visit and form acquaintances with ingenious and literary men, especially naturalists".[65] Such a course of action meant Smith would not have to spend another year in the dreaded dissecting rooms, and could instead immediately set up as a physician and botanical author, joining a long line of physician-botanists including William Withering, Richard Pulteney and Erasmus Darwin. Thomas Charles Hope encouragingly noted "the propriety of that step must strike every one, though I mention that an Edinburgh degree is far superior and more honourable than any other".[66] Thomas Charles's father, Dr Hope, was franker: "you have so happy a genius for botany, and so much unremitting zeal for the improvement of the science, that I heartily wish His Majesty, by a good pension, could induce you to give up physic". It appears as though Smith originally intended to embark on his journey before the end of the year but at the end of November James Snr wrote to persuade his son to delay until at least the spring, citing the benefit of the "milder weather, more favourable to your health" and "the safety of your museum and library in the long winter nights".[67] Smith acceded, and began planning for a departure at the start of June 1786 instead.

Smith continued his study of the Linnaean collections throughout the winter of 1785/6. In March, he informed Thomas Woodward: "I have now learned to decipher almost all [Linnaeus's] marks in the herbarium, and having gone through the whole with Sir J Banks am quite master of it. I now know which are the specimens from which he originally described species, and which are acquired since, the places each came from etc, etc, consequently know which are decisive authority and which are not".[68] In the same month he published another translation from the collections, Linnaeus's *Dissertation on the Sexes of Plants*, written in 1759 for the Academy of St Petersburg's competition on the subject, in which "that doctrine was either to be confirmed or refuted by new arguments and experiments".[69] Linnaeus won. This time Smith acknowledged himself as the translator, and dedicated the work to his old professor, Dr John Hope, "as a mark of unfeigned regard". Hope thanked Smith for the honour, and also for the "copy in English dress of a Dissertation I long wished to see".[70] Smith's principal reason for publication was the scarcity of copies of the original in England and elsewhere in Europe, but he also used the preface to defend Linnaeus against his detractors. He focused on refuting attacks made by Lazzaro Spallanzani, an Italian naturalist who had apparently attempted to disprove Linnaeus's theory without having read the dissertation, and Michel Adanson, a French botanist who spent his life developing a universal, natural system of classification:

> The greater part of his adversaries, having either been blinded by envy and prejudice, or most contemptibly ignorant and inexperienced in practical botany, their anathemas against his opinions have proved impotent; their prophecies respecting the success of those opinions, totally false. So that, in spite of all opposition, the system of Linnaeus is even now becoming universal, every part of the world abounding with his disciples; while the *Famille des Plantes* of Monsieur Adanson, professedly written to supersede it, is only occasionally read by those who are disposed to amuse themselves with whimsical paradoxes, presenting themselves in a preposterous orthography, which renders them still more ridiculous and unintelligible.[71]

(History has since pushed aside the artificial 'sexual system' of classification of Linnaeus in favour of the natural system, prototyped by Adanson and popularised by Antoine Laurent de Jussieu's *Genera Plantarum* (1789), but for the time being Smith and the disciples of Linnaeus were triumphant.)

As the time of Smith's departure for Europe came around, he was forced to delay yet again by a "contrary wind". On the 16 June, "after many an anxious look at the lofty plane and cedar trees of Chelsea Garden, still waving in an unpropitious direction", Smith's patience was finally exhausted, and he set out for the port of Harwich on the Essex coast.[72] Initially intending to be away for just a few short months, Smith was eventually absent from England for over a year, not to return to Paradise Row until 2 November 1787.

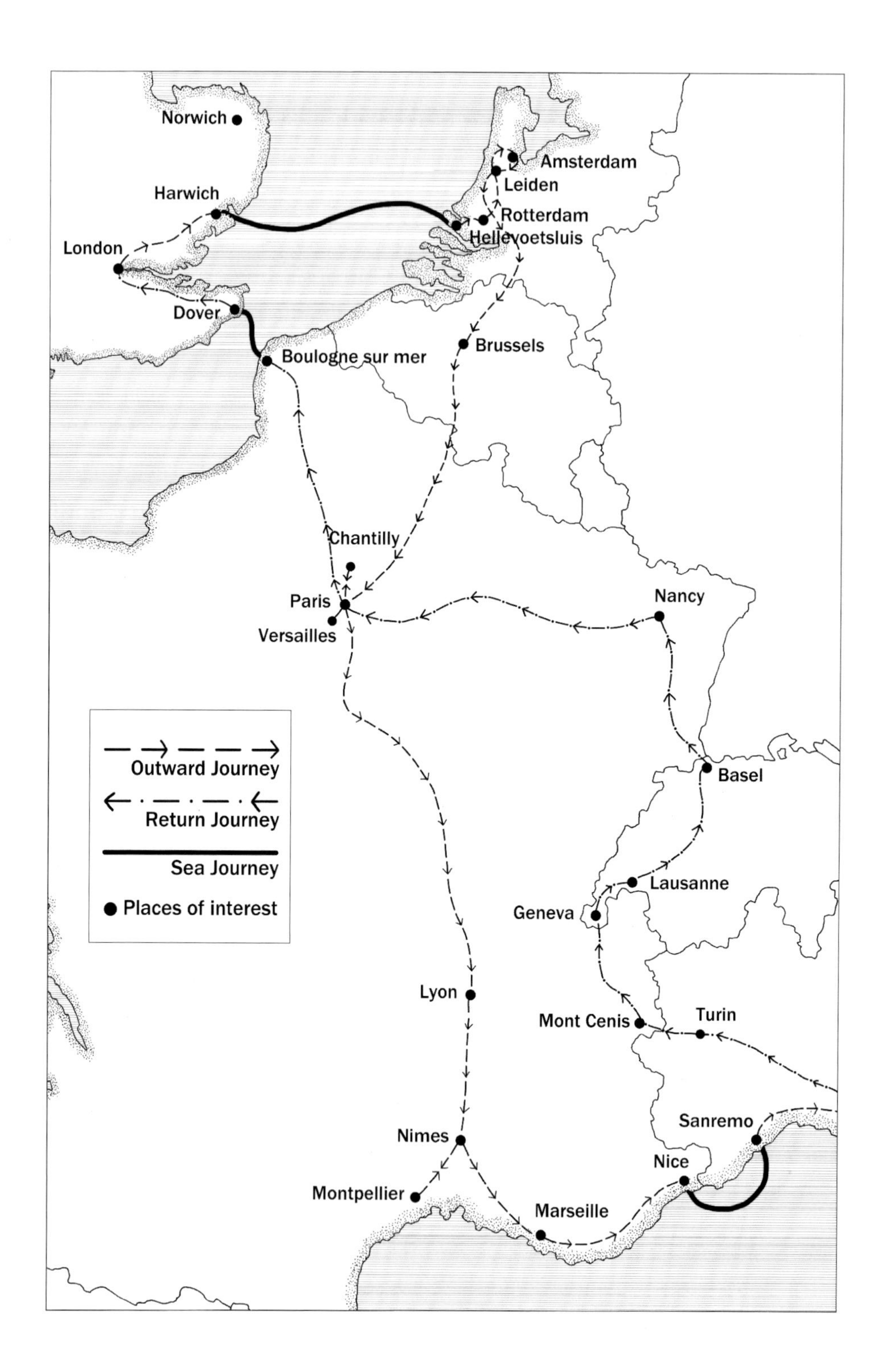

Smith's Grand Tour: The Low Countries and France.

CHAPTER THREE

The Grand Tour

Part I: Harwich to Paris

Smith reached Harwich on 17 June 1786, where he met two unexpected acquaintances also bound for Leiden MDs: Walter Vaughan, an Edinburgh contemporary, and a Mr Mitchell, previously known to Smith by name only. They boarded the boat for Hellevoetsluis in the Netherlands at 3pm that same day. A strong headwind ensured Smith a suitably memorable first sea voyage: he spent the majority of it lying down so as to keep from vomiting, and on the first night the wind blew so hard that the sea flowed over the deck and "came into my cabin dropping on the bed".[1] They disembarked, somewhat bedraggled, three days later.

Smith and his companions immediately set out for Rotterdam in a coach "sumptuously lined with red velvet, and drawn by three horses abreast".[2] They departed for Leiden on 22 June by 'treckskuyt' (horse-drawn barges), arriving at 4pm the same day.[3] The next day, Smith began calling on the professors of the university, in possession of a fulsome letter of introduction from Banks:

> Give me leave to recommend to your notice the bearer of this Mr Smith he is an enthusiast in nat[ura]l history & I really hope one day will become one of the chief supports of that science. He has purchased at a very liberal price the Herb[ariu]m Library & other collections of our great master Linnaeus [...]; you will find him particularly well informed in every branch of natural history but particularly so in botany.[4]

He visited Jean-Nicolas-Sébastien Allamand, Professor of Mathematics and Philosophy, David van Royen, the recently retired Professor of Botany, and Eduard Sandifort, Professor of Anatomy and Surgery. At Sandifort's, Smith and Vaughan were subjected to a 40-minute oral examination on the heart and circulation, "the lungs & most of the viscera, their principal vessels and nerves". Another oral examination on angina and its treatment, and a written examination on two aphorisms of Hippocrates followed the next day at the university. Sandifort objected "a little to them, but at last declared himself well satisfied with me & told me I might take my degree when I pleased".[5] All that remained was the publishing of his thesis (pre-prepared in England with assistance of SPNH colleague Samuel Goodenough, a noted tutor of Latin and Greek) and its successful defence before the professors. Smith's friends had apparently been correct when stating that the gaining of a Leiden MD from would not have anything "very terrific" in it.[6]

Leiden thus far had compared favourably with his time in Edinburgh. Here, all the students were treated "like gentlemen"; he was also impressed with the cleanliness of the streets and buildings, in particular the boarding houses, "though the spitting-pots [for tobacco] placed on the tea-table, [are] often much *too* like the cream-pot in shape".[7] He examined the university's numerous scientific collections, including Dr Vander Wynperse's collection of diseased bones, Professor Allamand's mathematical instruments and museum of natural history, and the university's famous botanical garden.

On 8 July Smith took his thesis, entitled *De Generatione*, to Professor Nicolas George Oosterdijk. Two days later he received approval for its publication.[8] Though it contains little original thought (Smith described it as "trifling" and "an exercise & a sketch"[9]), it demonstrates his desire to see medical science lifted from the "great obscurity [...] [into which it] has been plunged by our ancestors". Through his thesis he hoped "to reveal something about generation [sexual reproduction]; [...] from which it may well emerge how little, not how much, we know of the secret miracles of nature within the body".

Smith was an adherent of the theory of preformation, by which it was believed that the embryo developed from a miniature version of the parent organism. Citing leading preformatists Albrecht von Haller, Charles Bonnet and Lazzaro Spallanzani, Smith asserted that the "internal organs of the female sex" contained the inanimate fundamentals of the progeny, whilst the male seminal fluid provided the "stimulating and nourishing power [through which] life and growth are given to the tiny embryos".[10] Smith also seems to have absorbed something of Linnaeus's medulla-cortex theory, in which the plant was made of inner marrow or pith, and the outer layer or cortex. The marrow was the plant's life-bearer, through which the essential nature of the plant was transmitted to future generations. Preformation was challenged by the theory of epigenesis, championed by Erasmus Darwin amongst others, which held that an embryo developed progressively (importantly this allowed for the inheritance of new traits). Preformation and epigenesis were locked in theoretical battle for the remainder of the 18th century and most of the succeeding century, until cell theory vindicated the general tenets of epigenesis.

One final hurdle remained: on 15 July he defended his thesis *viva voce* against the ranks of 20 assembled "great wigs" of the university, "however thank God I came safe out of their hands, & now have nothing to receive from them except congratulations".[11] Two days later, having achieved his goal of becoming James Edward Smith MD, he left Leiden for Paris,

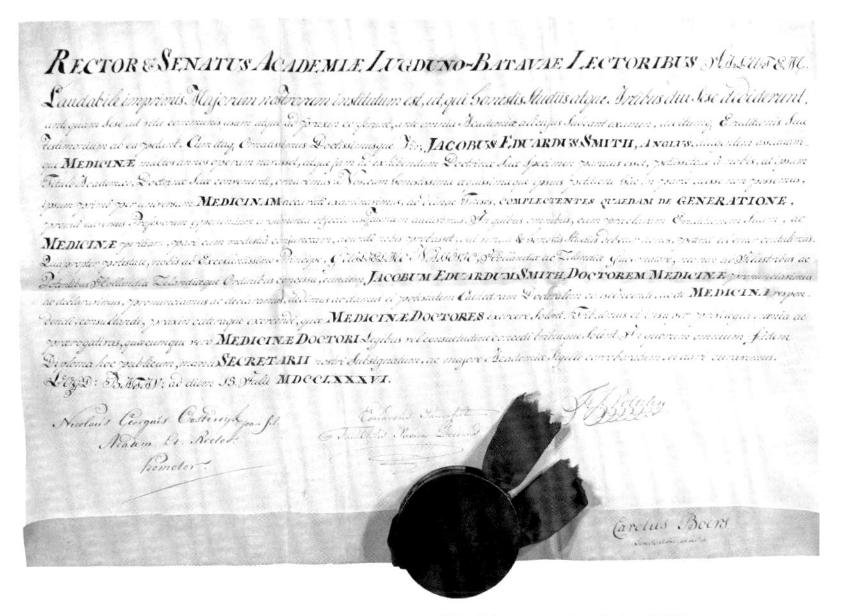
RECTOR & SENATUS ACADEMIÆ LUGDUNO-BATAVAE LECTORIBUS [illegible]

Laudabile imprimis Majorum nostrorum institutum est, ut, qui honestis Studiis atque Artibus diu sese dediderunt, [illegible] ... Testimonium ab ea petant. Cum itaque Ornatissimus Doctissimusque Vir, JACOBUS EDUARDUS SMITH, ANGLUS, [illegible] ... MEDICINÆ multos annos operam navasset, atque jam ad exhibendum Doctrinæ suæ Specimen paratus esset, [illegible] ... ipsum primo per universam MEDICINAM accurate examinavimus, ac deinde Theses, COMPLECTENTES QUAEDAM DE GENERATIONE, [illegible] ... MEDICINÆ peritiam, [illegible] ... Quapropter potestate, nobis ab Excellentissimo Principe, [illegible] NASSOVIO, Hollandiæ ac Zelandiæ Gubernatore, nec non ab Illustribus ac Potentibus Hollandiæ Zelandiæque Ordinibus concessa, eundem JACOBUM EDUARDUM SMITH, DOCTOREM MEDICINÆ pronunciavimus ac declaravimus, [illegible] ... MEDICINÆ respondendi, consultandi, praxin cæteraque exercendi, quæ MEDICINÆ DOCTORES exercere solent. [illegible] ... prærogativas, quæcumque vero MEDICINÆ DOCTORI legibus vel consuetudine concedi tribuique solent. [illegible] ... Diploma hoc publicum, manu SECRETARII nostri Subsignatum, ac majore Academiæ Sigillo corroboratum, [illegible]

[illegible]: ad diem 15 Julii MDCCLXXXVI.

Nicolaus Georgius Oosterdijk [illegible]

Academiæ [illegible] Rector

Promotor

Carolus Boers

Smith's MD, awarded by the University of Leiden on 15 July 1786.

intending to pursue his botanical and artistic interests for a few weeks and take a short trip to the South of France and Geneva, Switzerland, before returning to England.[12]

For Smith, passing through Protestant Holland, the ancestral home of his maternal grandmother, there was something "very delightful in [...] being in a country of universal toleration & unbounded liberty; the first country that afforded an asylum to the protestant reformers".[13] In Delft, he visited the house where, in 1584, a "bigoted hireling" of the Catholic King of Spain had assassinated the Protestant Prince of Orange, William I. On seeing the two holes left in the wall made by the pistol rounds passing through William's body:

> I could not help standing still some minutes in the street to picture to myself what must have passed in the town just after the accident: the running out of the house with the too interesting news, the terror, the despair, the wrath, what must they have been![14]

On 22 July, Smith crossed from Holland into Catholic Belgium. Like many Englishmen as the time, Smith held a deep-seated fear and suspicion of the Catholic Church, feeling that it "drew on credulity and superstition, [which] led to misery, poverty, clerical rule, and oppression".[15] Stopping at an inn on the outskirts of Antwerp, he saw his first ever monk: "his whole deportment was animated with zeal". A statue of Mary stood before the inn, "but it was not to *this* virgin the devotions of my monk were directed". Entering the parlour, Smith accidently disturbed the monk and the landlord's daughter "a pretty plump lass about sixteen. She no doubt was profiting by the holy father's lessons of piety".[16] Throughout his time in Europe, Smith exhibited an uneasy relationship with Catholicism. He was largely unconcerned with the religion of the people, remarking "whatever I may think of some unimportant points of any religion, I always consider such points as [...] entirely a matter of education". As long as religious feeling was utilised for the common good, Smith trusted "mistakes of judgement" would be forgiven. He was, however, less tolerant of those who possessed "scarcely any true principles of religion at all". He reserved most of his ire for the Abbés (the title once strictly referred to abbots, but its application was widened to include all lower-ranking clergy in France from the mid-16th century onwards). These clerics were often engaged as tutors or spiritual advisors in wealthy households. Smith wondered at the "strange blindness" that led parents to entrust the education of their children to men he considered irredeemably "dissolute" and given over to "irregular desires" on account of clerical celibacy.[17]

On 26 July, Smith boarded the coach for Paris. As they neared the city "every thing began to wear a frenchified appearance", as did the group's conversation. Despite the reputable professions and appearance of Smith's fellow travellers, and the presence of ladies, "the most undisguised and shocking descriptions were given of the debaucheries of the capital, and particulars, which would scarcely be whispered in England, discussed with the most minute exactness!"[18] Unfortunately, Smith did not elaborate in either account of his tour; Smith kept a journal for the duration of his time in Europe, writing in it almost every day. Later, in 1793, this journal would be published with much elaboration as *A Sketch of a Tour on the Continent, In the Years 1786 and 1787*. It proved to be both a blessing and a curse to Smith's fortunes.

On his arrival in Paris on 29 July, Smith took a room at the Croix de Fer, Rue St Denis, "a miserable dirty place"; an accidental tour of the kitchen stopped any idea of dining at the table d'hôte.[19] Despite the unfavourable introduction, Smith was to spend the next three months at the same hotel. Fluent in French since childhood, he communicated with the Parisians easily. His friend Pierre Marie Auguste Broussonet, first met at Edinburgh, procured him access to all the "collections, libraries &c, & to every body, at the same time making me acquainted with everything concerning their characters, connections, histories". Even without Broussonet, as possessor of the Linnaean collections, Smith found that "every body looks to me for information, & are eager to communicate any thing to me that I may want". He asked his father "to pray that I may not become too vain, of which I feel the danger, & dread it".[20]

On 6 August, Smith and Broussonet visited Versailles, an essential excursion for any tourist to Paris. In addition to the magnificent palace and gardens, visitors could witness King Louis XVI and family performing their public rituals. Smith saw the royal family process to chapel, part of the crowd all "adoring their grand monarque".[21] Smith noted that the king had "grown fat, & has an agreeable countenance; his ears are remarkable large & ugly. He had some very fine diamonds in his hat". Queen Marie Antoinette was still bedbound after the birth of a daughter.[22] As for the rest of Versailles, Smith was hard to impress. Though the palace was "more superb" than he had thought possible, it lacked "elegance or classical taste". The gardens, too, were "tiresome & not pleasing": the view from the great terrace was "a dreary barren waste", the lake "unpleasantly formal" and the waterworks tired one "with their noise and frequency", yet when they were not playing, "Versailles is the most melancholy spot upon earth".[23, 24]

These remarks were made in *Sketch of a Tour*, published four years into the French Revolution, and, though it is uncertain when he wrote them, they act as a comment on the inherent vacancy at the heart of the French monarchy. Even in 1786, there was little indication that France was on the brink of revolution. Though he made no mention in his manuscript journal, in his published account Smith recalled hearing "much unreserved political talk" in the Parisian salons, the prevailing sentiment being that "the people would not long bear the excessive taxes and excessive oppression under which they groaned". With the benefit of hindsight, Smith stated how this "would infallibly lead to the [storming of the] Bastil[l]e".[25]

They spent the night at the country house of Louis de Noailles, 4th Duke of Noailles in Saint-Germain-en-Laye, 12 miles from the centre of Paris. Noailles had been a correspondent of Linnaeus. Smith credited him with being the first patron of the sexual system in France and for giving Louis XV a taste for gardening and botany.[26] In the Duke's party was a Mr Le Breton, who was translating Smith's two pamphlets into French; according to Smith, when his preface to *Dissertation on the Sexes of Plants* was read to the Duke, "it drew tears from his eyes, & he expressed the highest approbation of it".[27]

Later that day, Noailles, Le Breton, Broussonet and Smith went to watch the King hunting in the forest about Saint-Germain. The King, on foot, was attended by eight pages, 10 or 12 Swiss Guards, a physician and a surgeon. The hunt left Smith shocked:

> On the right & left of the king were people with dogs to raise the game, w[hi]ch had all been collected in this spot as much as possible. Each of the pages carried a loaded gun, so as soon as the King had fired the one in his hand he had another ready straight away. The King walked up and down the field several times and killed almost every thing he aimed at, & the destruction on the whole must be very great.[28]

On hearing there were Englishmen in his train, Louis requested Noailles to ask if they had heard anything of the attempted assassination of King George III by the lunatic Margaret Nicholson, "& bade him tell us that he himself had had a full account of the affair, & that the king was safe". Smith considered this a "very polite piece of condescention"[29], particularly as when they returned to Paris that evening the city was full of reports of George "having been absolutely murdered".[30]

His time in Paris proved so successful that by mid-August Smith had abandoned his plan of travelling further south, resolved to fully exploit his crop of new contacts. Dinner at botanist Jacques Cels's with Charles Louis L'Héritier de Brutelle had garnered introductions to men including polymath Portuguese diplomat the Abbé José Correia da Serra, and naturalist Jean-Baptiste de Monet, the Chevalier de Lamarck, who would later develop the now-discredited Lamarckian theory of evolution. Smith attended the theatre with André Thouin and also looked over his herbarium and received specimens.[31] After a breakfast with botanist René Desfontaines he had the opportunity of looking over the plants and insects Desfontaines had collected in Morocco, and received several specimens of North African plants.[32] The greatest prize, though, was being granted access to the herbaria of Joseph Pitton de Tournefort, who had collected plants from all over Western Europe and the Levant, and Sébastien Vaillant, one of Tournefort's students.[33] Smith intended to look over the whole of Tournefort's herbarium from beginning to end; a daunting but rewarding project. By early October he had described 50 new species previously missed by Linnaeus, and hoped to find as many more.[34] Thomas Woodward was particularly envious of Smith's access to the valuable herbaria of Europe: "the names of the old botanists seem to carry one into enchanted ground, & the travelling thro' the herbaria of Tournefort, Vaillant &c is like taking a journey to Jupiter or Saturn, to verify the number of their satellites, & periods of their revolutions".[35] A less civil encounter occurred in the Jardin du Roi, where Smith ran into Michel Adanson, whom he had criticised in the preface to his translation of *Dissertation on the Sexes of Plants*. Smith reported to Jonas Dryander that Adanson:

> Immediately began to abuse Linn[aeu]s saying he was a great genius but had no learning nor judgement. I put him in mind of *Fundamenta Botanica* [1736 work in which Linnaeus set out his ideas for the reformation of botanical taxonomy]. He said indeed Linn[aeu]s was scholastic but that his abilities were merely artificial. Mark the absurdity! Adanson calls all the plants in the garden by his own hard names & makes the gardeners learn them.

Smith was equally dismissive of Antoine Laurent de Jussieu and Lamarck, snidely commenting that they "pretend to be working most prodigiously hard, doubtless the world will one day be the wiser for it".[36] Between Smith's writing to Dryander and publishing his *Sketch of a Tour*, Jussieu published his *Genera Plantarum* (1789) and established a new benchmark in botanical literature. Smith immediately recognised its value, and in 1793 acknowledged that *Genera Plantarum* would "immortalize" Jussieu, who he now described as a "true philosopher, profound in science, [and] ardent in the pursuit of truth".

The identification and classification of national character was a European obsession at this time, determined by a number of historical and cultural factors, including the country's form of government. Swiss writer Béat-Louis de Muralt summarised the differences between England and France in his *Lettres sur les Anglois et les François* (1725), in which England is depicted as "the land of common sense and reason, of science, of a fierce independence, and especially a spirit of liberty fuelled by a residue of ancient ferocity; whereas France is characterised by the dreary uniformity of custom, a passion for *spirit* which turns out to be vanity, a cult of exteriority, corruption of sexual mores, and political servility".[37]

Smith was gratified to find that the French gave the English "great credit for some particular things, as honesty, feeling, &c, as well as neatness and the conveniences of life". Yet he made no attempt to reciprocate, providing his father with a mean idea of French fashions:

> The daubing of the ladies cheeks is beyond conception, nature is quite out of the question: old hags ugly beyond what you can conceive (for we have very inadequate ideas of what an ugly woman is in England) are dressed like girls, in the most tawdry colours, & have on each cheek a broad dab of the highest pink crayon.[38]

In Paris he saw very few women who could be called "handsome, even if their mask of paint could be stripped off". He admitted that their eyes were "generally indeed good, till they look at you they may please, then the expression is infinitely too strong (may I say too gross?)". He joked to a friend that he expected to fall in love with the first English woman he met on returning.[39]

On 13 September 1786, just a month after deciding to spend the rest of his time on the continent in Paris, he again changed his mind, thanks to an invitation to accompany his friend Broussonet to the latter's hometown of Montpellier in early October. This was to be followed by a visit to the Marquess Ippolito Durazzo in Genoa, a relatively new acquaintance Smith had met in London, then Switzerland and a return to Paris, before arriving back in England in April 1787. Seeking his father's approval of the extension, he requested letters for Turin in order to investigate the textile industry there on James Snr's behalf, knowing "pretty well what you would chiefly examine into, & may perhaps get some hints".[40] He made no mention of his plans to also visit Rome and Naples; on the very same day he wrote to Sir Joseph Banks, requesting a letter of introduction to Sir William Hamilton, the British Ambassador to the Kingdom of Naples.[41] Such duplicity was, in the end, unnecessary—his father was more than happy for an extension to the excursion, which to all intents and purposes had now become a Grand Tour.

The Grand Tour had developed in Elizabethan England as a means of gathering information useful for the country and for training young gentlemen to take their place in an increasingly cosmopolitan world. Gradually the emphasis shifted to the latter and it became an enormously popular rite of passage for young men, both privileged and of more middling means. In 1772, it was noted "where one Englishman travelled in the reign of the first two Georges [(1714–1760)] ten now go on a Grand Tour". In the summer of 1785, just the year before Smith's arrival in Holland, 40,000 Englishmen were reported to be in Europe. There was no set itinerary—the threat of war closing borders and the individual interests of the Tourist meaning routes could vary significantly, but most went as far south as Naples via France and Switzerland, returning via Germany and the Low Countries. Smith reversed this route, starting in the Low Countries and returning via Switzerland, but had the same goal: Italy, the cradle of art, culture and Western civilisation. James Snr was already anticipating the results:

> A comprehension of a superior kind, a penetration, a judgement, a facility, that will soon discover itself, will set you in a distinguished point of view and give you a consequence, that you will reap every advantage from; and I assure myself will repay most nobly all your labour and expence.[42]

Needless to say, the expense remained entirely James Snr's. Before leaving, Smith had one more call to make in the vicinity if Paris: Ermenonville, the last home and resting place of the philosopher and writer Jean-Jacques Rousseau. Rousseau, who died in 1778, remains as controversial and divisive a figure today as he was in his own time, having been variously blamed or praised for nationalism, Romanticism, collectivism and the French Revolution. His *Social Contract* (1762) argued that all people were created equal, and that no individual should have political authority just by virtue of name, family or personal merits. Political authority could only come from the consent of the governed. In the same year he published *Émile, ou de l'éducation*, which contained a 'Confession

Jean-Jacques Rousseau (1712–1778).

of a Savoyard Vicar', a defence of natural religion and a rebuttal of revelation and Church hierarchy. Smith was a great admirer, and particularly recommended this section to his father: "it is what has made so many priests his enemies, but in my opinion is very excellent".[43]

On 13 September, with a Mr Ancram, a man of "great taste and sensibility", Smith set out for Ermenonville, 28 miles from the centre of Paris.[44] They spent that night at nearby Chantilly, and the next day enjoyed a "very romantic ride of 8 miles through the forest" to Ermenonville, arriving at dusk. The landlord of their inn had spoken with Rousseau on the day of his death: on display were the wooden shoes he had died in as well as his snuffbox. The shoes had since been inscribed an admirer, who wrote he was proud to leave his name "on the simple shoe of a man who only ever walked along the path of virtue".

The next morning they rose at 6am and had a "most enchanting ramble" through the gardens of René Louis de Girardin, Marquess of Vauvray. The gardens had been directly inspired by Rousseau's ideas about man's place in nature, and the philosopher was buried on an island in the lake. Smith brought away some moss from the top of the simple tomb "as a relick".[45] However, they were reluctant to visit Rousseau's common-law widow, Marie-Thérèse Levasseur, still living nearby at Le Plessis-Belleville, "lest we discover something in her that might excite disagreeable sensations, & even perhaps lessen our veneration for her husband". Curiosity got the better of them and they were received with the "greatest politeness". Smith was delighted by the insight he received into Rousseau's work, learning that the character of Julie from *Julie, ou la nouvelle Héloïse* (1761), a favourite book of Smith's, was drawn from Madame Bois de la Tour of Lyons, though the story itself had no connection. Rousseau's widow also confirmed that his *Confessions* (written 1770 and published 1782) were all his own writing, the only changes made were the expunging of several names and anecdotes of people still living.[46]

On his return to Paris, Smith found that Broussonet was no longer able to go to Montpellier. Smith, however, had no intention of changing his plans and instead persuaded his friend, Dr William Younge, another Edinburgh contemporary, to join him for the journey. Younge arrived at the beginning of October 1786. The goal of this Grand Tour was "instruction, not dissipation", to be achieved through avoiding "the society of our own countrymen, particularly of the travelling herd, whose general plan of operation would ill have accorded with our own". Instead, Smith and Younge were to "mix as much as possible" with the locals, resolving to "conform to their manners and customs, even their mode of travelling and living".[47] Their route was as follows: Montpellier, via Lyon, then Avignon, Marseilles and Nice, before heading to Italy and Genoa, Rome and Naples. From Norwich, the Smiths urged their son to interpose "a little of our <u>prudence sexagenaire</u> to your juvenile warmth of enterprise", and more specifically, to avoid travelling by sea, "Vesuvius, subterranean journies, and every extravagant pursuit of curiosity for vanity thro' dangers". According to James Snr, the written accounts were just as good as the real thing.[48]

Part II: Paris to Nice

On 31 October 1786, at four o'clock in the morning, "the snow beginning to fall", Smith and Younge boarded the coach for Lyon.[49] They paid 5 louis each (about £5) and were fed and lodged the entire way without further expense. This also meant frequent early morning starts and indifferent inns; Smith complained that his bed at Auxerre "seemed stuffed with potatoes".[50] True to his word, Smith fully engaged with his travelling companions, particularly on the barge from Chalons-sur-Sôane to Tournus, where he took part in an eye-opening conversation about clerical celibacy.

This led to a discussion on the Edict of Nantes of 1598, which granted substantial rights to French Protestants, and its revocation in 1685, the consequence of which was the emigration of skilled workers on a massive scale (including to Norwich). Smith was surprised by the looks of "generous indignation" on his fellow traveller's faces: "they seemed to indulge such rebellious ideas, as that governments ought to be wise and impartial!".[51]

They arrived in Lyon on 5 November, where they met the Comte de Charnacé, "a young gentleman of a literary turn and pleasing manners", who was also bound for Montpellier. Together they engaged a voiture, or carriage, departing on 10 November. As they journeyed south, Smith grew increasingly enamoured with the country. The Roman ruins, particularly the former aqueduct Pont du Gard, near Nîmes, and the amphitheatre in Nîmes itself, captivated him. On the final approach to Montpellier the country was covered with "olive trees, laden with fruit in greater abundance than has been known these 100 years" though the ripe olives were "of the most abominable bitter taste". The unfortunate weather improved, as did the inns; they lived "exceedingly well, indeed luxuriously", dining on "truffles, red-legged partridges, and great variety of small birds", and always with clean linen and silver forks, not excepting the "little dirty inn" called La Fourche, on the road between the Pont du Gard and Nîmes.[52] The slow pace meant they could alight at their pleasure to botanise along the roadside, collecting *Gnaphalium* [*Helichrysum*] *stœchas, Teucrium polium* and other plants not native to England.[53]

They reached Montpellier on 17 November. Professor Broussonet, father of his Parisian friend, met them with the "kindest reception", and provided further introductions. Smith was taken with Montpellier, comparing its narrow, crooked streets with those of Norwich. His highest praise was reserved for the Place Royale du Peyrou, which he considered the finest thing he had yet seen on his tour. He described it in great detail to his father, likening it to a "design in an opera, a fairy palace".[54]

He contented himself with several botanical excursions, though it was not the ideal season for it. A trip to Castelnau, near the river Lez, offered up several new lichens, as well as excitements in the form of the tree frog *Hyla arborea*, and "that singular insect" *Mantis religiosa*, the praying mantis.

Smith also met Antoine Gouan, a correspondent of Linnaeus and pioneer of the Linnaean system in France; an invitation to breakfast, a sight of his herbarium and a gift of several specimens followed.[55]

Smith also enquired into the local textile market for his father. On Broussonet Snr's recommendation, he visited Messrs Eston and Sons, merchants of Montpellier, who requested a pattern card of the woollen cloths in which Smith's father dealt, with their measures and prices. Smith urged haste, for a number of riders from Manchester and Yorkshire had already made extensive enquiries of their own across the region. When in Marseilles a few weeks later, Smith observed a young man at the post office putting in "an immense" number of letters for Manchester. He informed his father that English cloths were the preferred winter wears at Marseilles, but were currently difficult to get.

Smith and Younge regretfully departed Montpellier on 27 November, taking a voiture back to Nîmes with an "intelligent & liberal minded" superior of Cordeliers, an order of Franciscan friars.[56] Their next destination was Avignon, its route unfortunately necessitating a return to the "filth and misery" of the La Fourche inn.[57] Avignon was a disappointment to Smith, the "most striking objects [...] [being] the vast walls of the city, & the great old palace of the Popes; the town is lifeless and unpleasant".[58] They reached Marseilles on 3 December: thanks to its fine climate and busy cosmopolitan streets Smith thought it "by far the finest town I have seen in France, Paris [...] not excepted". He was overwhelmed by the abundance and variety of produce in the markets, providing his father with a vivid description, the stalls "loaded with vast variety of fish unknown to us, & with pomgranates, melons, dates, flowers of every season, & the finest grapes".[59] On 6 December he attended one of the biannual public assemblies of *Académie des Sciences, Lettres et Arts*, at which discourses on the progress of literature in France and Provence were read. One such discourse was a fable entitled *The Lion and Tygers*, supposedly outlining that mercy was the characteristic of the lion as he was king of the forest. It was not well received. Despite the author leaving ample space before and after speaking so that "no grateful murmur of applause might be drowned in his own voice; no such sound was heard after the first or second lines; and he had nothing to console him at the end but a slight mechanical clap of civility".

Smith and Younge spent only three days in Marseille, leaving on 7 December to continue their journey to Nice. They were surprised a few miles into their journey by a strict examination of their baggage by customs officials. His medicinal drugs were considerably disarranged. By "wonderful good luck" a parcel of chocolate sitting in the top of his trunk was not noticed: "if the chocolate had been a relick, or I a saint, this escape might have passed for a most important miracle".[60] No sensible Tourist travelled in Europe without a fully stocked, travelling medicine chest, not least a recently qualified MD with a history of poor health. Typical contents would have included Dr James' Fever Powders, a cure-all much used by Smith in later life, which contained the poisonous element antimony, tincture of jalap, a strong purgative, and ipecacuanha, an emetic, as well as apparatus for blistering and blood-letting, amongst a host of other curious powders and instruments. Despite this precaution, Smith's health remained surprisingly buoyant throughout the tour, with the inconvenience of just one bad cold in Genoa in June 1787, confirming his suspicion that he was "never better than when travelling or running about".[61]

Reaching Toulon two days later, Smith visited the military hospital, where lectures on medicine were given for free. There was also a small botanical garden in which the plants were, pleasingly, arranged according to the Linnaean classification. Oranges, *Orbea variegata, Solanum pseudocapsicum* and many other tender plants were all in the open ground, a curiosity for English visitors who were more used to seeing such plants in greenhouses.[62] Dinner that evening was unexpectedly exciting. At the table d'hôte were a number of French and Dutch officers. After supper the Dutch officers began smoking, having previously obtained permission to smoke from some ladies at the table. However, the French officers used this as an excuse to quarrel and a challenge was issued and immediately accepted by a "spirited young Dutchman". The combatants decided the affair with small swords in the street; the Frenchman was soon disarmed. Smith was disgusted by duels, particularly between soldiers, "whose profession is supposed to require their obedience to such savage principles of honour".

On 11 December they reached Cotignac, calling solely to see the aging Louis Gérard, author of *Flora Gallo-provincialis* (1761), and "one of the most famous European botanists of the Linnean school". They talked much of Smith's purchase of the collections, a "never-failing topic with all the botanists" he met on his tour. Smith felt that speaking to Gérard was like "paying a visit to the Elysian fields", so little did his "tales of other times" seem connected with what was then going on in the world.[63]

On 16 December they forded the river Var, "a very unpleasant business". The Var was intersected by deep channels that caused unpredictable currents, so it was necessary for carriages to be accompanied by guides, who felt the way with poles—a perilous endeavour for all. The guides' pay was fixed at six sous per passage (about threepence), and if any person was killed on the crossing the guides were hanged. Subsequently, most travellers paid much more out of generosity; Smith and Younge gave 36 sous, about 18 pence.[64] After a safe crossing they entered Nice, and though he admired the setting, Smith the swarms of his fellow countrymen gave it "exactly the style of an English watering place". There was a general unpleasantness in the air, in part due to the locals who "fawn upon, laugh at, & cheat the strangers who come here [...] to get rid of their consumptions and their money"[65], and the unsettling presence of galley-slaves in the streets, chained two together—"not an agreeable spectacle to an humane mind".[66] It was also at Nice that Smith learnt of the death of his old botany professor, Dr John Hope.

Despite having promised his father that he would not travel by sea, the terrible condition of the road from Nice to Genoa and the threat of bandits made it necessary. They hired a felucca, an open sailing boat, and were promised a "halcyon voyage". Inexperienced mariners, they trusted themselves "with light hearts to the insidious deep".

Part III: Nice to Naples

On 19 December 1786, at 8 o'clock in the morning, Smith and Younge boarded their felucca and rowed out into the harbour. The sea was already choppy, and Smith quickly retired to the bottom of the boat to keep from vomiting. Just four leagues later, at Monaco, they were forced to take

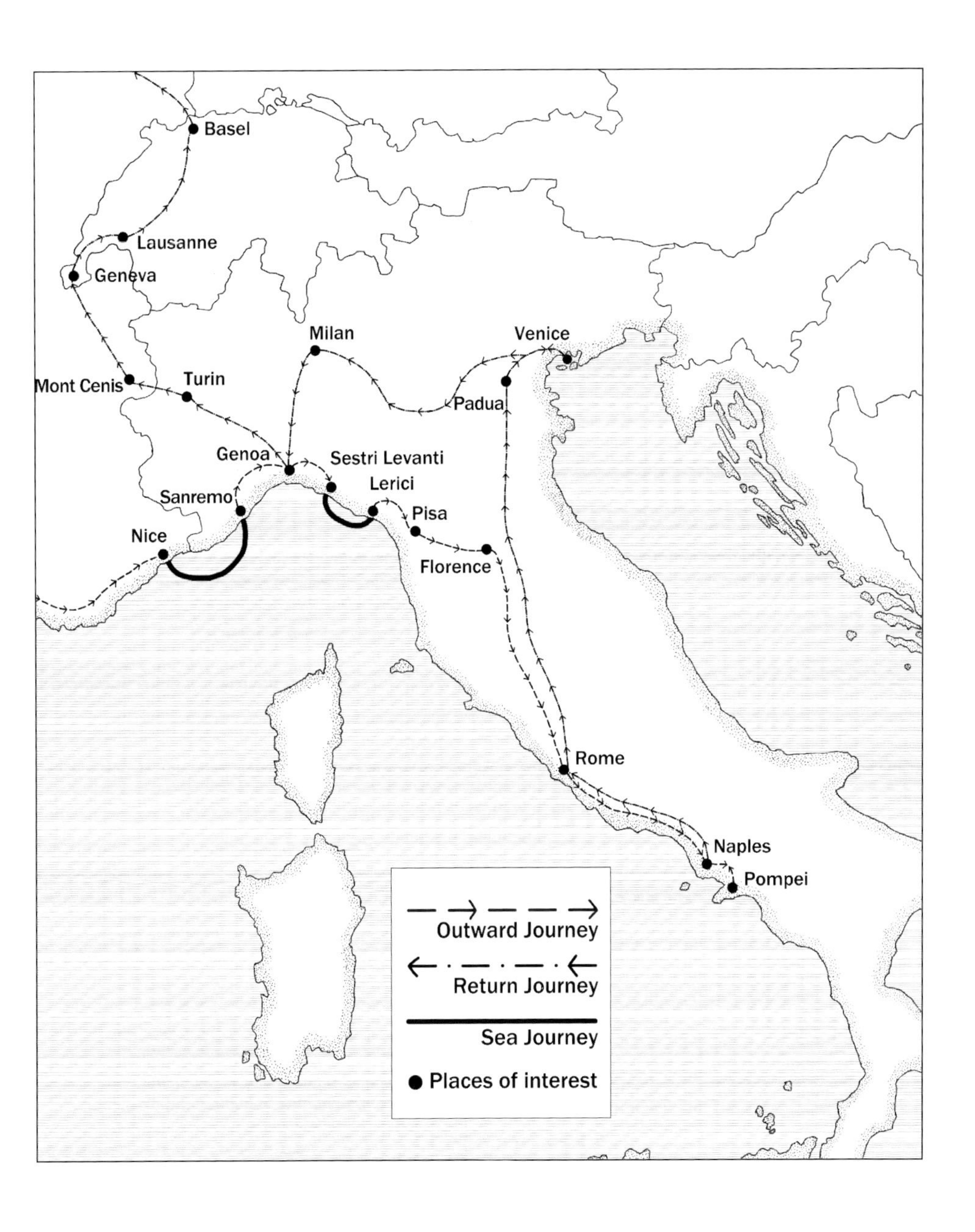

Smith's Grand Tour: Italy and Switzerland.

shelter, where they remained for the next two days. Smith was impressed with the locals' turn for nomenclature, noting with amusement that the dog at the inn was named "quattr' -occhi" (four eyes) on account of the two spots about its eyes.[67]

The sea was still rough when they departed Monaco on the morning of the 21st. Smith's refuge at the bottom of the boat no longer afforded relief and he spent the next eight leagues hanging over the side, though was rewarded with the sight of a very luminous sea before dawn, "which by far exceeded my expectations". At Sanremo, on the insistence of the sailors, they docked for another two days, but with the calming of the sea the wind had now moved round to the east, making sailing onwards to Genoa impossible. Smith, impatient and tired of feeling sick, resolved to travel the rest of the way by land, regardless of the accounts of "bad roads, precipices, robbers &c".[68] When the wind allowed, Younge was to follow in the felucca with their baggage. Smith hired a guide and two mules, made a small parcel containing two shirts, razors, and other necessities, including his pistols, and set out at about 11 o'clock of the morning of 24 December. Following a path along the rocky hills next to the sea, "more like a broken flight of steps or the [notoriously bad] pavement of Norwich than any thing else". That night, he stayed at an inn called the Crown, on whose promising sign was written "Ogn' ofteria e buona,/ Ma questa e la corona" ("Every inn is good, but this is the Crown, or the best of all"). Smith did not agree. He thought it a wretched place and got little sleep, thanks to the people in the street and the bells ringing for midnight masses. The next morning he was charged 6 livres of France (about £3) for his board and lodging, "the worst and dearest" he had ever had.[69]

Smith spent Christmas Day travelling. Stopping at the Pinco de Genoa inn at Alassio, a letter of introduction from the Marquess Durazzo got him an invite to the landlord of the inn's Christmas dinner.[70] The next morning, placing his confidence in his pistols (having been assured there were no robbers in the area), Smith set out for Finale, alone and on foot. This was a full 20 miles away—when needed, Smith could be very intrepid. Unfortunatcly, on descending the hill that overlooked Finale he accidently took the mule path, the bottom of which led through an icy rivulet. Rather than retrace his steps, Smith took off his shoes and stockings and waded across. On reaching his inn, he bathed his feet and legs in brandy to ward off any ill effects but sat too close to the brazier, suffered a "slight fainting fit" and had to be carried out into the fresh air.

Smith arrived at the outskirts of Genoa at dusk of 28 December.[71] The next morning, he walked into town to call on the Marquess Durazzo in the Via Balbi, one of Genoa's principal streets. On first seeing the grand house and its ranks of servants, Smith was seized with a sudden dread of the potential formality lurking within, but was pleased to find Durazzo the same "cheerful easy unassuming man" he had been in London. William Younge arrived that same afternoon, having sailed from Sanremo the preceding morning.

Smith and Younge spent three weeks in Genoa and were with the Durazzo family almost every day. The Durazzos were of high standing in Genoa, the grandeur of their palaces rivalled only, in Smith's opinion, by Chatsworth House in Derbyshire; he informed his father that a marble staircase at the Marquess's house had just been completed at the cost of £5,000.[72] The Durazzos had taken it upon themselves to introduce science, particularly natural history, into the area.[73] They spent the first day of 1787 at the Durazzos' country house, in order to see their vast natural history cabinet: three rooms lined with glass cases containing minerals, corals, shells, birds, animals and fish. Smith was pleased to find, sitting alongside Aristotle and Pliny, a bust of Linnaeus in the first room, by whose classification all the collection but the minerals were arranged.[74] Despite the grandeur of their homes, he was impressed by the reserve and restraint of the Genoese nobility's fashion. When in company they dressed in black, the only affectation being exquisite laces, and they wore no jewellery except rings, with which their fingers were often "enormously loaded".[75]

Smith and Younge spent several evenings at the opera, which was "pretty good" in Genoa, though it was "tedious" to see the same work, Angelo Tarchi's *La Virginia* (1785), performed night after night. They were received everywhere (Smith's Italian was not quite as good as his French), as the Genoese were Anglophiles and very "fond of our language, our literature, prints, manufactures & dresses".[76] Visiting the hospital, Smith was shocked to find that each year about 700 women and 1,200 men were admitted for stab wounds from knives and stilettos.[77] Though this "dreadful fact" would be sufficient to cast aspersions on the national character, he conceded that these "very people whose quick passions urge them to such horrors, would shudder at the deliberate brutality of an English boxing match".[78]

Smith and Younge left Genoa for Florence on 18 January 1787. Smith refused to re-enter the felucca so Younge followed with the baggage, meeting each evening at their inn. Bad weather again trapped them en route, this time at Sestri Levante, 30 miles down the coast from Genoa. In his boredom Smith etched his frustration on the wall of his room with a burnt stick:

> By adverse winds & faithless billows crost,/ A listless wanderer on a foreign coast,/ While rugged rocks refuse the opening flower,/ Nor e'er a moss beguiles the tedious hour,/ Nor, if to heav'n I turn my anxious eye,/ One ray of hope illumes the stormy sky.

Their next stop, Lerici, offered another "execrable inn", where it was advertised that the King of Sweden had slept in November 1773—little comfort as it seemed clear that monarchs were "indifferent travel guides". The next morning they were dismayed to find that their coffee had almost doubled the agreed amount, and were told, "with the most cool effrontery, that coffee was not in the original bargain".[79] In common with most Grand Tourists to Italy, Smith and Younge had failed to realise that an Italian innkeeper loved to bargain. As Leigh Hunt later observed, "if you pay anybody what he asks you, it never enters his imagination that you do it from anything but folly. You are pronounced a *minchione* (a ninny), one of their greatest terms of reproach. On the other hand, if you battled well through the bargain, a perversion of the natural feeling of self-defence led to a feeling of respect for you".[80] With his fainting fits, naïve poetry and plant collecting, Smith had been found wanting. In Pisa (arrived 21 January) they experienced a brief upturn in their relations with Italians. They managed to avoid being fleeced by their innkeeper and the driver of the carriage they hired to take them to Florence, Diego Baroncello, proved "always regular, sober, and obliging, and his carriage as good as most English post-chaises".[81] They ensured that he would be available for as much of their remaining time in Italy as possible.

They arrived in Florence on 24 January, soon running into more altercations. They had accepted the custom officer's proposal to examine their trunks at their inn rather than at the city gates, but on giving him the usual fee of two pauls (one paul was worth about six pence) the affronted officer saw to it that "much altercation ensued", and they were forced to give another two pauls to avoid a further scene.[82] Despite this inauspicious beginning, by the time they left eight days later they were both "quite in raptures", almost entirely owing to their time spent in the Uffizi Gallery, which was then, as now, one of the principal draws of Florence.[83]

Other aspects of Florentine life were less appealing. Searching the bookshops was a frustrating business, forced to tumble over "immense piles of old books in garrets and lumber-rooms", the proprietors as unaware of the contents as Smith and Younge. Attending a comic opera was also unpleasant. The audience were all wearing masks for Carnival, and many of the women were dressed as men, looking "awkward and ugly", and displaying "the most horrid perversion of taste and sentiment" in the male sex. A grumpy Smith similarly dismissed his "facetious encounters with several droll masks in the streets".[84]

On 1 February they left Florence for Rome, taking six days. The reliable Diego Baroncello was again their coachman, and they were "full of expectation & admiration at every step" for the wonders that awaited them.[85] They made for the hotel of Dominico Pio on the Piazza di Spagna—a favoured residence of Prince William Henry, Duke of Gloucester.[86] Prior to their arrival in the city, Smith and Younge had decided to dispense entirely with letters of introduction, intending to devote their time "solely and uniformly to the study of paintings, statues, and buildings"—avoiding any dalliances with Roman society. Unfortunately, their valet de place (tourist guide) soon "proved drunk & of little use", so they wandered the city by themselves. Almost by chance they stumbled across the Pantheon and were astonished by "its grandeur, & the immensity of its granite columns". On resting for a coffee at the English coffeehouse on the Piazza di Spagna,

Smith was surprised to run into the Abbé José Correia da Serra, to whom he had been introduced in Paris, and who was to become their new guide.

Organising their time to see the "principal things" in depth, they began with a visit to St Peter's Basilica.[87] For Smith, St Peter's seemed to invite a comparison with St Paul's Cathedral in London, and with patriotic pride was pleased to conclude that the exterior of St Paul's "may very well bear a comparison [...], except the colonnade". However, once inside, St Peter's superiority was "decided indeed". Descending into the crypt, the various tombs of Popes and monarchs generated much interest, particularly those of James Francis Stuart, the Old Pretender, and his wife Maria Clementia Sobieska.

Next was the Vatican. A harsh critic, Smith was initially disappointed by Raphael's frescoes, for though he could see the brilliance of the designs, the light was often bad and the colours faded, with evidence of damp. They were also encumbered with scaffolds to allow young artists to copy them.[88] Only after repeated viewings and close consideration could Smith see them as the works of genius they were generally considered to be; every part was "so well judged and ingeniously contrived". He was particularly struck by the fresco *Deliverance of St Peter*, in which "the radiance of the Angel is exactly what angelic light *must* be" – but he could still criticise, commenting that the "two strutting philosophers" in the middle of the *School of Athens* were "a little too theatrical". Inevitably, Smith's visit to the Vatican presented many opportunities for Smith to take umbrage with Catholic doctrine, finding much to ridicule at the Scala Sancta, by tradition the steps trod by Christ at Pontius Pilate's house. It was an act of penance to ascend these, on one's knees. Smith could not help note the ridiculousness of their being flanked by two other sets of stairs on which "a man may, without offence, walk in the upright posture", brought into relief by the "many gouty cardinals, fat priests, and corpulent old ladies, heaving one knee after the other" on the Scala Sancta.

On 10 February, the Roman Carnival began, one of Smith and Younge's chief reasons for coming to Rome. After dinner, Smith and Younge went with the Abbé Correia to the Via del Corso, the centre of activity. During Carnival time, the middle of this street was occupied by three rows of coaches on a looping circuit. The central row was reserved for princes and cardinals, but on this day there were interlopers: Charles Edward Stuart, also known as Bonnie Prince Charlie, the Catholic Stuart claimant to the British throne, and his legitimated daughter Charlotte Stuart, Duchess of Albany. The Pope had never recognised his claim to the throne, and his position in the central row at Carnival was now almost the only mark of rank he enjoyed. Years of frustration and disappointment had left him a broken old man. Smith thought him "the very image of a drunken Silenus [companion to the Greek wine god Dionysus], more asleep than awake". Whilst viewing the procession of coaches, someone asked who occupied the central position, to which another tactfully replied, purposely in Smith and Younge's hearing, "Il Pretendente".

Amongst the various characters rushing about the Carnival was a man dressed as a Quaker, who, with an idiotic stare, would run up to people making a "thrilling buzzing noise" with his lips. After witnessing him with another buzzing Quaker, shaking "one another violently by the hand", Smith and Younge concluded that they must be caricatures of Englishmen.[89] On 18 February, at midnight, Smith and Younge attended a masked ball, at the Aliberti theatre, where Smith saw "more bad dancing than I ever saw at one time before".[90] The last day of Carnival was 20 February. Smith and Younge walked out on the Via del Corso from eight o'clock in the evening; carriages were now at their most whimsical, with "transparent coloured lamps, & flowers in festoons". As dusk approached, everybody took a lit taper, the game to try and extinguish everybody else's light. Smith considered it "the most good humoured mob" he ever saw, despite the calls to variously kill those with lights, those without lights, the abbots, barbers, monks, and "my-lordi", directed at the English in the crowd.[91]

The next day was Ash Wednesday, the first day of Lent. Smith, Younge and the Abbé Correia returned to the Vatican to see Pope Pius VI placing ashes on the heads of his clergy in the Sistine Chapel. Smith reported that the Pope was "a very handsome man, & although said to be ashamed of this ceremony, yet he went through it with great dignity".[92] Smith was disappointed by Michelangelo's frescoes, particularly *The Last Judgment*, a "dark uncouth picture, the Saviour has great wrath but little dignity, & on the whole I was not pleased with this famous performance".[93]

Smith and Younge left Rome for Naples on 25 February, 141 miles away. As they travelled further south Smith was pleased to find that the flora "began to smile upon us more and more", with hedges full of myrtle, *Pistacia lentiscus* and the "fragrant and beautiful *Erica arborea* Tree Heath, in flower". They reached Naples on the evening of 28 February and though impressed by its opulent appearance they were appalled by the ranks of beggars who crowded into the coffeehouses, "covered with rags and filth".[94] He quickly came to the conclusion that the Neapolitans were "the most barefaced villains that ever I met with", an opinion that was only confirmed the longer they stayed.[95]

There was little to entertain Smith in Naples; despite its wealth there was little of good taste. However, there were three essential excursions for every curious traveller: the ancient city of Pompeii, buried by the volcano Mount Vesuvius in AD 79, Vesuvius itself and the ruined Roman resort of Baiae. Smith and Younge started with Baiae. Their next visit, on 12 March, was to Vesuvius. They left Naples at 6 o'clock in the morning in a calash, a curious four-passenger conveyance drawn by small horses; the reins were held by the passengers whilst the driver stood behind, brandishing the whip over their heads. At the foot of Vesuvius they swapped their calash for mules, and engaged guides for the ascent. They climbed the final mile by foot, on account of the loose ash, and walked around the inside of the old crater. Smith was a little disappointed, as "the smoke, although very moderate, prevented us from seeing far". Nevertheless, he was struck by the immense power of the volcano, observing "the chasms from which issue smoke & heated vapors, with snow at 3 feet distance from them, all this I had no conception of, much less of the lava of which we saw a fine stream of about a yard in breadth issuing from one side of the hill".[96] With regard to the volcanic flora, Smith noted with interest that a lava flow from 1771 was still completely barren, except for *Lichen paschalis*, which covered it in profusion. He later concluded that this lichen was "the first beginning of vegetation on lava, for which its shrubby figure and slender roots are admirably fitted".[97]

The next day they visited Pompeii, of which a considerable part had been revealed since its rediscovery in 1748. Smith was intrigued by the plants depicted in some of the frescoes, particularly what appeared to be *Agave americana*, which as the name implies, was indigenous to America. Smith dared not claim these figures as evidence for *Agave americana* in fact having been native to Europe since Roman times. Instead he inclined to believe they were representations of *Alœ perfoliata*, which would have had a more credible introduction from Africa.[98] Smith observed the different shops, identifiable by their contents, including "a coffeehouse in which were found the coffee cups, & a very neat surgeon's house in which the instruments of the owner were found". On the front of another, rather more explicit 'shop', Smith noted in his travel diary that there was "a stone carving of a great erect penis, from which that house is supposed to have been a brothel, & that strange ornament the sign".[99] Smith was much more discreet in the published version, describing the sign as "a certain carving in stone, which very expressively indicates this to have been a brothel".[100]

Part IV: Naples to London

Smith and Younge left Naples on 17 March to return to Rome. They stopped at Caserta, 25 miles from Naples, the home of Sir William Hamilton, the British Ambassador. Thanks to a letter of introduction from Sir Joseph Banks, in which Smith was described as one of his "most intimate friends", Smith and Younge were immediately invited to join the party, which included two extraordinary 18th century personages.[101] The first was Mrs Hart, "a fine buxom damsel".[102] This was in fact Emma Hart, born Amy Lyon, the muse of portraitist George Romney. She had only recently arrived in Naples, sent by her lover Charles Francis Greville so he could marry another. She soon became Hamilton's own mistress, and Sir William and Emma married in 1791. She later gained notoriety by becoming the mistress of Admiral Lord Horatio Nelson. Smith's description of her implies that he was aware of some incongruity in the relationship; no mention of Mrs Hart was made in the published *Sketch of a Tour*. The second person was Johann Wolfgang von Goethe. Smith described him as "prime minister to the Duke of Saxe Weimar, author of the well-known Sorrows of Werter, a polite unassuming man".[103] It was to escape these very two appellations as politician and author that Goethe was in Italy in the first place. Unfortunately no record of their conversation survives and Smith is not even mentioned in Goethe's corresponding journal, all the more curious as Goethe famously said of Linnaeus: "With the exception of Shakespeare and Spinoza, I know no one among the no longer living who has influenced me more strongly". This, however, was something of backhanded compliment. Whilst he truly admired Linnaeus, he believed his artificial system failed in presenting the full continuity and sweep of nature, something that, as a result, Goethe strove to uncover. Nevertheless, Goethe presumably would have had much to discuss with the possessor of the Linnaean collections.

The next day, after breakfasting, they walked together to a spot on the banks of the Vulturno River, the air scented by the flowers of an apparently undescribed species of *Daphne*. Smith took a specimen and later named it *Daphne collina*, the name it still bears today.[104] After meeting Emma Hart for a final time, Smith and Younge continued on their journey.

The next evening, whilst crossing a bridge, their carriage overturned and became stuck in a rivulet. When their driver started "howling aloud, and calling upon all the saints of heaven for help", Smith took it upon himself to make his way to the next village, San Germano, less than three miles away, where he found a "miserable hovel of an inn". With the help of the landlord the carriage was righted and brought back to San Germano, though his obliging nature arose solely from "sordid hopes of plunder". On being asked for a sequin each (3.5 grams of gold) for "one miserable bed [...] and a bad salad and eggs for supper", in addition to what they had already paid for his help, Smith said he would rather sleep in the broken carriage. The price was halved. The next morning it was discovered that one of his dressing gowns and a substantial part of the carriage were missing.[105]

They reached Rome on 23 March 1787, where they were to spend almost another five weeks, including Holy Week, again in the company of the Abbé Correia. Smith was in the crowd at St Peter's Square for the Pope's blessing on Easter Sunday, with "the great bell ringing, guns of St Angelo firing & the soldiers [...] trumpeting at the same time immediately after he has pronounced the blessing with his arms extended: all the people kneel to receive it".[106] Leaving again on 25 April, they cast "many a longing lingering look

Fig. 1 Smith's father, James, aged about 37.

Fig. 2 Smith's mother, Frances, aged about 33.

Painted as a pair in c. 1764 by Thomas Worlidge.

Fig. 3 "A space of parade-like appearance". Norwich Market Place in 1788; the Smith family shop and home is the second door from the right. By Thomas Rowlandson.

Fig. 4 Medal awarded to Smith by Dr John Hope for best Scottish herbarium, December 1782.

Fig. 5

"The daubing of the ladies cheeks is beyond conception, nature is quite out of the question". Smith had a low opinion of Parisian fashions.

Fig. 6 "No one has a greater claim on his gratitude & regard than I have, nor can any one be more ready to acknowledge it". Smith readily acknowledged the debt he owed his earliest patron, Sir Joseph Banks. By Thomas Phillips, 1809.

Fig. 7

James Edward Smith, aged c. 30 years old.

Figs. 8 & 9 In 1784, Smith purchased Carl Linnaeus's library, manuscripts, correspondence and incomparable collection of specimens, which included plants, insects, shells, fish and minerals. Smith later amalgamated his own insects into the collection, but their herbaria remained separate.

Fig. 10 *Smithia sensitiva* was named for Smith by Jonas Dryander, in honour of his work on the irritability of plants. Smith's former friend Richard Salisbury later claimed authorship, turning the commendation into an insult. From Richard Salisbury's *Paradisus Londinensis*.

Fig. 11 *Tradescantia discolor* (a synonym of *T. spathacea* Sw., or Boat lily). Once rare, Smith commented "it is now superabundant in the English gardens, insomuch as to almost be esteemed an incumberance". From Smith's *Icones Pictæ*.

Fig. 12 Marsh pea (*Lathyrus palustris* L.), from volume three of Smith and Sowerby's *English Botany*.

Fig. 13 Water avens (*Geum rivale* L.). This drawing is attributed to Smith, though his correspondence contains no references to his apparent artistic skill.

at the fine things" they passed by.[107] Their itinerary was now to take them back into northern Italy.

The Doge of Venice, by Smith.

Smith and Younge reached Venice for Ascension Day on 17 May, when the Doge "espouses the sea according to ancient custom", at the island of Lido in the lagoon. Smith and Younge hired a gondola to watch the festivities, though such was the press of other vessels they missed the moment the Doge cast his ring into the sea. Afterwards, however, they were able to board the bucentaur, or state barge, and saw the Doge "sat on his throne, the Nuncio [papal ambassador] (a keen sensible looking man) at his right hand, the senators in robes of crimson, silk & great wigs [...] intermixed with the strangers, some of whom I was sorry to see wear their hats, & in very shabby cloaths, particularly 2 or 3 frenchmen".[108] Ascension Day also marked the opening of St Mark's Fair and was the final act in the Italian social season for foreign tourists. Smith and Younge found themselves meeting several acquaintances from their travels, gathered for this "grand rendezvous".[109] Despite the prodigious numbers in dominos (eye masks) and other masks, Smith found the amusements repetitive. There was also an unsavoury air. He commented that Venice "may be called the Stews [brothel] of Europe, every lady of the highest rank amuses herself as she pleases at her casino".[110] Before leaving Venice, Smith witnessed the antithesis of this wantonness. Whilst visiting the church of Santi Cosma e Damiano he was present for the profession of a nun, a ceremony he had long wished to see. The woman, Cecilia Barbaro, about 20 years old, of an "agreeable countenance, but a little deformed", was liberated of her diamonds and finery, given a nun's habit and white veil, and crowned with a garland of flowers. Smith commented that she appeared "very chearful & talkative" but he feared a "flatness would follow when all the pomp & hurry were over", a sentiment shared with another spectator, who whispered to Smith: "Behold one more victim to prejudice".[111]

They left Venice on 28 May and travelled westward, stopping at Padua, Verona, Parma, Milan, and Pavia for a few days in each. A pall was cast by news from London: Molly Standard, the woman employed to keep house and look after Smith's collections whilst he was travelling, was "with child by the man that courted her". With the baby expected by the end of June, Smith's mother Frances took charge, coming to London and making arrangements for Molly to continue working until the first or second week of July. On receipt of the news, Smith expressed his sorrow at Molly's "folly & misfortune" but his sympathy did not extend much further; it would be of no use "to hurry home immediately, which [I] should be sorry to do".[112] Smith was franker when writing to his London friend Mrs Howorth a few days later:

> I am very much chagrined at the situation of my quondam virgin Mary, not only because in my arrangements at Chelsea I made no provision for a groaning [childbirth], but because I fear, as miracles have ceased, she cannot have a child without an impeachment of her virginity, notwithstanding her name. This is only between you and me.[113]

Smith's mother, later joined by his sister Esther Anne, looked after the house at Paradise Row until he returned. It is not known what became of Molly Standard.

They left Milan on 15 June and headed south, reaching Pavia, "a pretty little town devoted to the sciences" on the same day.[114] They stayed for four days, enthralled by the feud between Giovanni Antonio Scopoli, professor of chemistry, and Lazzaro Spallanzani, professor of natural history, both of Pavia university. A longstanding professional rivalry, exacerbated by Spallanzani's dismissal of Linnaeus (Scopoli had corresponded with the great Swede), finally reached crisis point in 1786, when Spallanzani accused Scopoli of stealing items from the natural history museum at Pavia, of which they shared the management. It quickly emerged that it was in fact Spallanzani who had been taking items, in order to supplement his own private museum in Modena. Smith had already publicly stated his low opinion of Spallanzani as a scientist in the preface of his translation *Dissertation on the Sexes of Plants* (1786), but "for the honor of philosophers" hoped Spallanzani was innocent. The Emperor, Joseph II (since 1713 much of northern Italy had been under the dominion of the Austrian empire), was informed, but as Spallanzani was so respected he was given ample time to return the items before a public examination was made. His subsequent acquittal was confirmed by imperial decree, but it was too late. Scopoli, furious at Spallanzani's duplicity, began "dispersing the true story all over Europe". Smith reported that Spallanzani was now in "little credit among real philosophers who examine for themselves, for many of his experiments are found false".[115]

On leaving Pavia, after eight months of travelling together through France and Italy, Smith and Younge parted; Smith to spent another month in Genoa, from 21 June to 30 July, and Younge to return to England, via Turin and Switzerland. They remained in contact by letter, Younge having "been so long used to a participation of the pleasures of travelling with you, that even in my present situation I meet with nothing new or pleasing which I do not wish you to see as well as myself".[116] Smith later dedicated *Sketch of a Tour* to Younge.

After leaving Genoa for the second time, Smith headed for Turin, for which his father had given specific instructions for investigating the silk market. Of most concern was to discover whether any of his suppliers sold silk to other Norwich merchants. Smith was to inform them "that I am the only dealer in that article here, & every bale they send besides mine interfere with my business".[117] By the time Smith left 10 days later he had investigated the market from almost every angle. On the processing of raw silk there was little to say, as the process was "just as in England", but brokers did all the purchasing, so James Snr would find little advantage of buying for himself.[118]

On 11 August, at 11 o'clock at night, Smith set out on a botanical expedition to Mont Cenis, in Savoy, then part of the Kingdom of Sardinia, just over a day's carriage ride away to the northwest of Turin. The trip was planned with several other Turin naturalists: the Portuguese Ambassador

Rodrigo de Sousa Coutinho, botanist Dr Carlo Bellardi, mineralogist Dr Buonvicino and the Abbé Vasco, a natural philosopher. Smith travelled alone, whilst the rest of the party went in a coach. They reached the pass of Mont Cenis at about noon, "a fine long plain, with 2 or 3 lakes, surrounded with very high hills on every side".[119] He was delighted to find the meadow still in bloom "with the rarest alpine productions". They spent four productive days exploring and collecting, and on 14 August ascended Little Mont Cenis, though two-thirds of the way up Smith was distracted by a particularly fecund meadow, and "returned laden with plants". Smith's herbarium contains almost a hundred specimens from this excursion. He also collected for his friends "as large a stock as I could well bring away". In an age before any real concept of conservation this was justified in the name of scientific collaboration: "the selfish dealer in mysteries and secrets, the hoarded of unique specimens, knows nothing of the best pleasures of science".[120]

Smith now headed into Switzerland, the final leg of his tour. He was joined by his own personal valet, engaged in Turin, the "Milanese lad" Francesco Borone. He considered Borone "such a treasure" that he intended to return to England with him; he would need a manservant when settled, and, furthermore, believed that he could mould him into a botanical assistant, and thus "make him earn what he costs me". Smith remarked to his father that it would not be possible for him to see "this country as it deserves, for want of time".[121] Smith followed the same route that Younge had taken, who had left good words for Smith wherever he went, and advised on accommodation, recommending an inn at Basel for "good bed, & good dinner; but bad tea & coffee".[122]

Smith reached Geneva on 23 August but was disappointed to find that most people were out of town for the summer.[123] However, he did meet naturalist and philosopher Charles Bonnet, who though "almost deaf & blind" was charming in his conversation, and recommended that Smith pursue the "physiology of vegetables in preference to nomenclature".[124] He also met physicist Horace-Bénédict de Saussure, often considered the founder of mountaineering, and geologist Jean-André de Luc. Smith left Geneva on 30 August for Basel, travelling via Lausanne and Berne, the glaciers of Mont Blanc, "another rich botanical harvest", and Lake Geneva.[125] They reached Basel on 8 September. Younge had already performed a sweep of the booksellers for botanical books, to little avail; "one crusty old fellow" wondered why anyone would even enquire for such works there.[126]

Smith eventually reached Paris on 19 September, where he had made arrangements to finish his consultation of Tournefort's herbarium, "a thing of too much importance to be omitted". His younger brother Francis joined him on 1 October. Francis's arrival gave Smith "the highest pleasure", even though he was so wrapped up in Tournefort's specimens he did not initially recognise him.[127]

On 29 October they left Paris, travelling north to Boulogne-sur-Mer, via Amiens. Bad weather prevented them from embarking for England until 2 November, but once on board the wind was so brisk that it took only two and three-quarter hours to get to Dover. Many ladies onboard were sick; for once Smith was able to hold his stomach. He had been advised by his friend Goodenough to avoid the temptation to smuggle home any French wine, as it hung "terribly on hand, so say the winemerchants, & no one calls for it".[128] Smith had a low opinion of custom-house officers, "whose duty it is to moderate the joy as well as the worldly affluence of all those that come in their way".[129] Smith and Francis arrived back at Paradise Row, Chelsea, on 2 November, where they had the happiness of finding their mother and sister, Esther Anne, who had been standing guard over the Linnaean treasures since July.

CHAPTER FOUR

Foundation of the Linnean Society

In spite of all Smith had experienced on his 17-month journey, it had almost been worthwhile just for "the pleasure of coming home again".[1] He and his brother Francis spent several days in London with their mother and sister, Esther Anne, before the whole Smith party left for Norwich in mid-November. On his return to London after the New Year he took possession of a new house, 12 Great Marlborough Street, moving on 25 March 1788.[2] In contrast to his previous neighbourhood, Chelsea, which at that time was still physically separate from London, Great Marlborough Street was a fashionable address in the heart of the city. Building on the street began in 1704, and, by 1714, author John Macky, in *A Journey Through England*, described it as surpassing "any Thing that is called a Street, in the Magnificence of its Buildings and Gardens". In 1788, Smith's neighbours included Lady Onslow at number 11, the anatomist Joshua Brookes at number 13, and at number 49, the actress Sarah Siddons. Smith described his house as decidedly "more commodious" than Paradise Row, complete with a "no[t] despicable garden" (the house still stands, the sole survivor of the street's original buildings, albeit with a modern shop front).[3] The garden backed onto the Pantheon, a magnificent building in Oxford Street, designed as winter assembly rooms; according to one contemporary, it was regarded "both by natives and foreigners, as the most elegant structure in Europe, if not on the globe" — the central rotunda was capacious enough to accommodate a hot air balloon on more than one occasion.[4] Much greater interest to Smith, though, was the fact that his new address was less than a 10-minute walk to Sir Joseph Banks's house in Soho Square.

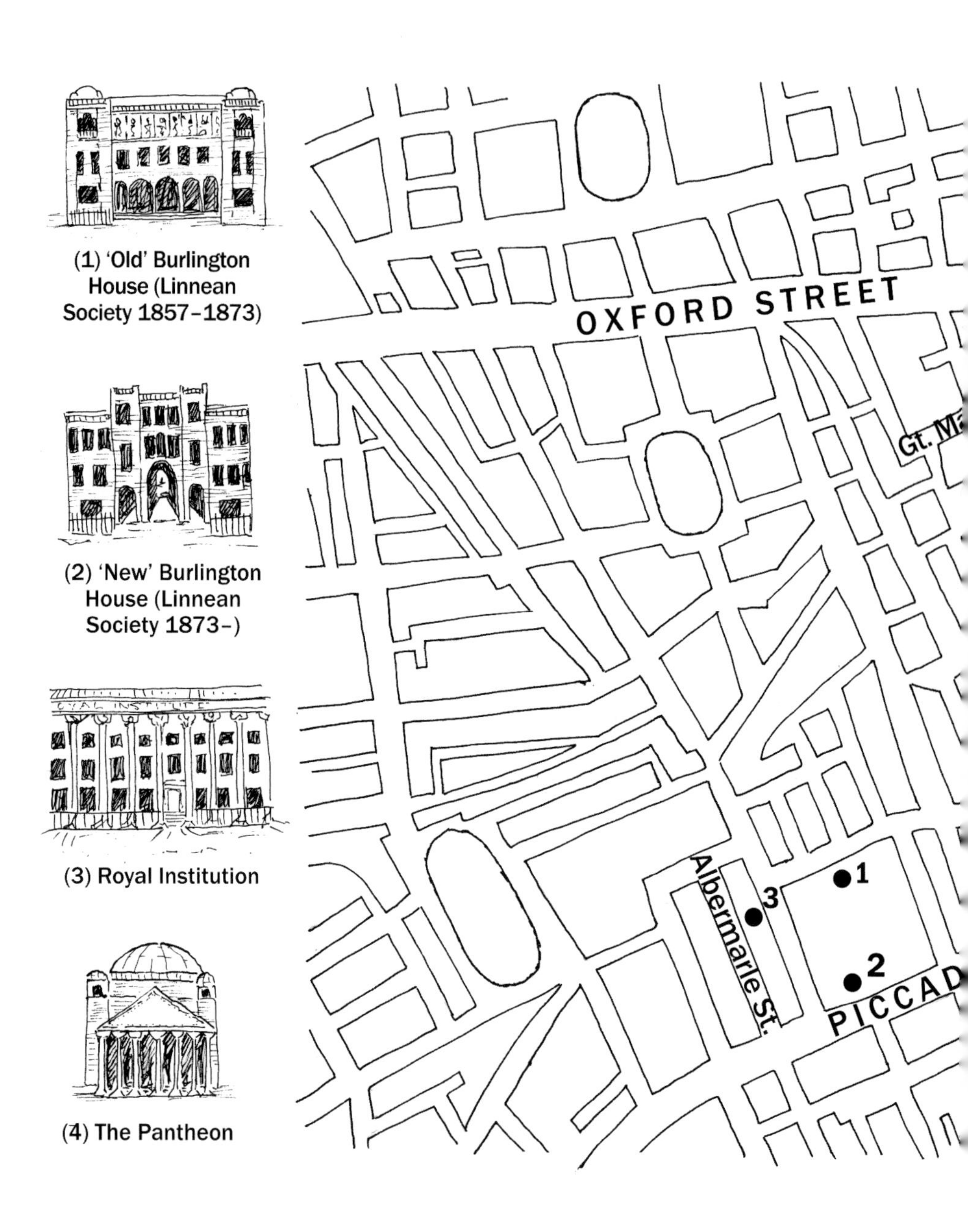
(1) 'Old' Burlington House (Linnean Society 1857–1873)
(2) 'New' Burlington House (Linnean Society 1873–)
(3) Royal Institution
(4) The Pantheon
OXFORD STREET
Gt. Ma
Albermarle St.
1
2
3
PICCAD

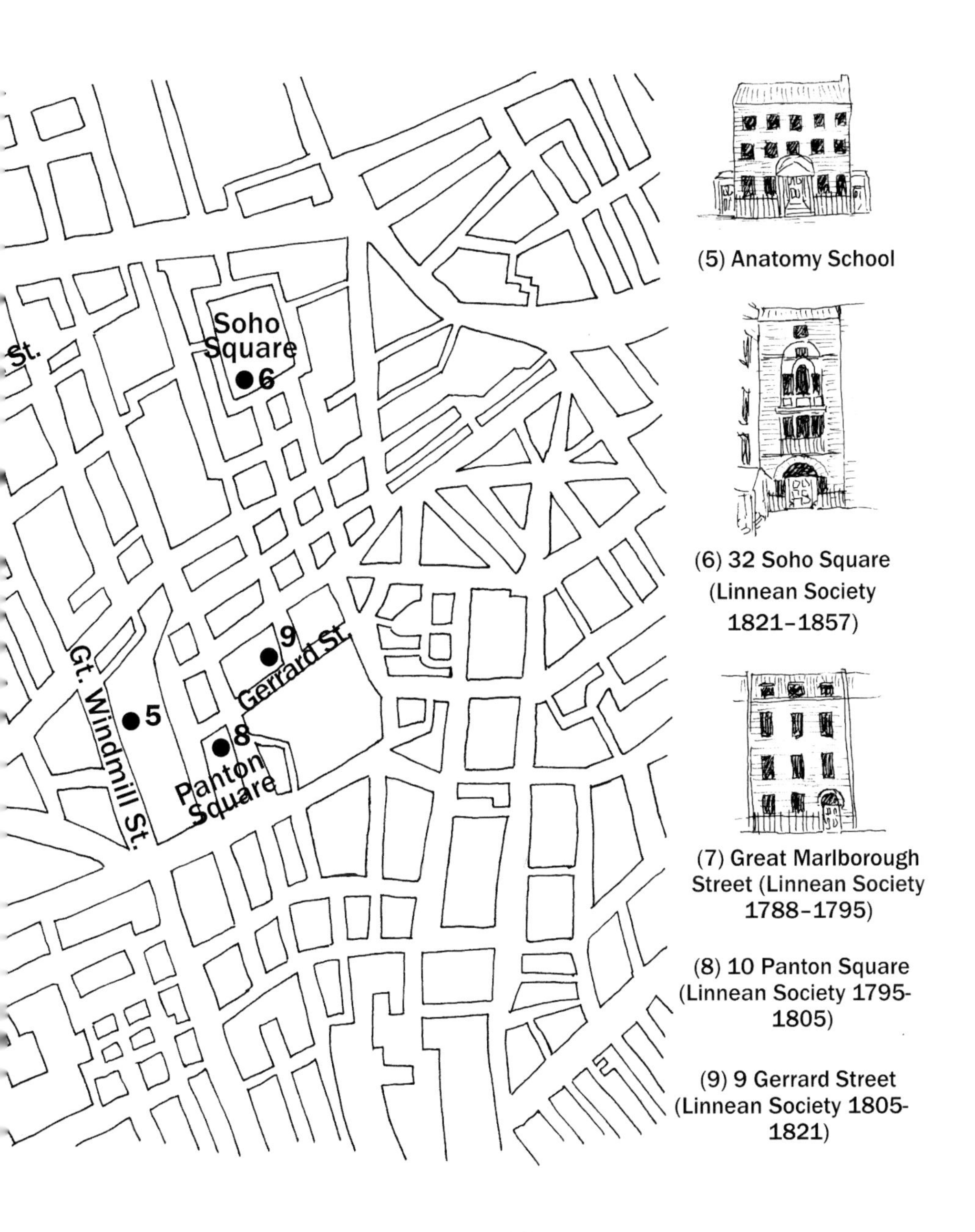

Map of Smith's London.

Smith was now 28 years old, and still entirely reliant on an allowance from his father. Before leaving for Europe in June 1786, James Snr reminded his son of the primary purpose of the journey: to gain an MD so as to begin practising medicine. James Snr expected physic to be, "the superstructure of your fortune, and I forebode your fame too".[5] This letter, however, was written before Paris and the Tour, and Smith returned to England having been courted by most of the leading natural historians of Europe, including more than one correspondent of Linnaeus. In early February 1788, Smith wrote to his father that he was leaving Chelsea with every "expectation of beginning [...] [his] medical career in London". He was careful to add that he remained as committed to the study and pursuit of natural history:

> A science to which I may say *I have raised myself,* with every prospect of taking a lead in the studies to which I am peculiarly attached. [...] You may depend on it Natural History will always be the main object of my life [...]. I rely on this to give me real lasting honour, and make me useful to mankind through ages when I am no more. [...] Do not think I mean to oppose it to my medical views; I have always meant them to co-operate.[6]

The penultimate statement was a direct reversal of James Snr's hopes; natural history, not medicine, would be Smith's path to 'fame', if not fortune. Smith quickly won his father round; James Snr hoped that his son's pursuit of science and medicine would raise him to a "very high degree of eminence". He lamented that he was unable to provide his son with an independent fortune to wholly dedicate himself to natural history, but was pleased to hear of his son's "determination to depend upon yourself and to be your own master".[7]

In private, however, Smith was as ambivalent as ever about a career in medicine. In April 1787, just months after acquiring his Leiden MD, he wrote to Banks about the vacancy that had arisen at the British Museum following the recent death the Keeper of Printed Books, Paul Henry Maty. A job at the museum would have allowed Smith to indulge his scientific interests whilst receiving an income, enjoying enviable access to the collections.[8] However, such vacancies were usually filled internally. The post went to botanist Dr Edward Whitaker Gray, and Gray's old position as Assistant Librarian to Samuel Ayscough, a "blundering kind of chap" according to Banks. Banks encouraged Smith by informing him that as Richard Penneck, Keeper of the Reading Room, was now "very old", and Charles Morton, Principal Librarian, had a "very bad life"—a "vacancy will soon happen".[9] Penneck and Morton, however, were to both give more than another decade each to the museum. Medicine, it seems, really was the only choice, though his finally setting up as a physician was to be delayed time and again.

For some time prior to his trip abroad, Smith and several others had grown increasingly exasperated at the ineptitude and inaction of the Society for the Promotion of Natural History (SPNH). The SPNH's problems were manifold. Numerous meetings passed with neither papers nor specimens presented. When they did appear, little was achieved, as according to Samuel Goodenough "it is referr'd to a committee to consider of it, the committee call it by some name & send it back to the society. The society desire the committee to reconsider it. The committee desire the society to reconsider it—in the mean time nothing is done".[10] The lectures were even worse, with one by Dr George Fordyce on a new arrangement of shells singled out for special condemnation: "such humming, such hawing, mumbling, snuffling, such interruptions in looking for his shells to illustrate as he went on, that not a soul could tell what he would be at".[11] Thomas Marsham frankly stated the facts: "after 4 years expectation I think I may venture to say that nothing has nor is there a probability that any thing will be done worth Publick notice".[12]

Plant a New Garden

In early 1786, Smith met with Goodenough and Marsham to discuss founding an entirely new society; they agreed that it should be dedicated to the study of all branches of natural history and named the "Linnaean Society", in honour of Carl Linnaeus. Since their first meeting at the SPNH in March 1785, Smith and Goodenough had forged a close friendship,

Samuel Goodenough (1743–1827), first Treasurer of the Linnean Society.

despite the 17-year age difference. Goodenough wrote to Smith frequently during his tour; Smith was one of the "very few people with whom I correspond for pleasure, because I can find nobody scarcely who loves to live with his eyes open, & has philosophy enough to talk of any thing but common occurrences".[13] Goodenough was possibly even more enthusiastic in his study of natural history than Smith, interrupting one of his letters to excitedly inform Smith: "just at this moment which is ten o'clock at night, I have caught the *Cimex personatus* [*Reduvius personatus,* the masked hunter insect], which settled on my paper".[14] Marsham was 11 years older than Smith and, in addition to working at the Exchequer Loan Office, was also a gifted entomologist; in 1802 he published *Entomologia Britannica,* the "first authoritative work on British insects based upon the Linnaean system".[15]

Before leaving for Europe, Smith met with Sir Joseph Banks to seek his advice regarding the new society. The details of their discussion are not known, but the endeavour obviously received encouragement, for Goodenough was glad to hear the results. This was also tacit approval that the Royal Society would not oppose the establishment of a society that had the potential to dilute its own scientific endeavours. Afterwards,

Smith would cite the Royal Society's inability to "pay sufficient attention" to natural history as a prime motivation for the foundation of the Linnean Society.[16] Before his departure, Smith had also informed William Forsyth, one of the founders of the SPNH, who, though aware of the SPNH's problems, was "inclined to weed the Old rather than plant a New Garden". Marsham was unconvinced: "the labor of weeding will be excessive & I fear will not answer the trouble".[17]

Smith urged prudence whilst he was away, preferring that their proposals be kept "quite in embryo at present", so as not to do anything "unwisely or hastily".[18] In practice, however, Goodenough and Marsham found it difficult to contain themselves. Goodenough longed to be able to present to the public a complete list of the Linnaean nomenclature "by a Fellow of the L. S."[19], whilst Marsham wanted their plans confirmed by the beginning of 1787 so as to counter the "little squibs of the Envious & Malevolent".[20] William Jones, a wine merchant and entomologist, who had also been involved in early discussions, was much more cautious. Jones proposed watching and waiting for a few years, and to arrange a quarterly breakfast for select, interested friends, from which a new organisation might organically grow, without raising "envious spirit against us [...] from the present existing society; and prevent in future that acrimony which I am sorry to say exists too much amongst ingenious people".[21] Meanwhile, Smith's discussions with "no small share of the scientific people of Europe" confirmed his opinion that:

> A society for the cultivation of Nat[ural] hist[or]y strictly, is much wanted, & would be ably supported; where then can it be fixed with such advantages in London, amid the first collections & libraries, & indeed amid the best naturalists that I have known or heard of?[22]

From early 1787 he was actively engaging prospective participants, as in Geneva, where Pierre-François Tingry, an apothecary and "excellent chymist" confirmed that he would "be glad to be a member" and promised to transmit a paper.[23]

By the SPNH's anniversary dinner in October, Goodenough had lost all patience with the old society. It seemed that all major decisions were being decided beforehand by "the Party"; at that meeting a motion was passed reducing the number of presidents from four to two, artfully proposed by George Fordyce, one of the two chosen. Prior to the meeting, Goodenough had sent a letter to George Prince, one of the founders, informing him that he was "quite disappointed in the Society—that it appeared to me that from their having no head, & such a profusion of honours they never would do any thing effectual". Goodenough was determined for the new society to learn from the mistakes of the old, and duly advised Smith:

> Pray take this into consideration—Members & Wealth are so far real necessaries to a Society: as it enables them to carry matters into effect—to purchase, reward, publish. A Society at Bruxelles is stopp'd at present for want of money to enable a publication going forward.[24]

Once Smith returned to London in early 1788, no further impediments remained and their plans quickly progressed. In late January, Smith, Marsham, and possibly Goodenough, convened at Paradise Row in order to settle the rules of the new society, a copy of which Marsham sent Smith on 28 January. This first draft shows the influence of both the Edinburgh Natural History Society and the SPNH, and does its best to avoid the pitfalls of both. Emphatically, the first item was that it was to consist of "one President to be chosen Annually by Ballot", rather than an unsettled number on rotation. Should any scientific question arise "which may require any particular attention", the President was to nominate "one or more proper Persons" to investigate, rather than delegation to a succession of committees. The Society was to consist of *ordinary members,* from which were chosen the officers who were to regulate the Society's business, and *corresponding members,* who would have free communication with the society but no say in its running. An admission fee of one guinea and an annual contribution of a further guinea were proposed. A provision was also made that every ordinary member, within one year of his admission, should communicate a "dissertation upon some subject of natural history under the forfeiture of one Guinea", the same to apply to corresponding members but without the forfeit.[25]

Smith, Goodenough and Marsham began submitting their proposals to both leading naturalists and interested amateurs, meeting with an enthusiastic response. By the end of January, Marsham had secured George Adams, part of the Adams family, makers of scientific instruments and globes, John Beckwith, a medical man and entomologist, and John Timothy Swainson, customs collector and zoologist, as Fellows.[26] John Latham, one of Britain's leading ornithologists, "did not wait to be twiced asked, but put down his name immediately".[27] Meanwhile, Goodenough was busy trying to secure his friend William Curtis, one of the most prominent botanists of the day thanks to his botanic garden at Lambeth Marsh and his publications *Flora Londinensis* (1777–1798) and the *Botanical Magazine* (1787–ongoing). He sent four letters in quick succession, and invited Curtis to the inaugural meeting, due to be held on the 26 February: "do come to it and have it to say in the annals of history that you were one of the founders [...]. Above all think what a body of *active* practical naturalists we shall have in our society, none else to be admitted—and be of the number". By Goodenough's definition, those that were "not practical men" would be denied entrance among the Fellows, the core membership, instead being allotted to a new class called "Associates".[28] This suggests some confusion about the levels of membership, for Smith described the Associates as "such people as dwell in this kingdom, but at a distance from London, or who cannot well pay, as gardeners &c, who yet may be of great use".[29] Nevertheless, the emphasis on practical, local naturalists was an important definition, by which means they hoped to avoid some of the SPNH's problems. An engaged and committed Fellowship would attend meetings, carry out research, and present and share their findings.

Smith's list of prospective members largely consisted of his Edinburgh friends, including William Thomson, Richard Salisbury and William Younge, in addition to London associates such as Aylmer Bourke Lambert and nurseryman James Dickson, as well as John Sibthorp, Professor of Botany at Oxford. A list of corresponding members numbered over 30, including many of the naturalists he met in Europe, in addition to the Norwich botanists and two further Edinburgh friends, Thomas Charles Hope and Francis Buchanan.[30] Marsham particularly asked him to pursue the respected Linnaean authors William Hudson and John Lightfoot and the mineralogist James Lewis Macie (later Smithson; his will enabled the posthumous foundation of the Smithsonian Institution in the USA). Marsham was also anxious for Lambert to join. An independently wealthy gentleman botanist, his participation would impart respectability to their early endeavours. Similarly, Sir Joseph Banks had been invited to become an Honorary Member, whose acceptance would allow the fledgling society to enjoy the patronage and approval of the President of the Royal Society, without compromising Banks's commitments or the new society's independence.[31] Goodenough was convinced that "were [Banks] not President of the Royal Society, I am sure he w[oul]d join us".[32] Banks accepted the invitation and became a great benefactor, donating books from his own library and even offering to pay for the plates for the first volume of *Transactions of the Linnean Society*. However, Macie declined to join, for unknown reasons, as did William Jones, "for the present only", though he approved of the rules and the proposed members. He eventually joined in 1791.[33] Norwich botanist John Pitchford modestly felt himself "unfit for it, as I don't see what I can send worthy of the Society's attention".[34]

On the 26 February 1788, the inaugural meeting of the Linnean Society took place at the Marlborough Coffee House, Great Marlborough Street, attended by Smith, Goodenough, Marsham, Swainson, Beckwith, Dickson and Jonas Dryander, Sir Joseph Banks's librarian.[35] William Curtis could not attend, but he sent his name to be put down as a Fellow.[36] This was a purely administrative meeting of the Fellows, as opposed to what would become the General Meetings at which scientific papers were read and discussed. The three initiators, Smith, Goodenough, and Marsham, were respectively named President, Treasurer and Secretary; Dryander would be named the Society's librarian at the third meeting, on 15 April. General Meetings were to be held on the first Tuesday of every month, Fellows' Meetings on the third Tuesday.

At the second Fellows' Meeting, on 18 March, the rules and orders were approved and entered into a book, to be signed by all incoming Fellows; this meeting was regarded as the Linnean Society's official date of institution. This new set of rules, which had been slightly amended from their first incarnation, clearly defined the Society's purpose as being "the Cultivation of the Science of Natural History in all its Branches; and more especially of the Natural History of Great Britain and Ireland". The admission fee for Fellows was increased to one and a half guineas (£1 11s 6d), and there were now four ranks of membership: Fellows, Honorary Members, Foreign Members and Associates. There was no charge for the latter three ranks. On admission, Fellows were expected to sign a bond for £20 to the President, Treasurer and one other Fellow so as to guarantee the one guinea annual contribution, which they could be excused from if they opted for a compound lifetime contribution of 10 guineas. Fellows of the Society could expect to have a say in its organisation and direction, as well as receiving all publications *gratis*. Other members had no vote, and only received publications if it featured their work. All papers submitted became the Society's property, to be "publicly read at any General Meeting", and published, if thought proper (the rule requiring all Fellows to submit a paper within a year was dropped). Lists were drawn up of the constituent members of each class of the Society. There were an additional 13 Fellows to the seven "founding Fellows"; the total should have been 21 but John Lightfoot, who accepted an invitation to join, died on 20 February, shortly before the inaugural meeting. Of the four Honorary Member positions, only three were filled: Sir Joseph Banks, Louis de Noailles, 4th Duke of Noailles, with whom Smith had stayed in France, and the Dutch physician and naturalist Petrus Camper. John Stuart, 3rd Earl of Bute, a former adviser to George III, botanist and patron of science was briefly considered but his politics were thought too dubious. In addition, there were 36 Foreign Members (largely Smith's Tour acquaintances), and 11 Associates, including Thomas Woodward and John Pitchford. Subsequent Fellows were to be proposed by at least two existing Fellows and then balloted.

One other significant piece of business was also enacted: provision for a permanent home, something that the SPNH had always lacked. Smith

No. 12 Great Marlborough Street, London; Smith's home and the first home of the Linnean Society of London.

offered two rooms of his Great Marlborough Street house to the Society, one for meetings, the other for its library and collections, for £20 per annum. The Linnean Society would also enjoy the distinction of sharing its home with the collections that once belonged to its namesake (access to which would remain entirely at Smith's discretion).

The Linnean Society's most important function was to act as a facilitator of scientific communication, consultation and research. From the collection of specimens in the field, to the preservation and examination of species conducted in the study, natural history had historically been a largely solitary pursuit, often for no specific audience. Prior to the formation of scientific societies in the 17th century, isolated scientists could only communicate their findings via correspondence, a slow and limiting medium, or by publication, which, whilst it could reach more people, was undertaken at great, personal financial risk. A case in point was provided in early 1789. Smith, always adroit at attracting new members, proposed Fellowship to Richard Pulteney, one of the earliest English followers of Linnaeus. Since publishing his landmark *A General View of the Writings of Linnaeus* (1781), Pulteney, a physician in Blandford, Dorset, had found his scientific life had stagnated:

> Engaged as I am, in the practice of Physic, I have no opportunity for simpling [botanising]; &, [...] at this Distance from London I can have little or no Amusement with Exotics; which confines my botanical studies wholly to Books; & of these I see none, but such as a I buy, so that I have long felt it impossible to go on with any activity, or to any effectual purpose, in botanical Researches.[37]

Pulteney also bemoaned his lack of a London correspondent, which further isolated him from botanical news. He was unanimously elected in December 1789, to the mutual advantage of both the Society and Pulteney. Smith rejoiced to have his name on their list "as one of the main pillars of our infant undertaking", whilst the Society provided Pulteney with a much-needed scientific lifeline.[38] From this point on a regular correspondence was maintained between Smith and Pulteney. Smith also acted as his book agent, sending a small but steady stream of the latest publications into the depths of Dorset. Inspired once again, Pulteney went on to submit four papers to the Society, three of which were printed in the *Transactions*.

Ten Fellows attended the first General Meeting, held 8 April, in addition to three Associates and three visitors. Smith read the first half of a discourse, which would go on to be published in 1791 as "Introductory Discourse on the Rise and Progress of Natural History", the first article in the Society's first volume of *Transactions*. With a Europe-wide perspective, Smith analysed the development of natural history from its imagined prehistoric beginnings to its "most flourishing period", ushered in by the innovations of Linnaeus. It was also a manifesto: Smith ended with the foundation of the Linnean Society itself, and his hopes and desires for this new endeavour.

The Minutiae of Natural History

The Society was to act as a channel through which scientific findings could be disseminated, at meetings and via publication, preventing "all the pains and expence of collectors, all the experience of cultivators, all the remarks of real observers, from being lost to the world".[39] It would also act as a repository of knowledge, pooled resources enabling the acquisition of expensive or rare texts and scientific cabinets of specimens open for consultation by all members. The Society would also be able to exploit, and transmit, the wealth of undisclosed information in London's rich botanic gardens such as Kew, constantly augmented by the arrival of new exotics from Britain's colonies:

> Is it not a reproach to the naturalists of Great Britain that so many rarities should remain in their hands undescribed? that foreigners should eagerly catch at one or two plants obtained from our gardens, which we for years have been trampling unnoticed? Yet how, till now, could such nondescripts have been made publick?[40]

Smith's discourse ended with a justification of the Linnean Society's name, which implicitly bound the members to abide by "the laws and principles of Linnaeus, so far as they have been found to be good". In particular, he emphasised Linnaeus's system of nomenclature, now so well established that anyone purporting to be a naturalist could not "avoid conforming" to his principles. The bedrock of the Society was to be Linnaeus's publications, and its overarching *raison d'etre* "to endeavour to give them the perfection of which they are capable, and to incorporate with them all new discoveries". Nothing could be "more useful to the science of natural history", and Smith pledged Linnaeus's collections to the cause. He considered himself a trustee to the public, holding the "treasures only for the purpose of making them useful to the world and natural history in general, and particularly to this society [...] [as] a never failing resource to us in every difficulty, as well as a fund of information not easily to be exhausted".

The Society's other main function was to enable the publication of "detached descriptions" of species and specimens. The Society actively encouraged the receipt of "the slightest piece of information which may tend to the advancement of the science", making no proscriptions on length or subject: "whatever relates to the determination of species, even in the lowest and seemingly unimportant tribes of nature's works, ought never to be neglected". A publishing committee was set up in June 1789, and after several delays the first volume of *Transactions* appeared in 1791.

Here the Linnean Society offered, and actually delivered, something unique. The SPNH had always harboured intentions of publishing, but were far too ineffectual to realise their plans. The only other viable outlet at this time was the Royal Society's *Philosophical Transactions,* too general to "enter into the minutiae of natural history".[41] In the period 1783 to 1788, just 19 of the 188 papers printed in *Philosophical Transactions* related to natural history, and the final volume of this period contained just one natural history paper, ironically from the pen of Smith himself. Entitled 'Some Observations on the Irritability of Vegetables', it had been read on 14 February 1788. Devising his own experiment, he provided an explanation for the irritability of the stamens (the male parts of a flower) of *Berberis communis* (*Berberis vulgaris*, or the European barberry), which could be induced to spring from their initial sheltered position next to the petals towards the stigma (the tip of the female part of a flower). Several authors had previously described this phenomenon, but as Smith noted, none had identified the mechanics involved, having "mostly [...] copied one another".[42] (Poor research would consistently remain one of Smith's greatest grievances with botanical literature.) Through a series of experiments, Smith surmised that the movement was caused by a high degree of irritability on the inside of each filament (stalk of the stamen). When touched, the filament shortened on that side, bending the stamen towards the stigma and enabling pollination. Smith surmised that the purpose of this behaviour was that when the stamens were in their original position, the anthers (stamen tips) and their pollen were sheltered from rain by the concave petals, but if an insect came into the base of the flower, it would inevitably activate the irritable filaments, and so effect pollination. The paper continued with examples of other irritable plants, and concluded by noting an analogy between plants and animals: "their constitution is capable only of a certain degree of action consistently with health; when that degree is exceeded, disease or death is the consequence".[43] He speculated that the real purpose of the corolla (petals) could be discovered by investigating the habit of double flowers (from which the stamens were absent)

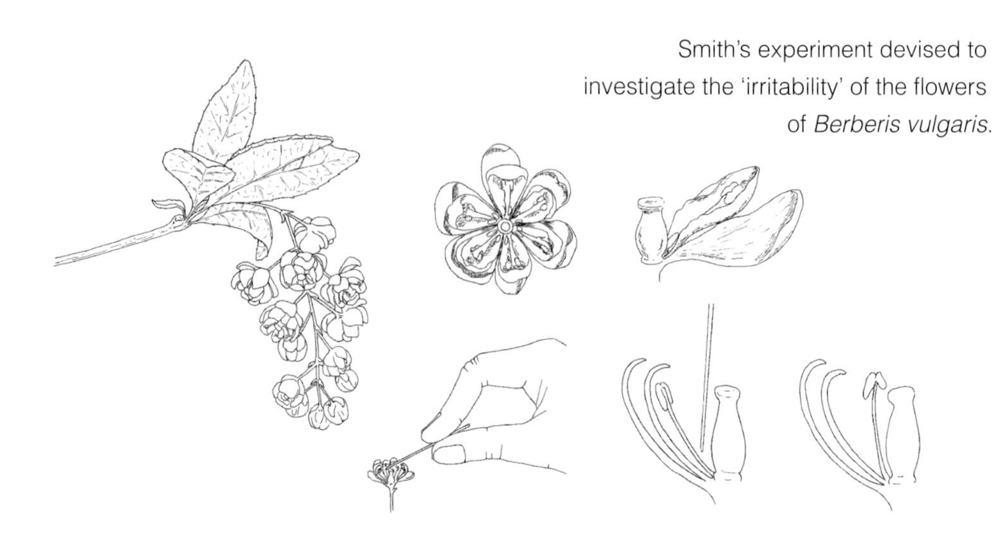

Smith's experiment devised to investigate the 'irritability' of the flowers of *Berberis vulgaris*.

to remain in perfect condition for much longer than their single flowered counterparts of the same species. The paper even generated interest outside of the Royal Society, receiving a mention in *The General Evening Post*, which described it as "a most ingenious paper [...] of a very interesting and entertaining nature". The experiment Smith had described was particularly lauded, as, due to its simplicity, it could be put to the test by anyone.[44] This was to be Smith's first and only paper for the Royal Society, the Linnean Society having first refusal on all his subsequent papers.

The status of the Linnaean collections within Great Marlborough Street was an important distinction. Despite his claims of being merely a trustee to the public, the collections remained emphatically Smith's. This was a shrewd decision, through which we can see much of his character. The original purchase had been an extraordinary gamble made with a significant portion of his family's money. He was determined to make it turn to account, both for his family and for botanical science. From the time of the collections' arrival Smith exhibited an extraordinary drive, belying his supposed delicacy and timidity. The Tour of Europe and the MD were an integral part of his plan, giving Smith a respectability to justify some of the honour reflected by the Linnaean collections, as well as contacts for founding the new Society. Smith was an astute observer: at Edinburgh, at the SPNH and above all at Soho Square, where Sir Joseph Banks provided the model of scientific patron, controlling access and yet generous, the consummate scholarly gentleman. Like Banks, Smith had been deeply passionate about botany from a young age, and in purchasing the collections Smith too had become a patron of learning. Banks, however, had money, whereas Smith was still receiving an allowance from his father. Nevertheless, at 28 years of age, Smith had brought together a disparate group of physicians, clergymen and clerks, most at least 10 years his senior, to discuss and debate natural history. This would take place not at the breakfast table, as in Soho Square, but in an ordered Society, with rules and regulations, funds and collections, and a will to publish and disseminate information. Smith's first act of generosity was granting the Linnean Society a permanent, respectable home: for a price. Despite his already extraordinary achievements, vanity never entered the equation; at Great Marlborough Street the presiding deity was always Linnaeus, never Smith.

In his introductory discourse, Smith acknowledged that not everyone would agree with all of Linnaeus's theories, but he did not expect that one of those selected for Honorary Membership would reject the invitation on exactly those grounds. In late June, Smith received a letter from Petrus Camper. Whilst flattered by the invitation to become an Honorary Member of a natural history society, he thought it would "do me little honour, I fancy, to be it of a <u>Linnean Society</u> whatsoever". Camper regarded "the Swedish author"—his dismissive name for Linnaeus—as "a mere Catalogist, and the most superficial naturalist" he had ever encountered, and believed he had done "little honour" to the science of natural history over the course of the 18th century. Even when allowing him credit for the sexual system of botany, he stated it was not new, and he was furious that Linnaeus had become "universally accredited by the Natural Historians of Europe". Camper was further incensed by "the pompous Greek titles of his Classes, Ordines &c" which he saw as being imposed "upon the ignorants". Camper thought that the naming of a British natural history society after Linnaeus was an insult to eminent home grown naturalists such as John Ray or Robert Hooke. He concluded by asking why it could not be named "for the prosecution of natural history? Or of the Naturae Curiosorum? Of the Naturforschende Freunde as in Berlin? Why not the London Society for Natural History? Or any other except that of Linnaeus?".[45]

Camper had edited Linnaeus's *Amœnitates Academicæ* (1749), so Smith was particularly shocked by Camper's response. He remonstrated with Camper in his response, remarking that he had not in Camper "any thing like narrow jealousy, or the petulancy of little minds, who are angry with Linn[aeu]s because he cannot teach them what they have not abilities to learn". Not wishing to enter into a defence of Linnaeus, he focused on Camper's objection to the Society's name. He explained that the Linnean Society was a body of naturalists whose sole intention was the cultivation of the study of natural history, not a group whose goal was to "enlist themselves as the followers of any person whatever". The name was "peculiarly proper for us, who have among us the very museum & lib[rar]y of Linn[aeu]s in the house where we meet". Several Fellows of the Society agreed in some measure with Camper "as to the merits of the illustrious Swede", but all had approved of the Society's name for the reasons Smith had given. Unable to hide his disappointment, he ended the letter by stating his wish that respected men like Camper would always be "free from weaknesses & prejudices, but perhaps that cannot be". For this reason, he informed Camper, he was keeping the letter to himself, claiming that he was protecting him from common gossip—"I could not bear to hear you slightingly spoken of"—and would wait for either confirmation of his refusal, or acceptance of the offer.[46] No further correspondence survives (Camper's letter and Smith's response are both later copies), but the original refusal was maintained.

Smith's friends in Paris had actually anticipated London by founding their own *Société Linnéenne de Paris* on 28 December 1787. Though Smith had remained in Paris until 29 October 1787, he appears to have been unaware of their plans, if they even existed at that stage. Pierre Broussonet's letter of March 1788 informs him of its foundation with no reference to earlier conversations. It is even possible that Smith, who at the time was corresponding with his friends in England on the matter as well as engaging potential Foreign Members, inspired the Paris Linnaeans. Other members included L'Héritier and Desfontaines; they met every Friday at Broussonet's house, and read their papers in Latin.[47] Just over a month later, Broussonet provided a vindication of the London founders' careful planning when he conceded that his own Society "will have difficulty surviving, as many here are envious and subject us to ridicule".[48] Broussonet's fears unfortunately were to prove correct; *Société Linnéenne de Paris* was unable to survive the destabilising effects of the French Revolution and ceased functioning in 1789, only to be revived in 1790 as the *Société d'Histoire Naturelle de Paris*, before ceasing yet again in 1795 with the establishment of the *Institut National des Sciences et des Arts*.

The Linnean Society of London, meanwhile, went from strength to strength. Each meeting saw the reading of at least one original paper, often accompanied by presentations of unrelated specimens for the Society's growing collections. As intended, this was natural history in *all* its branches: Goodenough provided the first entomological paper ("Remarks upon the Linnean and Fabrician Systems of Entomology" 3 June 1788), and John Latham the first ornithological ("An account of a singular Bird sent to him by Mr Lewin of Oare near Faversham accompanied with an elegant drawing" 1 July 1788). It was not until the meeting on 7 October that the first exclusively botanical paper was read, Richard Salisbury's "On 2 new Species of *Cypripedium*". The first anniversary meeting was celebrated on 21 April 1789, at which Smith, Goodenough and Marsham were re-elected to their respective offices. At the same meeting the Society agreed to hire its first paid member of staff; Francesco Borone, Smith's Milanese valet, who was to receive 20 guineas annually for his attendance on the Society "at all times" as a housekeeper and errand boy. The first anniversary dinner was held immediately afterwards at the Old Slaughter Coffee House in St Martin's Lane, attended by 21 members of the Society. A flurry of activity followed; a list of the Society was printed, now numbering 32 Fellows, 46 Foreign Members and 13 Associates, and the *Transactions* committee established.[49]

In May 1788, Smith accompanied Sir Joseph Banks and Jonas Dryander on a visit to Oxford to consult John Sibthorp's collections. Sibthorp had spent the years 1784 to 1787 studying and collecting on the continent, including a year and a half in Greece with botanical artist Ferdinand Bauer. He returned with around two thousand specimens and drawings for an intended flora of the Hellenic region, inspired by the *De Materia Medica* of Dioscorides, a first-century Greek army surgeon. In Smith, Dryander and

Sir Joseph Banks (1743–1820), President of the Royal Society.

Sibthorp, the visit brought together three of the most prominent English botanists of the day; curiously, at this point, each had a conspicuous lack of published scientific work, though all three had great ambitions in this area. Indeed, unbeknownst to Smith, these collections were to eventually play a pivotal role in his life, following the untimely death of Sibthorp in 1796. Later, in 1799, Smith would be chosen by Sibthorp's executors to edit (and in the event, write) his monumental *Flora Græca*, a project that would also see Smith to his own grave. Smith's Norwich friend, John Pitchford, commenting on Smith's visit to Oxford, was particularly prescient when he stated that Smith was "born under an auspicious planet".[50]

From Oxford, Smith travelled to Chapel Allerton, near Leeds, Yorkshire, to visit his old Edinburgh colleague Richard Salisbury, formerly Markham (Salisbury had changed his name in 1785 as a condition for inheriting a substantial request from a distant relative of his mother), and was back in London in time to chair the Society's General Meeting on 3 June 1788. Inevitably, Smith's fragile health felt the impact of this relentless activity; having suffered from a persistent cough since February, he now rapidly developed a fever and a pain in his side. He spent most of July confined to his room, tended by his mother and sister by the fireside, with all visitors barred, missing the General Meeting at the beginning of that month. Writing to Thomas Woodward over a week later he assured his friend he was feeling better and gaining strength every day, but he soon relapsed, later diagnosing himself as suffering from a "peripneumony" (pneumonia)—his lungs, again.[51] By the end of July it had become apparent that a full recovery would only come from taking the waters at Matlock Bath, Derbyshire. Smith's father had long been a proponent of the curative powers of hot springs, having utilised those at Matlock and Bristol many times himself. Smith had fully recovered by 8 September, though with a strict injunction "to vary study with exercize avoiding much hurry, company & the night air".[52] Harking back to Edinburgh days, James Snr recommended taking "as stout a walk as [he] could bear approaching to fatigue".[53] By such a regime he made it through the winter without further complications. Smith resumed his duties as President (in his absence the chair had been filled by Goodenough or Dryander), beginning with a successful attempt to convince Thomas Woodward to upgrade his Associate membership to Fellowship.

Smith's convalescence had given him ample time to consider his future prospects; throughout this period he had made no further steps towards establishing himself as a physician, despite continued pressure from his father. To Johan Gustaf Acrel, the Linnaean collections agent, he stated that he was intending to "attempt lecturing in Natural History; perhaps too I may practice physick, but that is uncertain".[54] His other friends were still under the impression he was to become a physician, and his correspondents, particularly those on the continent, kept him well informed of the latest medical developments, publications and intriguing cases from their own practices. John Pitchford wrote of a case of *retroversi uteri*, which he had treated according to the directions in Thomas Denman's *Introduction to Midwifery* (1762), only to result in a miscarriage, and Walter Vaughan, Smith's companion in Leiden, sent a detailed description of a woman with "functional supernumerary nipples".[55, 56] Neither of these graphic accounts would have done much to induce the squeamish Smith to finally begin his practice, and as 1788 drew to a close he developed his continuing campaign to become a respected practitioner of science in his own right, with an ambitious lecturing and publication schedule.

CHAPTER FIVE

Establishing Smith

On the night of 16 May 1702, a huge fire broke out in the Swedish city of Uppsala, destroying large swathes of the city. Alongside houses and livelihoods, the fire also consumed the lifework of Olof Rudbeck the elder, contained within the vaults of Uppsala Cathedral. Rudbeck was a scientific genius, mastering, amongst other subjects, anatomy, chemistry, mathematics, architecture, linguistics, music and botany. Much of his life was spent in preparing the *Campi Elysii* (1701–1702) — a monumental endeavour to figure all the known plants of the world, together with their synonyms. Rudbeck drew, coloured and cut the woodblocks for around 11,000 plants, to be published in 12 volumes, his son gradually taking over production as his father aged. The first two volumes (grasses and bulbous plants) had been printed and were being stored underneath Uppsala Cathedral, awaiting distribution, when the fire struck. All was lost: the woodblocks, the drawings and the printed volumes, except for just two copies of the first, by chance still at the printer's, and a handful more of the second. Rudbeck, devastated, died the same year.

During the negotiations for the purchase of Linnaeus's collections, Smith had been led to believe that the library, thrillingly, contained one of the surviving copies of the now incredibly valuable first volume — Banks was prepared to give Smith £100 for it. In fact, there were only two copies in existence, and neither was in Linnaeus's library (one was in William Sherard's library at Oxford University, and the other at Castle Löfsta, Sweden). Instead, Smith received a copy of the second volume and another (partial) survivor of the conflagration: the woodblocks for 90 of the first volume's 130 plates.

Smith immediately realised the publication potential represented by these blocks, and made plans to visit Oxford in the summer of 1785 to compare them against Sherard's *Campi Elysii*.[1] The trip never took place, but the idea stuck, and he probably consulted the copy when in Oxford with Banks, Dryander and Sibthorp three years later. With 40 missing blocks, a standard new edition was impossible, as acknowledged in the title of the eventual publication: *Reliquiæ Rudbeckianæ*. It went to press in February 1789 and was published in May, dedicated to Linnaean sale agent Johan Gustaf Acrel and priced at half a guinea. It was a simple work: each of the 35 pages contained as many as four woodcuts, accompanied by Rudbeck's brief diagnostic descriptions. Smith, as editor, rearranged the figures according to Linnaean principles, as well as providing the current scientific names. The sniffy assessment in *The Monthly Review* stated that the woodblocks may "exhibit nature indeed, but it is in her coarsest attire". The most curious thing about this work was its editor: "whatsoever comes from the pen of Dr Smith, the worthy possessor of the Linnean Cabinet, necessarily demands the attention of the naturalist", but the production itself could only satisfy the "curiosity of the antiquary, rather than promoting the knowledge of Botany".[2]

Smith's friends seemed to share this view. Though many requested or received copies as gifts, there is a deafening silence in the correspondence as to their opinion. Elsewhere it struggled to find an audience at all—three years later, Acrel wrote to Smith that the copies sent for sale in Uppsala remained unsold, and asked if Smith would like them returned.[3]

Almost simultaneously with the publication of *Reliquiæ Rudbeckianæ*, adverts for "A Course of Lectures on Botany, by James Edward Smith M.D. F.R.S., Possessor of the Linnaean Collection[s]", commencing on Tuesday 5 May, began appearing in the London newspapers, with instruction to enquire at Great Marlborough Street for further particulars.[4] Details are scant, but Smith commented to a friend that it was to be a short course, suggesting that this was an investigative foray into their potential popularity and profitability.[5] Setting up as a lecturer in natural history, as a side-line to being a physician, had been the very first argument Smith had used when trying to convince his father to provide the money for the Linnaean pur-

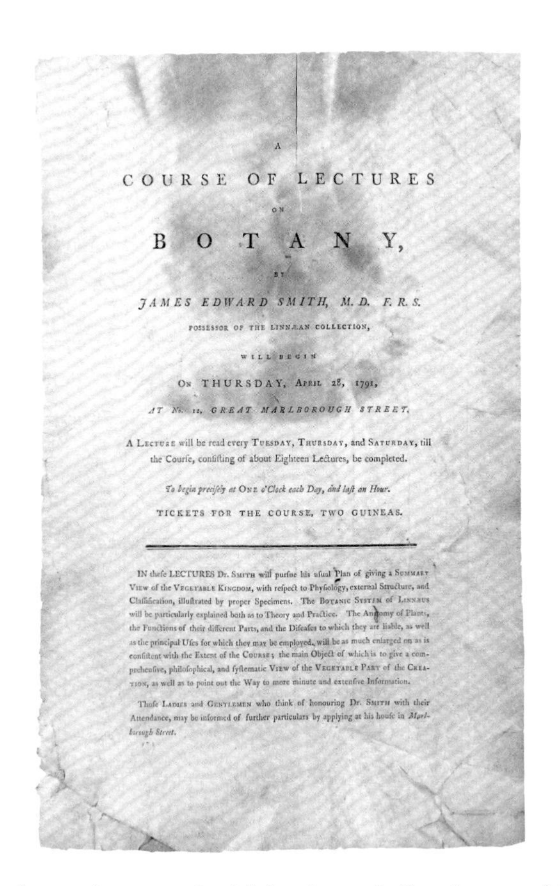

Notice advertising a course of botanical lectures at 12 Great Marlborough Street, commencing 28 April 1791.

chase. As ever, Smith had carefully observed the current offer before commencing on his own plan. His most obvious model was William Curtis, with whom Smith shared many parallels. Curtis had initially trained and established himself as an apothecary but struggled to suppress his botanical inclinations. Before long, "the apothecary was soon swallowed up in the botanist, and the shop exchanged for a garden".[6] From this garden (variously at Bermondsey, Lambeth Marsh and Brompton), Curtis lectured and demonstrated the principles of practical botany, and led "herbarizing excursions". Curtis also began publishing—the respected, though poor selling, *Flora Londinensis*, and the phenomenally popular *The Botanical Magazine*, which sold upwards of 2,000 copies an issue; Curtis reportedly said of the two works "one brought him pudding, and the other praise".[7] Curtis's absence from the 1789 lecturing circuit was noted by Smith: "his Mag[azi]n[e] has made him too rich to want it. Tis not so with me!!!".[8] The reception to Smith's own course of lectures was encouraging enough for him to consider also covering zoology the following spring, and for which adverts began appearing at the end of 1789.[9]

Reliquiæ Rudbeckianæ was followed within weeks by another publication, *Plantarum Icones Hactenus Ineditæ, Plerumque Ad Plantas In Herbario Linnaeano Conservatas Delineata* (1789–1791).[10] *Plantarum Icones* was an entirely new venture for Smith, being his first part-issued work, the first dedicated to taxonomy and the first to feature original illustrations, or figures. The plan of *Plantarum Icones* was to provide figures of plants previously unpublished, drawn largely from the herbariums of the two Linnaeuses, father and son. Smith also planned to feature plants from the Tournefort herbarium in Paris. Though he was relying on the collections of these "illustrious predecessors" to provide his source material, he promised "to set down faithfully, in words and by illustration, only things that I have observed in person".[11]

Illustrated botanical works often had to serve two audiences: the scientist and the art lover. Indeed, in his first preface, whilst acknowledging that botanical plates could be useful in identifying plants, he complained that the same, ostentatious specimens were figured again and again. This new work was aimed at the scientist, where utility and accuracy were the most important qualities. The uncoloured figures were largely taken from the dried specimens and in some instances from drawings sent by Linnaeus's correspondents. In the second fascicle (instalment) Smith defended his use of dried specimens as the model for the figures: "the task and the duty of the illustrator here is to observe the parts of the dried plants with such subtlety and care, and so to fix them in his mind, that in the end they become alive to him".[12]

The uncredited illustrator was the remarkably talented James Sowerby. Two years older than Smith, Sowerby had been born and raised in London. Apprenticed to the marine artist Richard Wright, it was not long after the latter's death in 1775 that he began working for William Curtis as an artist and engraver on *Flora Londinensis*. By the time he met Smith, he had already established a reputation for producing illustrations both accurate and beautiful, his work appearing in publications by John Lightfoot, Charles L'Héritier de Brutelle and Richard Relhan. Though

Sowerby's work on *Plantarum Icones* was not credited, it signalled the beginning of what was to become an incredibly fruitful partnership.

Each fascicle was to contain 25 uncoloured figures of plants, described, in Latin, by Smith. It was priced at a guinea and published by Benjamin White & Son, one of the first publishers to specialise in natural history books. Smith acknowledged the huge debt he owed to Sir Joseph Banks, dedicating the first fascicle to him under the triple character of "consummate botanist, most excellent patron, and above all, a most sincere friend to the author".[13]

In the first fascicle, Smith introduced 13 new species, including two new genera, *Roussea* and *Thouinia*, largely through correcting mistakes made by Linnaeus the Younger in his *Supplementum Plantarum* (1781). With *Roussea*, Smith fulfilled the elder Linnaeus's intention to name a plant after the philosopher and botanist Jean-Jacques Rousseau: before his death, he had designated a plant for this purpose, but his son, by mistake or design, had instead named the intended plant *Russelia*. Smith bestowed the name *Roussea simplex* on a curious plant restricted to the island of Mauritius; this plant has since been found to be pollinated by geckos, and remains the

Roussea simplex, from Smith's *Plantarum Icones*.

sole species of its genus. *Thouinia spectabilis* was named in honour of French botanist, André Thouin, who he had met in Paris. It is now a synonym of the earlier name *Humbertia madagascariensis*. In any case, there was already a *Thouinia*, described, interestingly enough, by the younger Linnaeus in 1782.

The work was received with great interest. *The Monthly Review* was so enthusiastic it ignored its general rule not to review serially issued works, considering it "a publication, on which the opinion of the public ought to be taken at once; for the trouble and expence attending it demand a quick return of countenance and patronage; lest so useful a purpose, unable to establish itself, should be frustrated, and the public lose a great convenience".[14] *The Critical Review* commended Smith for "uniting accuracy with so much elegance as to render his work not a costly collection of pictures, beyond the reach of many private individuals, but a real acquisition to science and the natural historian".[15] The figures were "exceedingly clear, distinct and expressive", their veracity tested by the reviewer using them to draw up his own description and then comparing the results to Smith's description; the only difference occurred in the colour and thickness. All were united in their hope that the author would continue such a worthy publication. The very highest praise, however, came from Johan Gustaf Acrel, who ever since the Linnaean purchase had thought that Smith would become:

> The worthy successor and scientific heir to Linnaeus, and now I must believe, with all the world's scholars, that it has come to pass. [...] Anyone here with a scientific knowledge of botany who has had the good fortune to see them, recognises that this [is] no mere essay, but a template for the most exact botanical observation.[16]

The original intention was to produce two fascicles a year; however, 1789 passed with just one, as did 1790, and in 1791 the third and final fascicle was published. The correspondence is silent on the cessation of *Plantarum Icones*, but it can be assumed that despite the early praise it received, it struggled to find an audience.

A steady stream of accolades started coming Smith's way as his botanical reputation spread across Europe. On 4 June 1789 he was elected a Corresponding Member of the *Regia Scientiarum Taurensis Academia*, with a promise of being upgraded to an Associate Foreign Member if he sent a paper (Smith's 'Tentamen Botanicum de Filicum Generibus Dorsiferarum', a new arrangement of ferns, was printed in the Academy's *Transactions* in 1793[17]), as well as an invitation to join Turin's *Reale Società Agraria*.[18] By the end of the year he had also been elected a Foreign Member of the *Société des Botanophiles* of Angers, France.[19] The ultimate honour, though, came in September, with the publication of the third and final volume of William Aiton's *Hortus Kewensis* (1789), a definitive catalogue of all the plant species cultivated at Kew (in reality constituting the vast majority of all cultivated plant species then in England). This was a collaborative effort between Aiton, who provided the material and basic information, and Sir Joseph Banks's successive librarians, Daniel Solander and Jonas Dryander, who contributed the scientific classification and descriptions. The three volumes contained around 5,600 species, many of which were rare exotics brought back from Britain's colonies, making it highly anticipated. Since at least April 1789, Dryander had been promising Smith that it would include a plant named in his honour, and on 2 July, Smith informed a friend that the "Kew Cat[alogue] not yet out, but here is a harbinger of it—*Smithia sensitiva*".[20] A low-growing annual plant with small yellow flowers, indigenous to eastern Asia and Australia, it was first sent to Banks in 1785 by John Gerard Koenig from the coast of Coromandel, India, in the form of seeds. Identified and classified by Dryander and Richard Salisbury, who had successfully cultivated it at Chapel Allerton, the species name *sensitiva* referred to the action of the leaves folding together when touched—a punning tribute to Smith's work on the irritability of plants, and also perhaps to his bashful nature. As a further tribute, *Smithia sensitiva* was one of only three plants figured in the volume, engraved by James Sowerby.[21] Smith sent copies of the engraving to several correspondents, including the Marchioness of Rockingham, Spanish botanist Antonio Cavanilles and Italian botanist Carlo Bellardi. He also distributed seeds, and a *Smithia sensitiva* was flowering in Turin by 1790.[22] For over 25 years,

Smithia sensitiva was to remain the sole species, until Smith identified a second, *Smithia conferta*, in 1816. At the same time it was thought that the genus *Smithia* was almost indistinguishable from the genus *Aeschynomene*, and Smith had doubts over the propriety of keeping them separate.[23] *Smithia*, however, has endured and now comprises 22 species.

This early period in Smith's professional life saw the development of two highly typical friendships, examples of which were to be repeated throughout his days. The first, and most important of the two—indeed, one of the most important of his life—was with Edmund Davall. Born in 1763, Davall had spent his first 20 years in London, following his mother to her native Switzerland after the death of his father, a Holborn shopkeeper, in 1784. It was at this time that Davall first developed an interest in botany, leading him to procure Philip Miller's *The Gardener's Kalendar* (1757), in which he saw a sketch of the Linnaean system. Like the childhood Smith with the gorse flower, Davall was "suddenly inflamed & at this critical period resolved to pursue a study which I was certain would be productive of better happiness than any plan that might lead to pecuniary advantage".[24] In Switzerland, Davall exhausted his finances in acquiring a "proper stock of Books" (£600 by 1795[25]), but quickly made a name for himself amongst the local botanists, contributing papers and information to the 'Private Society of Friends of Natural History in Berne'. In 1788, for unknown reasons, he made a long visit to England, taking with him two letters of introduction to Smith provided by Jean Senebier and Jacob Wyttenbach, two eminent Swiss naturalists Smith had met in 1787 in Geneva and Berne, respectively. Davall was announced as both "an admirer who would like nothing better than to become your disciple" and a "fervent lover of botany".[26] Smith and Davall quickly became friends, united by a shared passion for botany and possessing the same romantic ideals of friendship. Taken under Smith's wing, Davall received a full introduction to London's botanical scene, which included admittance as a Fellow of the Linnean Society on 16 September 1788. Davall would later describe his time in England as "surely the most memorable & the happiest period of my whole life" for both spurring his botanical zeal and procuring him Smith's "inestimable Friendship which I prefer to every other blessing that Providence could grant me".[27]

Davall was forced to return home to Orbe, Canton de Berne, in January 1789, following the death of his mother. A regular correspondence was established, initially botanical, but intensifying in a matter of months, much like Smith's earlier friendship with Robert Batty. In May, Davall wrote of the "inexpressible satisfaction & delight" he received from the sight of Smith's letter:

> From the portion of my thoughts which you occupy, from the anxiety concerning your health you are of all other beings the one who interests me most & were Botany quite out of the question I think I could say as much from the high esteem your conversation & character have created in me.[28]

Though Smith reciprocated, his responses were more restrained. Nevertheless, he assured Davall, "that 'there is no love lost between us'. Now indeed I feel the value of botany when it procures me such friends!".[29] Davall's valedictions quickly morphed from the standard "y[ou]r obedient humble servant"[30], to the truly heartfelt "believe me ever yours most sincerely & affectionately".[31]

Davall lived at the home of his three spinster aunts, whose lives revolved entirely around the card table—one actually died with cards still in hand. Increasingly disgusted, he described "the Society of this little place [...] [as] composed of that too numerous herd who are constantly desirous of killing time they know not how to employ".[32] Since his meeting with Smith, Davall had resolved to dedicate his life and patrimony to the pursuit of botany, revealing his newfound focus on "the establishment of a good herbarium, you have set me all on fire & the sight of L.H. [the Linnaean Herbarium]!". In anticipation, Davall had two cabinets made, and the covers of 800 genera written, but declared himself as "poor as Job in plants!". He confessed his imitation of Smith "in preferring neat & instructive specimens"[33], and even went to the extreme of ordering a herbarium case to the same design as Smith's, "with a top in pyramid & Wedgwood's medallion of Linnaeus in the middle!". In his excitement, he included a tiny sketch of the case, helpfully pointing out the location of the medallion.[34]

Davall's herbarium cabinet.

The second friendship was enabled entirely through Davall, who introduced Smith to Mary Watson-Wentworth, the dowager Marchioness of Rockingham. Lady Rockingham was the widow of Charles Watson-Wentworth, second Marquess of Rockingham, Whig Prime Minister of Great Britain 1765–1766, and again in 1782, before dying of influenza. Lady Rockingham, who had been an influential political hostess, spent her widowhood indulging her taste for gardening at Hillingdon House, near Uxbridge in Middlesex. Smith first visited in early December 1788 and quickly cultivated her friendship and patronage. Shortly after the first visit he received two *Portlandia* flowers, one of which was to be passed on to Jonas Dryander.[35] The next day, he sent a gift in return; a copy of the one (unnamed) work by Linnaeus missing from her collection, which she declared she "should have despaired of obtaining". Smith had gone all out: not only was it "one out of actual Linnaean Library" (a duplicate!), he had also gone to the trouble of having it rebound in the same style as the Marchioness's books. She promised to take up Smith's invitation to come to town to see his collections, "tho with the most ignorant eye they ever were view'd with".[36] Her garden became one of the principal inspirations for the most beautiful of all Smith and Sowerby's publications, *Icones Pictæ Plantarum Rariorum* (1790–1793), or *Coloured Figures of Rare Plants*.

Lady Rockingham became a generous patron; in October, she gave Smith a generous gift from her own library: six (of the 12) volumes of Hendrik van Rheede's *Hortus Malabaricus* (1678–1703), a treatise on the medicinal plant properties of the flora in the Indian state of Kerala, though she later asked him to "shake those books well" for any memoranda written by her late husband. The next month, Smith wrote to Davall, stating that his introduction to her had been "peculiarly fortunate", for she was a "worthy woman, & her sentiments accord with mine in many things.

She treats me with peculiar affability & attention, & sometimes consults me medically as well as botanically".[37] Her patronage extended beyond Smith. On the publication of *Hortus Kewensis* she ordered enough copies "to set up a shop", intending to distribute them as gifts to her botanical friends. Lady Rockingham is also the first known patient of Smith the physician. She implicitly trusted Smith's medical advice regarding her chronic stomach complaints, exclaiming that it was "rare to meet with Physicians with your sentiments of the imperfection of human knowledge but they are so just, that it must always in my opinion give a great pre-eminence to the person who possesses them".[38]

Peculiar Triangles and Toad Eaters

Davall comes across as the more junior of the partnership, eager for Smith's approval. This is mawkishly acknowledged in October 1789, when Davall confessed that he was:

> Very well aware that to be on good terms with you is enviable—that I am highly interested in cultivating your good will—that from your peculiar advantages & knowledge the common run of men should court you—but in the name of God I can assure you that were Botany quite out of the question I know not a man on earth whose friendship I so much desire nor whose sentiments harmonize so perfectly with mine as yours—I love you from my heart & I know well enough to be certain of its return.[39]

Smith was never as florid with his affections, showing a marked maturity in comparison to his earlier, more youthful outpourings with his cousin Nathaniel Kindersley and Edinburgh friend Robert Batty. Despite the physical gulf separating them, they were in almost constant communication. Davall also acted as an emissary for the Swiss Foreign Members of the Linnean Society, on one occasion distributing the Fellowship diplomas, laws and lists of members to Jacob Wyttenbach, Pierre-François Tingry and Berthout van Berchem. The delivery to the latter, in Davall's words, resulted in a "complete farce" when van Berchem's father, having misconceived the reason behind Davall's visit, "boasted at dinner in the presence of 14 persons that there were only 4 honorary Members & that his son had been chosen as one¡¡¡ they suffered no little avanie [humiliation] when I corrected the mistake observing at the same time that distinguished knowledge & rank united were essentially requisite".[40] Smith sniggered, thanking Davall for his care of the diplomas and "Van Berchemian anecdotes thereto belonging¡¡¡".[41]

Smith showed his regard more quietly. In November 1789, he sent Davall a specimen, from the Linnaean herbarium, of *Diapensia lapponica*, a small, evergreen perennial shrub indigenous to Arctic regions. Davall went into raptures on receiving the specimen, exclaiming: "a piece of the Cross is less precious to a bigot Catholic".[42] He had it framed and glazed, along with a specimen of *Smithia sensitiva* also sent by Smith, kept together in "the sacred corner between the Bookcase which contains Linnaeus's works & my (little as yet) Herbarium".[43] Davall, though, had a secret. On 4 September 1789, he married Henriette-Louise-Stéphanie Crinzos de Cottens, the only daughter of a poor but distinguished local family. Smith did not find out until late November, probably through a mutual friend, even though Davall had had the opportunity to inform Smith in a letter written 10 days later on 14 September. Hurt, Smith wrote to Davall: "how is it that you tell me not one word of your marriage? Could you think I should not be interested in an event so important to your happiness?". Smith earnestly hoped this woman was "no enemy to flora!".[44] An unfortunate consequence of the slow transit of letters between Switzerland and England meant that when Davall finally informed Smith at the end of November, he was convinced that it would be fresh news for Smith.

Desperately lonely, with only his botanical work and correspondence with Smith to shield him from that "herd of silly beings called gens du monde, eternal players of [the card game] Quadrille", his aunts and their friends, he could no longer resist the agreeable conversation and turn of mind of Henriette, which perfectly matched his own. Henriette was apparently fully aware that she was entering an unusual, romantic-platonic love triangle, and would be sharing her husband's heart with an Englishman. Even their neighbours had noticed something unusual about Davall. In August, just weeks before the marriage, he embarked on a botanical expedition to Great St Bernard near the Swiss-Italian border. This was solely to collect fresh specimens of *Lichen cucullatus* (*Flavocetraria cucullata*) for Smith, who had accidently spoiled his own by soaking them in warm water. Davall was "firmly resolved that no consideration whatever should prevent me from doing as soon as possible all I might to keep my word with you". The neighbours were scandalised, muttering "M. Davall cannot be much in love since he runs along to the Alps at such a time. Has anyone seen such behaviour? He is an Ostrogoth—surely he is mad, etc etc".[45]

Davall was thrown into despair on receiving Smith's hurt missive, reading it as "an accusation to the most conscience-wounded criminal. Yet on my honour I did not dare tell you of it [...] I thought you would consider me as a deserter of the good cause [botany]".[46] Smith, of course, was delighted for his friend, and joked that he should hold a grudge against him for suspecting he would not rejoice "with all my heart" at the marriage. It seems as though much of the misunderstanding stemmed from the fact that Davall and Smith had never spoken of their ideas of marriage before. Smith stated that Davall had certainly done him an injustice in thinking him "not sufficiently attentive to the first great end of man & his truest means of happiness, virtuous love". In a rare moment of vulnerability, he confided to Davall that he had been:

> Unfortunate in this respect, partly alas by my own fault, & perhaps am never doomed to be happy in this point. If not I have enough to be thankful for, & must submit—after having said this much I must say there is one woman I am persuaded would make me happy & compleatly so, & but one: if I have not her I shall probably never marry. I cannot merely take a wife as a piece of furniture, without real attachment. I would rather be single & have some my dear relations to supply the want (as much as possible) of a still dearer companion.[47]

This 'one' woman was probably Pleasance Reeve, whom Smith would marry in 1796. She was the daughter of Robert Reeve, a Lowestoft attorney and merchant, and a close friend of Smith's sister, Esther Anne. At the time of this letter she was just 16 years old. An undated portrait of Smith from this period exists, drawn by a Mrs Louisa Lane. It shows him as a young man, with short, slightly curled hair, a long nose, pert lips and a slight flush to the cheeks, handsome even. This, along with the above quoted letters, are rare artefacts of Smith's private life at this time.

In many respects, Smith was quite a catch. Known across Europe (in certain circles) as the possessor of the Linnaean collections, founder and president of the Linnean Society, published author and lecturer—now all he needed was an income. Smith's success had started to cause tensions with Smith's prestigious friend in Soho Square that Davall had certainly picked up on whilst in London. In October 1789 he asked Smith if Sir Joseph Banks was "steady" with him, which drew an enlightening response. Swearing Davall to secrecy, Smith believed that both Banks and Dryander "mean to be as civil to me as they can, & why should I enquire farther? Every body is not blest with an heart". There were several obvious causes of tension, one being *Icones Pictæ Plantarum Rariorum*, Smith and Sowerby's projected new work. As Smith reported, this was "not relished" by Banks, as he wanted to employ Sowerby himself on a similar work based on Kew's plants, which Smith's work would now forestall. Despite this, Smith used the resources at Soho Square "generously as I ought, & they are very communicative to me. Every body thinks us the best possible friends", belying the fulsome dedication to Banks of his *Plantarum Icones*.[48] There were some awkward scenes at Soho Square. When visiting with Richard Salisbury, Smith commented on a plant that Banks had received from Karl Dietrich Koenig in India with the name *Hastingia*, in honour of Warren Hastings, the first Governor-General of Bengal from 1772 to 1785. In 1788, a trial to impeach Hastings for misconduct and corruption began, generating much popular interest. A rare example of Smith's sense of humour, he observed that if the name of the plant were preserved, it should be called "*Hastingia sanguinea*", referring to both the plant's striking red flowers (*sanguinea* translates as 'blood-red' in botanical Latin), but also to Hasting's resigned stoicism during the trial, in which he saw himself as a heroic lone individual battling against malignant adversity. According to Smith, "Dryander & Salisbury laughed much, but Sir Joseph said nothing,

& seemed grave!!!".[49] Smith dismissed Banks's miserable reaction with some venom, claiming he was "a meer toad eater to the King", George III having always been a staunch supporter of Hastings. Smith named the plant *Hastingia coccinea* in 1806.[50]

This may, in fact, have been nothing other than professional jealousy. In a very short space of time, Smith had succeeded in establishing himself as a botanical patron, and unwitting rival to Banks, the man who had created him. Great Marlborough Street was now an essential port of call to any natural historian visiting London. As Linnaeus's ideas continued to spread across Europe, the possessor of his collections held a privileged and unassailable position as the keeper of his scientific legacy and the authoritative source for the publications. Smith reaped the dividends. When the esteemed Austrian botanist Joseph von Jacquin visited in 1789, Smith took him under his wing, arranging introductions to Richard Pulteney and taking him to see Lady Rockingham and the gardens at Hillingdon.[51] Smith's international botanical network was also expanding. Where his previous pool of European correspondents had largely been established through his Tour when still an untried, unpublished botanist, he was now acquiring new contacts through his botanical reputation as author and president of the Linnean Society. Previously, in 1788, via his cousin, Nathaniel Kindersley, Smith had received a box of Indian plant specimens from William Roxburgh, an assistant surgeon for the East India Company at Madras. After a second parcel in 1790 came again via Kindersley, Roxburgh's next missive was sent directly to Smith, in which he acknowledged the "honour of corresponding with so distinguished a Botanist".[52]

Botany on the Rise

Smith's next course of lectures began on 19 January 1790, and covered both botany and zoology. This was a huge undertaking for both Smith and his audience: every Tuesday, Thursday and Saturday morning, for 13 weeks, Smith gave an hour and a quarter lecture, a grand total of 40 lectures for 2 guineas. Great Marlborough Street was again the venue. The design was to "give a summary view of the Animal and Vegetable Kingdoms, with respect to Physiology, external Structure,

Classification", and was aimed at both the beginner and the advanced amateur. The first two lectures were to consist of Smith's 'Introductory Discourse on the Rise and Progress of Natural History'. The remainder were to encompass the "delineations of Methods and Systems, will be intermixed with the more entertaining disquisitions of Physiology; and the infinite variety, and admirable economy of Nature". Smith wanted the series to stimulate an uninformed audience "and excite their curiosity to know more".[53]

Smith appears to have enjoyed lecturing, and was relaxed enough to leave their composition until the very morning they were due to be delivered.[54] Writing after his death, Pleasance Smith claimed that "when pressed for time, he frequently wrote most to his own satisfaction", citing in particular his prefaces and dedications, always left till he was being hurried by the printer.[55] Smith's lectures were open to both ladies and gentlemen, making them much more accessible than the Linnean Society meetings, which were, by default, exclusively male. However, the barrier of class still remained. In February, Lady Rockingham specifically sent her gardener, Grieg, to London on a Friday "so that in case it should not be improper, nor impossible to you to let him stand behind a door to hear you lecture he will be ready for Saturday morning: I perceive it will be the highest of all Treats".[56]

The first part of 1790 again saw Smith hard-pressed, barely finding time to even write to his friend Davall. When he did, he breathlessly listed his current commitments, which, in addition to the lectures, included printing the second fascicle of *Plantarum Icones*, writing the letterpress for *Icones Pictæ*, developing plans for two or three other works, as well as tutoring a private pupil (presumably paying, though this is not known for certain), Lady Amelia Hume, another possessor of extensive gardens and hothouses full of exotics: "judge then whether I am busy or not!".[57]

Barely stopping for breath, almost as soon as the zoological-botanical lectures finished, Smith commenced on another course of lectures dedicated purely to botany. Beginning on 22 April 1790, this course was to consist of 18 to 20 lectures, three days a week from one in the afternoon, again for 2 guineas for the series. This run garnered Smith the attention of yet another society lady, the Hon. Mrs Jane Barrington, wife of Shute Barrington, Bishop of Salisbury. Jane Barrington had a confessed love of plants, and her wish of being "well informed in every thing concerning them", led her to write to Smith soon after attending the lectures. She had been particularly taken with Smith's description of the different formation of leaves and the relative "perspiration" of evergreen and deciduous leaves, and now wrote offering an explanation as to how the Lucombe oak (*Quercus x hispanica*, a hybrid of the deciduous Turkey oak, *Quercus cerris*, and the evergreen cork oak, *Quercus suber*) retained its leaves longer than deciduous oaks. Barrington proposed that the cause came "from its having accidently the same kind of outer cuticle on the leaves as evergreens are observed to have", this cuticle preserving "within the leaves that juice & nourishment which retain them green so much longer on the tree".[58] This was to be the first of many letters between the two, and though Smith's letters have not survived, it is clear that there was much mutual advantage to the correspondence. Barrington became something of a botanical patron, making her extensive collection of exotic plants available to Smith for his publications. In return, Smith allowed Barrington access to a scientific world from which she was otherwise excluded. Smith kept her informed of botanical news, and he regularly sent her seeds and roots received from his more far-flung correspondents. In 1799 Barrington anonymously offered to pay the Linnean Society dues for life for the Revd John Harriman, a County Durham based botanist, the first to discover *Gentiana verna* in England and a collector of rare lichens.[59]

Botany, and specifically Linnaean botany, had become increasingly popular with women throughout the latter half of the 18th century. Female participation was actively encouraged as both a fashionable and 'improving' study in line with social and cultural values.[60] Many botanical works were written specifically for women, such as Thomas Martyn's hugely popular *Letters on the Elements of Botany, addressed to a Lady* (1785), a translation of Rousseau's *Lettres Élémentaires sur la Botanique* (1782). Dedicated to the "Ladies of Great Britain", it was intended for those "fair countrywomen and unlearned countrymen as wished to amuse themselves with Natural History". It went through eight editions in 30 years. Martyn discouraged the 'student' from reading the work "in the easy chair at home". "Botany", he stated, "is not to be learned in the closet; you must go forth into the garden and fields, and there become familiar with Nature herself".[61] A contemporary review of Martyn's book noted its appeal: "Noble and ignoble; learned and unlearned; men and women; even boys and girls, all, are delighted with Botany, and are curious to know the names and the nature of plants and flowers". For women in particular, it was regarded as a more constructive pursuit than "visits, cards, and public diversions".[62]

For Jane Barrington, who admitted her own relative botanical ignorance, the contemplation of natural history filled "the soul with wonder & gratitude to Providence for giving us such proofs of his universal power & wonderful works".[63] William Withering had employed a similar tone a decade earlier in the preface to his *Botanical Arrangement* (1776), a popular English handbook, in which botany "furnishes amusement at every footstep of the solitary walk, and above all, [...] it leads to pleasing reflections on the beauty, wisdom, and the power of the great CREATOR", an interpretation very much in keeping with Smith's own view of botany.[64] Anticipating that botany "in an English dress would become a favourite amusement with the Ladies", Withering had attempted to both demystify and de-sex Linnaeus's Latin terminology: the stamen, pistil and calyx respectively became the chives, pointals and impalement. Yet, such an approach came in for stern criticism from the likes of Erasmus Darwin who accused Withering of making his work "unintelligible to the latin Botanist; equally difficult to the English scholar, and loaded the science with an addition of new words".[65] (Withering reverted to Linnaean terminology for the third edition in 1796.) Even Queen Charlotte herself had caught the botanical bug. In a letter to Smith whilst he was still on his Tour, Sir Joseph Banks had written that "Botany flourishes here most abundantly the Queen studies diligently under [William] Aiton [head gardener at Kew]", and after other botanical news, including the establishment of a new botanic garden in Bengal and another soon to be established in Madras, Banks concluded: "in short botany may again raise its head & I think it will".[66]

CHAPTER SIX

Academic Success

The year 1790 was to be something of a watershed for Smith, both personally and professionally. In early March he stated that the forthcoming summer would "probably determine many things respecting me—whether I shall be supremely happy—or must put up with lesser happiness".[1] Smith intended to produce two further works in 1790, in addition to his other publishing commitments: a new edition of *Species Plantarum*, in gestation since the acquisition of the Linnaean collections, and "a sort of journal" of his European tour, which he intended to be quite general but that natural history and "observations on mankind will have the first place in it".[2] Smith freely communicated his intentions, with both Richard Pulteney and Thomas Woodward expressing their approval. Woodward particularly urged Smith to not let the tour journal "sleep, [...] do publish it to convince the World that a botanist can write English intelligibly".[3] Smith's flurry of lecturing and publishing activity (he also had longstanding plans to publish a volume of *Observationes Botanicæ*) was driven by necessity. His allowance from his "most indulgent father" had been uncomfortably stretched for some time. His Milanese servant, Francesco Borone, had spent the second half of 1789 in Europe visiting his family, and on his return Smith was forced to find another position for him, promising to take him back as soon as he could afford it. Though there are no surviving family letters from this period, it is clear that Smith's father had been placing increasing pressure on Smith to return to medicine, convinced his son would earn more by it. However, to Davall, Smith emphatically justified his resistance, knowing that "nothing is to be got by a young physician in London".[4]

One Good (Botanical) Battle

His first publication of the year was the much-delayed second fascicle of *Plantarum Icones*, which appeared in May 1790. Smith apologised for its tardy appearance in the preface, and rashly recommitted himself to producing two issues a year. The remainder of the preface was dedicated to Smith's first botanical feud, which had erupted over the latter part of 1789. Pierre Broussonet, to whom this issue was dedicated, reported Jean-Baptiste Lamarck's surprise that Smith had not cited him in his description of *Thouinia spectabilis*. A new genus according to Smith, it could also be found in Lamarck's *Encyclopédie Méthodique Botanique* (vol 2, 1786) as *Humbertia madagascariensis*. The slighted Lamarck felt his description had priority, which, indeed, it did. In addition, both Lamarck and Antonie-Laurent de Jussieu observed that Smith had also ignored Antonio Cavanilles's priority with his two new *Turrea* species, also in *Plantarum Icones*.[5] Lamarck lost no time in making his feelings known. Publishing a riposte to Smith and anyone else he felt had ignored his priority (in this case Charles Louis L'Héritier de Brutelle and Giovanni Antonio Scopoli), Lamarck listed the offending plants and his corresponding names in the third volume of *Encyclopédie Méthodique Botanique* (1789). Smith had transgressed with *Thouinia*, as well as *Calceolaria nana*, *C. plantaginea*, *C. ovata* and *Ehrharta panicea*. Lamarck claimed that by offering the plants as new to science, Smith and others had "not only lacked in justice, but they have also deprived their readers of an additional means of obtaining explanations they might desire". Lamarck acknowledged that his plants had not been accompanied by figures, but believed the descriptions of their characteristics were undertaken with utmost precision. He pointedly selected Smith's *Thouinia spectabilis* to compare with his own *Humbertia madagascariensis*. Lamarck listed the numerous additional pieces of information his description had included, such as its relative size, native name and the natural affinities of the plant with other genera whose characters were closest to it. He concluded that the plant was "more completely known by the description which is given in this Dictionary, rather than Mr Smith's *Thouinia* article" and that, consequently, the situation should not be taken lightly by those with an interest in botany.[6]

Smith responded to this public accusation with surprising ferocity in his preface. He had told Richard Pulteney that "a little chastisement of an impertinent fellow would save me future quarrels, as one good battle when a boy first goes to school saves him many more".[7] Addressing the situation with a quote from Horace's *Satires*, "*Men'* autem *moveat cimex Pantilius?*" ("But shall the louse Pantilius upset me?"), Smith claimed that Lamarck had inadvertently elevated those whom he sought to criticise. Wrote Smith, "his jealousy seems above all to be aroused by the mere existence, anywhere, of someone worthier than himself". Smith made clear that, in the interests of thorough research, it was his practice "to quote books even more worthless than his, if that is possible", but that he had been deterred from using Lamarck's *Encyclopédie* on account of its arrangement. He mockingly asked the reader to "Restrain your laughter" as *Encyclopédie* had been arranged as "an alphabetical list of barbarous technical names! How, and by what miracle, can anyone find what he is looking for in such an obscure work?". The criticism thrown at *Thouinia spectabilis* was dismissed in a similar manner. Smith argued that he could not be expected to include things he was obviously not aware of, and derided Lamarck for the high status he placed on what Smith considered the unnecessary elements of his descriptions. Lamarck's work, and botanical priority with his species *Ehrharta erecta* (which Smith had ignored by naming the plant *E. panacea*), was the subject of Smith's final disparaging comment:

> When he demands that I admire what he wrote on the genus *Ehrharta*, as most certain proof of his scholarship and erudition, it does indeed, in my opinion, do him credit. For I willingly acknowledge that I learned from it an important lesson, which was that, using the wonderful skills that only he possesses, he confused two plants that are utterly different in nature, to wit Linnaeus's *Ehrharta capensis* and Richard's *Trochera striata*. I truly cannot be sufficiently astonished that so outstanding a man should be so angry with me. Why is a scholar not permitted to scrutinise another man's work, when it seems obvious that there is a problem with it? What more can I say?

The tirade finished with Smith urging Lamarck to "either stop his nonsense, or at least try to heap less opprobrium on those who are minded to appreciate in due measure the wisdom of Linnaeus".[8] Smith's riposte to the anti-Linnaean Lamarck arrived in France at exactly the right time. Nikolaus von Jacquin, Professor of Botany and Chemistry at the University of Vienna, praised Smith, and revealed that, with regard to Lamarck, he had "found nobody who had the least pity with him".[9] Smith's correspondent René Louiche Desfontaines gaily informed Smith "the bug Pantilius is not very happy. You boxed his ears very soundly. I hope that that will teach him how to behave. We laughed heartily over it".[10] Smith's apparently decisive answer did stop Lamarck's accusations, at least publicly. (The fiasco was also later to be resurrected against Smith in a much more bitter botanical feud, and from a very unexpected source.) However, having made his point, Smith graciously included an addendum for additions and corrections to the first issue, and provided Lamarck's corresponding names for the plants in question. He also cited Lamarck in the third fascicle (1791) in his description of *Andromeda salicifolia*.

Though there was a great deal of personal rancour fuelling this dispute, it should be properly viewed as an engagement in the long-running battle between the Linnaeans and anti-Linnaeans (followers of the natural system). France, and in particular Paris, had always been hostile to Linnaeus's ideas, and though binomial nomenclature and generic reform eventually saw universal adoption, the sexual system and the concept of genus and species were never fully accepted. Many French botanists had remained committed to Joseph Pitton de Tournefort's native system, unsatisfied with elements of Linnaeus's simpler system, which failed to show *la marche de la nature* (the course of nature). Linnaeus's religious outlook led him to proclaim that "we count as many species as there were created in the beginning", and that the law of generation provided only for "the production of identical, unchanging forms".[11] The natural system took a much more progressive view, analysing a host of morphological features to determine the relationships between plants, but at this time struggled to find many adherents outside of France. Even within France, as Broussonet complained to Smith, "our botanists do not always agree with one another; indeed, lacking any systematic method, they can barely understand one another".

Broussonet, along with L'Héritier, was one of the few Parisian Linnaeans; predictably, he firmly believed that L'Héritier was "the only one on the right track". Despite the veneer of scientific respectability, relationships between the two groups were often strained. It seems no coincidence that the three men Lamarck singled out for attack in *Encyclopédie* (Smith, Scopoli, L'Héritier) were all committed Linnaeans. Broussonet commended Smith's response to Lamarck, describing him as "an irascible man who wishes to have everything his own way, and as a result makes himself unhappy". Lamarck engaged in his own retaliatory pettiness; in June 1789 Lamarck and Jussieu, in alliance with botanist Michel Adanson, had attempted to prevent L'Héritier being elected to the *Académie des Sciences*. L'Héritier eventually joined, but only after the anti-Linnaeans had gone too far in saying that L'Héritier's book *Stirpes Novæ Aut Minus Cognitæ* (1785–1791) "was the work of a mere draughtsman, that a man who foisted Greek personal names on plants was not a true botanist".[12]

Smith's relationship with the anti-Linnaeans was not any more subtle, even considering the geographical distance. Lamarck and Adanson, two staunch anti-Linnaeans, are conspicuously absent from the list of Foreign Members of the Linnean Society, which otherwise contains most of the other eminent European naturalists of the period. This can, in part, be attributed to the acrimonious encounters Smith had had with both men whilst in Paris, since the more welcoming Jussieu was accepted, as both a founding Foreign Member of the Linnean Society and one of Smith's frequent European correspondents. Jussieu was flattered to join a society "devoted to the advancement of the science, and I shall do my utmost to deserve its confidence and esteem", even though he was "not quite Linnaean". "I part company with that great man", he elaborated, "on the systematic question, in which he seems to me to distance the science from its true aim. But I do greatly value his nomenclature, his genera and species, and I believe that in this area he has performed a great service for botany."[13]

Smith truly esteemed Jussieu as both a botanist and friend, "profound in science, ardent in the pursuit of truth, open to conviction himself, and candid in his corrections of others; [...] his manners are gentle and pleasing, his conversation easy, cheerful and polite". They differed on many points, for example "the laws of nomenclature and the merits of the Linnaean system", but with truth as their common cause, their many discussions in Paris were "productive of instruction as well as pleasure".[14] This communication continued once Smith had returned to England. Smith was extremely liberal in sharing information with him, sending samples from the Linnaean herbarium that were invaluable for the preparation of Jussieu's *Genera Plantarum*.

Genera Plantarum, published in 1789, was a true departure, and eventually led to the dominance of the natural system over Linnaeus's sexual system. Despite the ease with which Linnaeus's system could be adopted by beginners and amateurs, it had considerable limitations, not least the difficulty of classifying plants out of flower. Its didactic nature also forcibly separated plants otherwise considered 'naturally affiliated'. By greatly expanding the characteristics used for classification, Jussieu was able to present a natural system of classification, reflecting the natural relationships between plants. Where Linnaeus used just the stamens and pistils to group plants into classes and orders, Jussieu used the number of seed leaves and the relative attachment of the sepals, petals, stamens and pistils to one another. Other characteristics were used to further classify plants into families, genera and species. According to Georges Cuvier, *Genera Plantarum* "produced a real revolution in botany since it was not until after its publication that one studied plants from the point of view of the relationships between them, and according to the totality of their organisation".[15]

Genera Plantarum was received with enthusiasm and curiosity by botanists across Europe, not least in England. Dryander feverishly wrote to Smith following the book's release stating that he was "studying hard", adding that it would be essential for Smith to study it before publishing any further work. He also astutely summarised its great advantage and disadvantage over Linnacus; after mastering this new text, Dryander hoped to achieve "what I never could [...] with certainty from Linnaeus's books, which is to tell if a new plant is a new genus or not. From what I hitherto know of the book, it is a very good one for those who are advanced in Botany, but I defy a beginner to make anything of it".[16] Smith was initially cautious, replying to Dryander before even seeing the work that it "must be a book of real observation & the work of no contemptible botanist [...] [though] many of his names will I suppose be bad".[17] Smith repeated this sentiment within the second fascicle of *Icones Plantarum*, which earnt him the opprobrium of Broussonet, who thought that *Genera Planatarum* was "a rough, disordered mass set out in barbarous Latin".[18] Smith, however, soon recognised Jussieu's achievement and in 1793 presciently stated that *Genera Plantarum* would "immortalize its author, and probably go down to posterity with the *Genera Plantarum* of Linnaeus, to which it is an excellent companion".[19] Unlike previous attempts at a natural system, such as Adanson's, Jussieu had accepted Linnaean generic reform and nomenclature, which enabled its eventual adoption across Europe and the rest of the world. It is now the starting point for the list of conserved family names for flowering plants by the International Code of Nomenclature for algae, fungi and plants (ICN), just as Linnaeus's *Species Plantarum* (1753) is for plant names.

All Minds are Turned to Politics

Jussieu's *Genera Plantarum* was published a month after the fall of the Bastille in Paris, which ignited the French Revolution. Having a large French correspondence, Smith naturally received numerous updates on the political situation. Broussonet threw himself into the endeavour, signing himself up for military service and being placed in charge of his district, and just two weeks after the storming of the Bastille, announced to Smith that "we are free, at last, and most unwilling to allow our liberty to be removed". He was aggrieved to see the situation misrepresented in the English press, "where the nation has been called a Mob. I can assure you that nothing could have been more respectable, and that all citizens were present. We are a new nation which will prove to be full of energy".[20] Unfortunately, that energy was to turn on Broussonet, as with so many others, and within a few years he was to become a fugitive from revolutionary France, holed up in Saragossa, Spain, begging Smith and Banks for their assistance in getting him safely to England. Another victim of the turmoil was *Société Linnéenne de Paris*, which dissolved in the tumultuous summer of 1789. It was small wonder that at the beginning of 1790, Smith noted that "all science stands still at Paris at the moment".[21] This was confirmed soon after in a melancholy postscript from Desfontaines—"learning is in decline here; all minds are turned to politics".[22] L'Héritier, too, was swept up in the revolutionary fervour. A Paris magistrate in the Cours des Aides before the revolution, he afterwards served as an Elector, responsible for nominating deputies and judges, and was himself appointed a judge for the Paris Department. At the end of 1790, he wrote to Smith stating how his duties as Elector had prevented him from attending to any of his personal affairs, and on his appointment as a judge, "despite the appeal of botany, patriot that I am, I could not refuse to accept such an honour". Yet his letter also included a portentous indication of the coming violence, where in a mysterious crime "several botanists, including myself, have—of all things—been poisoned by arsenic. I shall remember for the rest of my life the plant that I was describing and getting drawn at that moment".[23] The Revolution would prove to be the downfall of L'Héritier; he lost much of his private wealth and his social and political standing, and had to find paid work. Years later, on 16 August 1800, he was murdered close to his home, his murderer never discovered.

The Revolution itself did, however, have an unanticipated effect on the cult of Linnaeus in France. A public subscription was established in order to commission a marble bust of Linnaeus, to be placed in either the newly renamed *Jardin des Plantes* (formerly the *Jardin du Roi*), or in the School of Botany. This generated considerable interest amongst the French botanists; Smith received at least four accounts of its commissioning and its unveiling, on 23 August 1790, under the giant cedar of Lebanon in the *Jardin des Plantes*, where "all the naturalists" signed a document to be placed in the shaft of the plinth.[24] Desfontaines was particularly enthusiastic, the marble bust proving that "at last we are doing justice to the father of natural history and to one of the most rare and beautiful minds of our times". Hopefully such public recognition would "at last silence the enemies in France of that celebrated man and that henceforth they will be able to do no more than mutter darkly". He clearly despaired at the chaotic political situation and its effect on scientific discourse, but also against an unpleasant aspect of the French character, *la basse jalousie*—the vile jealousy—that the French held against men of distinction. Desfontaines envied England's political stability, as well as its respect for learning:

> I believe that you are more philosophical than us in this respect. The English will recognise merit regardless of time and place. This is not said to flatter: it is my true opinion, and you give proof of it every day. Some of these detractors of Linnaeus would put themselves on a par with him, or even above him, but in truth they will never come close.[25]

The unveiling of the bust gave the Parisian Linnaeans a boost, and soon afterwards they re-formed *Société Linnéenne de Paris* as *Société d'Histoire Naturelle de Paris*, dedicated to the advancement of natural history. Smith was elected an Associate Member almost immediately, and applied to provide a complete bibliography of Linnaeus's works. Though the name had changed, the new Society's allegiance was perfectly clear. The anti-Linnaean Adanson and Jussieu were once again absent from the list of names, and the Society's first (and only) volume of *Actes* (equivalent to the Linnean Society's *Transactions*) contained a folio-sized engraving showing Linnaeus's bust in the shadow of by the cedar of Lebanon.[26]

Elevating the Hothouse

On 2 July 1789, Smith announced to Davall that he and Sowerby "are about a work of superb col[oure]d plates, 6 in a fasciculus, to be dedicated to Lady Rockingham".[27] Entitled *Icones Pictæ Plantarum Rariorum*, or *Coloured Figures of Rare Plants*, this was a significantly more ambitious work than *Plantarum Icones*, though again the intention was to figure plants previously unrepresented in botanical literature. This time, however, they were to be drawn from living cultivated, specimens, with the "most rare and beautiful plants only to be admitted". Smith and Sowerby intended to draw on the wealth of new and exotic plants then being cultivated in the hothouses, stoves and conservatories of England's magnificent gardens, which had "long demanded the attention of a scientific botanist to rescue them from oblivion".[28]

Preparations were already underway when Sowerby visited Lady Rockingham's estate at Hillingdon in May 1789 in order to draw specimens of

James Sowerby (1757–1822), Smith's long-time artistic collaborator.

Catesbæa spinosa, *Portlandia grandiflora* and *Euphorbia punicea*, all then in flower. (Unfortunately, the *Catesbæa* proved ineligible for inclusion, having previously appeared in Mark Catesby's *The Natural History of Carolina, Florida and the Bahama Islands* [1729–1747] "tho' but ill done".) Lady Rockingham kept Smith updated on when certain plants were expected to flower, and hoped that he would be able to come to Hillingdon in time to see the *Aralia capitata* (*Oreopanax capitatus*) bloom, which she believed had never flowered anywhere else in the country but her hothouse for the last two years. She exerted gentle pressure regarding the appearance of certain plants. She particularly wanted *Euphorbia punicea*, the Jamaican poinsettia, to be included, as her late husband had been the first English possessor of the plant.[29] It duly appeared in the first fascicle. Lady Rockingham deferentially hoped that the dedication really applied to her plants "as a Collection which was amongst the earliest, & choicest of this Country", & would have been carried on to perfection" but for her want of skill following her husband's death. Though by July three plates had been completed, two from specimens provided by Lady Rockingham, the first fascicle was not to appear for a full year and a half.[30] As it approached publication, it generated considerable interest amongst Smith's botanical acquaintances. Banks's displeasure in Smith's poaching Sowerby for the work has already been touched upon, but William Aiton, the King's gardener at Kew, was also "jealous of my col[oure]d work I hear in secret".[31]

The first fascicle appeared in October 1790. Smith and Sowerby published it themselves, having "both drained our purses from an ambition (laudable I hope) of bringing out our great work without being under the thumb of booksellers".[32] This was a work for learned and unlearned in separate Latin and English editions, 12 shillings for the English version or 14 shillings for both English and Latin. Botanist and artist succeeded in producing a spectacular work, thanks to Sowerby's exceptional hand-coloured figures and Smith's detailed and precise descriptions. The engravings filled the page, with the first fascicle even featuring a foldout in order to accommodate the *Portlandia grandiflora* drawn from Lady Rockingham's collection. The other plants featured in the first issue were *Passiflora lunata* (*Passiflora biflora*) and *Antirrhinum reticulata* (*Linaria reticulata*), both from Chelsea Physic Garden, *Euphorbia punicea* and *Hedera capitata*, from Lady Rockingham's, and *Wachendorfia paniculata*, from James Lee's Hammersmith nursery. The rich colours even today remain startling in their intensity. Before publication, Smith had conceded that the "merit of [the] work will be Sowerby's, not mine".[33] Though his name did not appear on the title page, Smith fully acknowledged Sowerby's contribution and skill in the preface, acknowledging him as "one of the best botanical draughtsman this country ever possessed".

In his English descriptions, Smith had favoured a loose translation, keeping some Latin words as technical terms, in preference to a "rigid rendering of word for word, and that obsolete language, in which elegance and perspicuity are too often sacrificed". Smith conspicuously ignored the 'de-sexing' scheme William Withering had tried to introduce. In Smith's work, his *stamens* and *pistils* retained their Latin names, but English words replaced others: *Radix* became root, *Caules* stems, *Folia* leaves and *Semina* seeds. Smith's intention was to entice the less botanically educated "into a familiarity with scientific and classical language, so that at length the learned and unlearned may [...] cultivate the same science, use the same terms".[34] As promised, the publication was dedicated to the Marchioness of Rockingham, who was credited with having "considerably enriched" the issue. In fact, the work can be seen as a testament to Smith's considerable social skills and his ability to ingratiate himself with valuable patrons. Half of the 18 plants featured across the whole publication were from the gardens of society ladies; five from Lady Rockingham, two from Jane Barrington, one from Lady Amelia Hume, and one from the Viscountess Cremorne, Philadelphia-Hannah Dawson, a close friend of Queen Charlotte.

The Monthly Review described the first fascicle as "*grand* and highly elegant", and thought Smith "particularly happy in his English botanic language [...] entirely free from the quaint terms attempted to be introduced by some other writers; and is more intelligible, with all the necessary conciseness of the original".[35] Subscribers included Lady Rockingham and her stepsister Elizabeth Weddell, the Duchess of Portland and the Earl Fitzwilliam.[36] Davall, on receipt of the work, was predictably effusive, proclaiming with no fewer than seven exclamation marks, "I have just received your *Icones pictæ*!!!!!!!" and was utterly convinced that it had surpassed every other "production of art".[37]

Despite such praise, Thomas Woodward acutely articulated the tension between the aesthetic and scientific present in *Icones Pictæ*. The second fascicle, published in February 1792, contained a slight deviation from the exotic beauties: *Ligusticum cornubiensis* (*Physospermum cornubiense*), an extremely rare, though thoroughly plain, British plant that had not been seen for almost a century, and which had recently been rediscovered in Cornwall. Woodward recorded for Smith the conversation that ensued with his wife on observing the plate:

Ligusticum cornubiense, from Smith's *Icones Pictae.*

Mrs Woodward:	"What vile thing is that?"
Mr Woodward:	"It is one of the scarcest English plants, & the figure is particularly curious."
Mrs Woodward:	"It may be, but for my part, they are all alike, & I can pick up an hundred in the Garden, that can't be told from it."

Though, for Woodward, it was the "most desirable figure" of the volume, he conceded that Mrs Woodward's reaction would be a frequent one for those who "consult only beauty in these publications".[38]

Despite the attention and acclaim, Smith was still waiting for a financial recompense from botany. After another gruelling double series of lectures commenced at Great Marlborough Street in January and April, Smith reluctantly admitted that they "answer but ill", though it was the expensive periodicals he had committed himself to that "principally embarrass[ed]" him. He was confident that time would prove him right, and that *Icones Pictæ* would repay him. He defiantly declared he would "live on bread & water" before giving up botany. He had, however, secured his position enough to be able to take back his Milanese servant, Francesco Borone. There were several other indicators of success, including the announcement in April 1791 that the first fascicle had sold out (the print run is unknown), and, the next month, the news that "the Queen takes 3 copies of my *Icones pictæ* large paper".[39] Unfortunately, as with *Plantarum Icones*, ultimately *Icones Pictæ* struggled to find a sufficiently large audience. A second fascicle appeared in February 1792, and the third, and final, in 1793 (although there appears to have been a reprinting in 1814).

During the course of the 18th century, part-works had become an extremely popular medium for presenting botanical information to the public, allowing subscribers to pay in instalments and spreading the costs for publishers (with works often self-funded by the author and the bookseller). There were pitfalls, however, as shown by William Curtis's *Flora Londinensis*. Though adored by botanists, Curtis's intermittent publishing schedule caused untold frustrations. John Lightfoot impatiently wrote to him of *Flora Londinensis*: "I lament only that the numbers do not come out oftener", whilst Sir Thomas Cullum, 7th baronet and surgeon, proposed that if Curtis was to commit to publishing it within a specific timeframe he would be "ready to subscribe [to] any proposition in advance", it being the only way Curtis could "ever think of getting thro' such an undertaking". Like Smith, Curtis overstretched himself in managing his botanic garden, lecturing and issuing other publications. However, they differed in that Curtis had a phenomenally successful publication in the *Botanical Magazine* that he could use to subsidise *Flora Londinensis*. Smith, as yet, had no such resources.[40]

The Germination of English Botany

In December 1790, one further Smith-Sowerby production appeared. Or rather, in the eyes of the public, it was a new Sowerby work that hit the bookshops, entitled *English Botany; or, Coloured Figures of British Plants*. Sowerby had astutely identified a gap in the market for a "work on English plants on the plan of Curtis's Mag[azi]ne", which dealt in ornamental and exotic plants. The plan was entirely Sowerby's, who as well as engaging

Smith to provide the descriptions, produced and published the work. The result was a monthly issue of three coloured figures, with accompanying English descriptions. As the first preface (written December 1792) later elaborated, a "knowledge of the plants of our own country is in many respects preferable to that of exotics", on account of the greater ease of access and utility. The study of native flora was not only essential to those occupied with the "rural economy", but, echoing many a previous evocation of the spiritual and physical joys of botany, "doubles the pleasure of every journey or walk, and calls forth to healthy exercise the bodily as well as the mental powers". Simply put, *English Botany* had the potential to appeal to all who were interested in botany. Indeed, it was surprising that among the "many merely descriptive works on British plants" no successful attempt had yet been made to "illustrate them by original figures on a cheap and compendious plan".[41] The figures were executed with Sowerby's usual grace, skill and accuracy, often featuring magnifications or cross-sections of the flowers or fruits. *The Analytical Review* immediately recognised Sowerby's "known skill, and happy talent in giving faithful as well as beautiful portraits of plants" would highly recommend the figures to experts and amateurs alike.[42] The figures have been consistently praised in the succeeding centuries, showing "what a dexterous engraver could accomplish; the lines are economical, unmarred by any excess of cross hatching, and admirably suited for subsequent hand-colouring".[43]

Sowerby initially offered Smith half a guinea per description but Smith decided to provide the text "gratis, till he [Sowerby] sees whether it will answer or not".[44] Sowerby's name was the only one to appear on the title page, and it was Sowerby who dedicated the work, to George Legge, Viscount Lewisham, later 3rd Earl of Dartmouth, a Fellow of both the Royal and Linnean Societies. Smith elected to remain anonymous, though he played a full role in the preliminaries, including the selection of the motto: "Quos ipsa volentia rura sponte tulere sua".[45] Taken from the *Georgics*, Virgil's long poem on agriculture, it translates as the subject of *English botany* being the fruits "which the countryside has freely borne". Smith was particularly proud of this, and thought it "quite [...] original".[46] The reasons for Smith's anonymity are diffuse, though one happy consequence of it meant that when Smith was indisposed in the summer of 1791, the text for the sixth issue (figures 16, 17 and 18) could be taken over by Linnean Society colleague George Shaw without causing any undue fuss. Ultimately, though, Smith appears to have been uncertain about attaching his name to such an accessible, and by inference, unscientific work. In the preface to the fourth volume (1794), the first he signed his name to, he revealed his passion to help improve "the botanical language of this country" as being the main impetus behind his involvement, an extension of his work with the English letterpress for *Icones Pictæ*. In the same piece, he stated that his botanical friends had persuaded him to come forward "by way of giving it consequence".[47]

Published in octavo (6" x 9"), it was considerably smaller than the folio sized *Icones Pictæ* (12" x 19"). This also made it much cheaper; each issue of *Icones Pictæ*, which contained six figures, cost 12 shillings. *English Botany*, by contrast, contained three figures per issue, but cost just 1 shilling—the same as Curtis's *Botanical Magazine*. Meanwhile, *Flora Londinensis*, the nearest comparable work to *English Botany* in terms of content and format cost 2s 6d for an uncoloured copy, 5 shillings for coloured and 7s 6d for superior colouring. Such a consideration was very real; John Pitchford, though he praised it, had to turn down the opportunity of purchasing *Icones Pictæ* on account of the cost.

Each figure was accompanied by a one-page description, which was divided into three parts. First was the Latin binomial and common English name. The second part gave a scientific description of the plant, consisting of the Linnaean class and order, plant characteristics and the synonyms (previous Latin names by which the plant has been known) and other publications in which the plant had been described. Finally, section three offered "occasional remarks", including habitats, locations, flowering times and even horticultural advice, by far the greatest portion of the text. Here, Smith would include various other details like medicinal uses and differences in cultivated specimens, amongst other digressions. The preface acknowledged that whilst much of the British flora had already been depicted in previous publications, to actually study it from these sources would entail the acquisition of a "voluminous and expensive" library. In addition, incorrect citations had perpetuated themselves across various editions and decades, inevitably leading botanists into error and confusion. The genius of Smith's letterpress was in the accuracy of the botanical characters and synonyms. He started afresh, resolving to avoid "copying what others have said", and to refer only to "the most popular and useful descriptive and systematic books", such as Linnaeus's seminal *Species Plantarum*, and the floras of Hudson, Curtis and Withering, Lightfoot and Ray, amongst others.[48]

Though the plates were not issued in any systematic order, the very first plant to be depicted, *Cypripedium calceolus*, the lady's slipper orchid, was carefully chosen. Referring to it as "the queen of all the European Orchideae", Smith remarked that "if the beauty or scarcity of a plant, or the singularity of its structure entitle it to our notice the Ladies Slipper certainly merits the first place in a work on British plants".[49] The second and third figures detailed the slightly more prosaic *Veronica spicata*, spiked speedwell, and *Erica vagans*, Cornish heath. Smith managed to imbue a certain humour into his text. Writing of *Erica dabœcia* (*Dabœcia cantabrica*) Smith recounted John Ray's statement[50] that Irish girls would "gird themselves with its long trailing branches as a protection to their chastity". "With what success", Smith cheekily responded in his text, "he unluckily has omitted to inform us".[51]

Along with Thomas Woodward, Edmund Davall was one of the few people Smith had informed of the true authorship. Even close associate John Pitchford was unaware; having immediately registered his interest in the work, he wondered, in his ignorance, whether Smith would offer his assistance to Sowerby.[52] In fact, the text abounded with hints as to its authorship, in the form of numerous nods towards "Dr Smith", thanked for his identifications, even going so far as to offer previews of plants to feature in *Plantarum Icones*. Woodward was certain that Smith would be found out in no short time; indeed, writing after publication of the third fascicle in February 1791, the reviewer in *The Analytical Review* thought himself "pretty certain, that we differentiate the pen of the learned possessor of the Linnaean collections in the remarks".[53]

Almost all of the initial reaction was couched in reference to William Curtis's works, to which all agreed it bore a strong resemblance. Smith

White Water-lily (*Nymphæa alba*), from Smith and Sowerby's *English Botany*.

privately informed Davall that he believed *English Botany* "excells Curtis's Mag[azi]ne, & if he does not exert himself may hurt his flora [Londinensis]; but he deserves no pity for that".[54] Both *The Analytical Review* and Thomas Woodward noted the quality of the production: the "paper, print & execution of the plates, is so much superior to Curtis, that there can be no fear of its succeeding".[55] Woodward warned Sowerby not to let the subsequent numbers "be inferior to the first beginning, as Curtis is much complained of for that".[56] Davall was particularly desirous of seeing *English Botany* continued on a monthly basis, a remark pointedly aimed at the notoriously slow Curtis, as if the competition might rouse him "from his lethargy".[57] There was, however, at least one unfavourable comparison with the *Botanical*

Magazine, from a reader aggrieved that Sowerby's plates were a full inch smaller than those of Curtis: "they not only have a bad effect, by the figure coming so near the edges of the plate, but, what is worse, frequently oblige the artist to cut the flower-stalk [...] where the addition of an inch would have given room for the plant at full-length".[58]

For Curtis, the publication of *English Botany* was a personal affront, and Smith was soon embroiled in the second botanical feud of his career. Curtis was particularly angry with Smith for helping Sowerby, Curtis's former collaborator, and considered *English Botany* a complete "infringem[en]t of his domains".[59] Curtis held longstanding plans to begin a national illustrated flora once *Flora Londinensis* was complete. In a vain attempt to avoid conflict, Smith and Sowerby had made a conscious decision not to feature plants in *English Botany* also delineated in *Flora Londinensis*, or indeed any plants at all that grew within a 10 mile radius of London, the original bounds of Curtis's work. According to Smith's public account of the dispute, recorded in the preface to the seventh volume of *English Botany* (1798), the authors informed Curtis of their prescription, only to be informed that "he should ever consider our undertaking, in any form, as in all respects hostile to his".[60] Curtis became completely estranged from Smith, to the point that he stopped attending the Linnean Society for some years, though Samuel Goodenough made repeated attempts to reconcile the two. It is unclear how close the two were, if ever, before this episode, though Sowerby and Curtis had a relationship going back some 15 years. Even as the first rumblings occurred, Smith clearly had little time for Curtis outside of his botanical work, describing him as "a man of very unsound principle, & a bad temper".[61] The blame for almost the entirety of this unfortunate spat can be laid at the door of Curtis though, who became increasingly hypochondriac with age. With his spirits weakened, he grew convinced of a host of "malevolent enemies" about himself, including Smith. Curtis died in 1799, having finally completed the long-awaited second volume of *Flora Londinensis* as well as apparently reconciling with Smith.[62]

In May 1791, yet another Smith-Sowerby publication appeared, the first part of *Spicilegium Botanicum* (1791–1792). Dedicated to Lady Amelia Hume, its subtitle was *Gleanings of Botany*; like *Icones Pictæ*, its purpose was to depict rare and beautiful plants, but of a smaller size, containing such specimens "as do not require so ample a page to exhibit all the necessary parts".[63] In his preface Smith stated that the plants contained in *Spicilegium* would be "generally, though not entirely, exotics".[64] Thomas Woodward immediately recognised the conflict between the two works: "the Spicilegium, & English Botany seem to rather interfere, as the same subjects in fact belong to both". Indeed, of the first fascicle's 12 figures, three were native to England, though one, *Lycoperdon* (*Battarrea*) *phalloides*, was a fungus, a group excluded from *English Botany* by the authors.[65] This was another ill-fated publication, and though it had been advertised "to be continued occasionally", the second fascicle, published 1792, was the last. By contrast, in July 1791, Smith was pleased to report that *English Botany* "sells amazingly, & is by no means like to stop".[66] The success seems to have surprised them, having neither anticipated the "importance to which this little work might attain, nor of the utility it might be of as a vehicle for botanical criticism upon British plants". The work subtly changed, with Smith's text becoming more scientifically rigorous. He later admitted that the early remarks had no real structure or purpose other than to "say something which might allure the careless observer, and stimulate the curiosity of the inexperienced".[67] His flights of fancy were replaced with detailed accounts of the location of collection and habitat of the specimen, and a more thorough description that greatly increased the length. By way of example, plant descriptions in volume one could be as short as 80 words (although the average was closer to 150), whilst those of volume four (1794) were generally between 200 and 250 words. Sowerby, and Smith, though he was yet to claim the text as his own, had finally succeeded in producing a popular, financially viable botanical work.

CHAPTER SEVEN

The Botanical Radical

Smith intended to dedicate the summer of 1791 to the published account of his Tour, the long-promised *Genera Plantarum* and *Flora Britannica* (in gestation since his Edinburgh days). Even when visiting Norwich for a month, he intended to isolate himself from everybody and divide his time "between writing & country walks for air & exercise".[1] In addition to the three works mentioned, Smith was also committed to producing the next fascicles of *Plantarum Icones* and *Icones Pictæ*, as well as the first fascicle of the similarly ill-fated *Spicilegium Botanicum*.

On 13 August, the first volume of the *Transactions of the Linnean Society of London* was published. Though it had received considerable support, most notably in Sir Joseph Banks's sponsorship of the plates, it suffered from constant delays. A final push was made in July 1791; awaiting only the plates, Smith wrote that "it must be out July 19", being the Society's final Fellows meeting before the annual summer break, though even with this determination it was delayed once again. The publication process had been arduous, as he complained to a friend: "you cannot conceive what a trouble it has been to get it done & after all there are some typographical errors".[2] The first volume began with Smith's 'Introductory Discourse', as given at the inaugural General Meeting, followed by 14 botanical papers, 10 zoological and one mineralogical, illustrated by 19 plates. The list of authors contains some of the period's most prominent natural historians, including William Curtis, George Shaw, Thomas Martyn, Olof Swartz and Charles Louis L'Héritier de Brutelle. Most fittingly, the first volume included three papers from former pupils of Linnaeus.

Adam Afzelius submitted a paper on *Trifolium*, Jonas Dryander on the genus *Begonia* and Carl Peter Thunberg—the successor of Linnaeus the Younger as Professor of Botany and Medicine at Uppsala—sent a paper on the plant genus *Dillenia*. The latter in particular was recognised as being of great significance.[3] *The Monthly Review* remarked: "it must be no small satisfaction to the members of the Linnéan Society, that to the names of Sir Joseph Banks, Dr Smith [...] &c. they have to add that of Dr. Thunberg, Linné's truly worthy successor".

Smith's 'Introductory Discourse' met with particular acclaim and was described by the same review as being "the richest in the volume".[4] Smith received so many compliments that he worried he was "in danger of being really vain of it", especially on hearing it was being translated into Italian by Gregorio Fontana, professor of mathematics at Pavia University. To Thomas Woodward he modestly determined to list all of its faults, though conceded that there were some "merits in the performance".[5] Woodward refused to countenance the author's criticism in response, comparing the discourse to the "bold drawings of a Raphael" and relating that it had convinced Revd Thomas Zouch, an eminent scholar and Yorkshire clergyman, to become a Fellow.[6]

The work did not pass all reviewers without some criticism. It was almost universally acknowledged that Adam Afzelius's paper on *Trifolium*, at 46 pages the second longest in the volume after Smith's discourse, was "too tedious".[7] *The Monthly Review* was "almost at a loss for words" regarding the paper's laborious construction.[8]

In three years, the Linnean Society had managed to achieve what the Society for the Promotion of Natural History (SPNH) had not yet managed in its nine years of existence, and presented a volume of their scientific activities. Undoubtedly aware of their dwindling significance, in early 1791, William Forsyth of the SNPH had written to Smith suggesting a union of the two societies. The proposal was put before the Linnean Society's Fellows meeting of 15 March 1791, and was firmly rejected on the grounds that neither society "would be benefited by such a Union".[9] The SPNH struggled on for several more years; the last regular meeting to be entered into the minute book was held on 14 November 1800. The book was opened, for the last time, in the Linnean Society's rooms, on 30 May 1822, where it was recognised that the Linnean Society, "which originally emanated from this Society and embracing its principle objects is now in full operation and activity", should become the recipient of all the SPNH's property, including £190 of 3 ½ per cent Consols and £136 10s 6d of accumulated dividends. The SPNH was no more.[10]

A Work of Real Excellence

About the same time as the publication of the Society's *Transactions*, another of Smith's works entered the press. Unlike his constantly delayed works with Sowerby (bar *English Botany*), barely a year passed between the first mention of a new edition of Linnaeus's *Flora Lapponica* and its publication in 1792. First published in 1737, *Flora Lapponica* was a groundbreaking work, listing the 534 species Linnaeus had encountered on his 1732 tour of Lapland, and outlining the first practical use of Linnaean binomials and classification. In addition to listing and describing the plants, Linnaeus also discussed their economic and medicinal uses, as well as providing anthropological notes on the Laplanders. It quickly became a classic work, described as "the most elegant of all the local floras", but since its original publication had become extremely scarce.[11] By the 1790s, it was considered lucky to find a copy priced at a guinea.

Smith's second edition, published in February 1792 and priced at 12 shillings, was eagerly received. *The Monthly Review* commended the republication of "works of real excellence" for allowing "the less *fortunate* to receive the pleasure of possessing them", and for their efforts, Smith, and the publisher Benjamin White & Son, received the *Review's* "best thanks", and their wishes for "an abundant sale".[12] Diplomatically acknowledging the publisher's role (and financial investment), Smith promised that he was only gifting copies to Woodward and "1 or 2 other country friends", whilst sending all his London friends to buy it at White's.[13]

The timely, efficient appearance of *Flora Lapponica* can be attributed to its publisher, who had also taken on the publication of Smith and Sowerby's first collaboration, *Plantarum Icones*. As Smith acknowledged in his preface, it had been produced entirely at their instigation after their recent acquisition from Holland of the original copperplates used for the first edition. Benjamin White had a reputation for re-issuing scarce natural history publications; in 1771 he published the third edition of Mark Catesby's *The Natural History of Carolina, Florida, and the Bahama Islands* (1729–1747) and in 1789 the second edition of Patrick Browne's *The Civil and Natural History of Jamaica* (1756). Linnaeus's manuscript for *Flora Lapponica* remained in Amsterdam, where the first edition had been published, but amongst the manuscripts in Smith's possession were many working papers from the Lapland tour, including Linnaeus's journal, and Smith immediately offered his services for the new edition. The result was a complete revision of Linnaeus's text. In his overhaul, Smith added the specific names and references from the second edition of *Species Plantarum* (1762–1763), in addition to 55 new Lapland plants discovered since the first edition, and an exhaustive survey and correction of erroneous synonyms and typographical errors.

Smith was a conscientious editor. In the preface, he claims to have been "very cautious" in emending Linnaeus's work, with all his changes intended to "purge an excellent book of the occasional rare slip". He refrained from adding new synonyms, intending the book to be "useful, rather than merely long". To ensure that the references in the first edition corresponded with the second, he left Linnaeus's numbering unchanged, new species being given the same number as the preceding related plant and marked with an asterisk. He put his name to any textual additions of his own, so as not to "detract from the glory of our Linnaeus".[14] So confident was he of his editorial integrity that he boasted to Thomas Woodward that it would be "the most correct edition that ever appeared of any of Linnaeus's works, his own Stockholm ones not excepted".[15]

The smooth production of *Flora Lapponica* was the first of Smith's successes for 1792, which was to prove another significant year. Yet it could have been entirely different. During the early hours of the morning of 14 January, just three doors down from Smith's house in Great Marlborough Street, the Pantheon theatre spectacularly burst into flames. By morning, the entire edifice had been razed to the ground. One unnamed Great

Marlborough Street resident reported that he was awoken "by the shrieks of females, and the appalling accompaniments of watchmen's rattles. I threw open the window, and heard the cry of fire. The watchmen and patrol were thundering at all the neighbours' doors, and people were rushing to their windows, not knowing where the calamity was seated". Even the famous actress Sarah Siddons, "who resided opposite, had, *en chemise,* thrown up the sashes of their bedroom, on the second floor, and called to us, that the Pantheon was in flames".[16] Smith was awoken at about 2am, and for a moment there must have been considerable panic, for he "really thought the fire had been at next door, so bright were the flames".[17] Fortunately, a windless night and the presence of several fire engines ensured that his row of buildings was safe; the Pantheon was the only structure to suffer any damage. The total destruction of such a prominent theatre received extensive coverage in the press, and though the majority of reports stated no other buildings were damaged, several of Smith's correspondents wrote, anxious to hear of the safety of himself and his collections. Smith's Edinburgh friend, Robert Batty, was less fortunate. After completing his studies (without taking an MD) Batty had remained in London, establishing himself as an apothecary with a shop under the stage of the Pantheon. Completely destroyed in the fire, Batty, his wife Ann and their infant child, were forced to take refuge at Smith's for a week, as their house next door temporarily lay under threat from the unstable remnants of the Pantheon walls. By the time *Flora Lapponica* appeared in February, Smith was able to report that all were now safe, escaping only with minor colds.

In his preface to *Flora Lapponica,* Smith acknowledged the invaluable assistance provided by Adam Afzelius, Demonstrator of Botany at Uppsala, who had visited England whilst Smith was working on the text. Early in 1792, Afzelius was commissioned to travel to Sierra Leone by the newly formed Sierra Leone Company, ostensibly to search for anything that might be "profitable as articles of trade", but also allowing for a more general exploration of the region's flora.[18] The Sierra Leone Company was formed the previous year, with the intention of founding a second British colony in Africa for freed American slaves, to be named Freetown, after the first settlement at Granville Town failed in 1789. The Company was supported by leading abolitionists such as Henry Thornton and William Wilberforce, and made no secret of its abolitionist views in its 1790 prospectus, which stated that its subscribers had done so "not with a view of any present profit to themselves, but merely, through benevolence and public spirit, to promote a charitable measure".[19] Though not explicitly stated in the surviving correspondence, it can be assumed that the Unitarian Smith family were all abolitionists. Some proof is offered in the fact that Smith's father and brothers Francis and John Frederick each quickly became shareholders in the Sierra Leone Company, with Smith acting as their agent.[20] Many of Smith's friends leaned towards abolitionism. Thomas Woodward, a magistrate for Suffolk, informed Smith in February 1792 that "we are going to petition against the slave trade, all over Suffolk", and a month later Smith sent Davall several pamphlets on the issue, stating that it was "a matter much talked of now".[21, 22] Smith arranged for his servant Francesco Borone to accompany Afzelius as his botanical assistant for the duration. This endeavour had every opportunity of being highly advantageous to Borone, if he lived—a very real consideration when voyaging to hostile climes. Smith was assured that the climate was healthy except for "the great heat", and in any case Afzelius and Borone were both "very sober & prudent".[23]

Departing England in March 1792, Afzelius and Borone arrived at Freetown on 6 May. The first news arrived in a letter written to Smith by Afzelius in early July. Though they had been in perfect health since arrival, it was not a favourable report. The territory itself had much to recommend it, "the soil good, the woods abounding of game, the water of fine fishes & the whole country of the most wonderful plants", but the colony was "in confusion & divided into parties". As yet they had been unable to collect any specimens, particularly disappointing when "surrounded by so many curious & unknown productions", owing to the lack of a house, or even a room, within which to dry their specimens, shelter their supplies and write up their observations. The saving grace was John Clarkson, the Company's agent in Sierra Leone and eventual first governor of Freetown, who had shown them both "so many civilities, and [also] promised us to have very soon a house for ourselves". Sadly, Afzelius was less optimistic for the grander project. Clarkson was "now almost the only man who supports the Colony & endeavours to put all things in order again; but it shall be a long time before he shall gain his laudable intentions".[24]

Queen Charlotte (1744–1818), botanical patron.

Windsor is a Courtly Place

Such was the pace of Smith's own social success that by February 1792 he was paying court to Queen Charlotte at Frogmore House, a short distance from Windsor Castle. His role was to advise on the preservation of the late Revd John Lightfoot's herbarium, which King George III had purchased for £100 as a gift for her, on the recommendation of Samuel Goodenough.[25] The Queen was already aware of Smith's botanical skill, as she was a subscriber to *Icones Pictæ*. Another influential mutual friend, Lady Cremorne, also recommended Smith. It was via Lady Cremorne that the Queen invited Smith to a three-day visit to Frogmore in mid-February in order for both to make an initial assessment—he of the collections and she of the botanist. The visit was successful; on his return to London, Smith reported back to various friends, describing the king as "very gracious", and relaying that the Queen had professed that she "hoped to become better acquainted with me". The visit concluded with an invitation to return in the summer, at his leisure, to work on the herbarium, and a possible course of lectures on botany for the Queen and Princesses was also discussed.

Smith had tactfully signified that he was above "pecuniary reward" for the work. In any case, this presented a golden opportunity to consult Lightfoot's herbarium, particularly valuable in British plants, making it an essential resource for the long-projected *Flora Britannica*. He also acknowledged that, if nothing else, it would be "at least a feather" in his cap.[26] Thomas Woodward was particularly anxious that his friend play his cards right, and unwittingly became his mentor for dealing with the royal family: their Majesties were "famous for being satisfied with the honour which their acceptance of obligations confers".[27] A careful balance had to be struck. Too eager, and Smith risked losing his dignity and possible future favours. Showing too little interest, and the "penurious disposition" of the Queen would prevail; the honour alone might be sufficient. Woodward recommended that should any appealing position open whilst in her employ, Smith should "boldly" ask the Queen for it. "Her love of money", he wrote, "will induce her to procure for you something better worth having, rather than she will part with her bank notes".[28] Smith was already aware of this from his own personal experience. On the publication of the third fascicle of *Icones Pictæ* in November 1793, he requested Sowerby "to send this day to Buckingham house 3 copies large paper [...] let them be perfect – & rolled up directed For Her Majesty. I am still unpaid for the 1st & 2d".[29] Heeding Woodward's advice, Smith resolved to say nothing of the personal benefit received from consulting the herbarium "lest it should be thought an equivalent for my trouble, which it is not", and instead relied on his charm.[30]

An attempt to return to Frogmore in late March was abandoned after Smith became ill with a cold and fever, and a course of botanical lectures beginning on 3 April prevented any further visits until the end of May.[31] The 1792 botanical course is the first for which attendance figures have survived: 17 pupils, of which 15 paid, though none were women. The only named attendee was Lord Stormont, David William Murray, later 3rd Earl of Mansfield, a conscientious student who industriously took notes; the remaining students were all "very respectable". Smith's dedication was starting to bring returns; he had never heard his lectures spoken of "with applause" before, as they now were, and he was confident of their gaining more ground in the future.[32]

Following the conclusion of the lectures in mid-May, Smith's health spectacularly collapsed, resulting in his worst bout of ill health since his 1783 journey from Edinburgh to Norwich. Months of incessant toil in the bad London air had taken their toll on his delicate respiratory system, and his fever in March was exacerbated by a sudden hot spell in April, further aggravating the condition of his lungs. At the end of May he left London for Matlock with Richard Salisbury, resolving to spend an extended period of time at Matlock Bath in order to take "a little air water & repose".[33] Though the waters initially disagreed with Smith, by the end of June he was in large part recovered. He missed the Linnean Society's July meeting, but kept himself busy, sending Sowerby a box of plants for inclusion in *English Botany*, and he assiduously avoided socialising. He wrote to Jonas Dryander of the "abundance of odd beings of the human kind that would exercise your risible faculties".[34] More constructively, Smith did meet Erasmus Darwin, who lived in nearby Lichfield. In the 1780s, as part of the Lichfield Botanical Society, Erasmus Darwin helped translate two of Linnaeus's works into English, and between 1789 and 1791 he published *The Botanic Garden*. The second part, *The Loves of the Plants*, was a poetic treatment of Linnaeus's sexual system of classification. On meeting Darwin, a "fine old man, full of enthusiasm", one of his first requests to Smith was to become a Fellow of the Linnean Society. Later in the year, Smith sent Darwin a copy of his doctoral thesis *De Generatione*, which Darwin read with great interest, though stated their theories "would not agree".[35]

Fully recovered, Smith returned to London on 12 July, and paid a 10-day visit to Frogmore at the end of the month. Smith's time was chiefly devoted to working on the herbarium, which left him with a sheaf of valuable notes for *Flora Britannica*. Windsor was a flurry of activity; a great encampment of troops at nearby Bagshot Heath commanded much attention, as did the presence of Princess Frederica of Prussia, who the previous year had married Prince Frederick, Duke of York and Albany. Consequently, the Queen only spent two mornings with Smith, and there was no time for any botanical studies, though he often saw her and the Princesses Elizabeth and Augusta on the terrace. Smith was in his element. Always a keen social observer, he revelled in the opportunity to study the customs and protocol of this privileged world. Smith thought the Queen, Augusta and Elizabeth were "very worthy sensible people".[36] His leisure hours were spent in great part with the Queen's reader, Jean André de Luc, a Swiss geologist, and his family; they honoured Smith "in a style far superior to my merits or pretensions, but Windsor is a courtly place". He left with an invitation to return again in October, this time as royal tutor.[37]

Smith was engaged for at least five weeks to instruct the Queen and Princesses in botany and zoology, though he returned to London for Linnean Society meetings. The lessons at Frogmore were to take the form of a daily, hour long conversation, though as the family had "the knack, more parentis, of talking all at once", he expected to have "little to say—but no matter—if they fancy they learn".[38] A much more sensitive issue lay in the content of the conversations, namely, how to decently convey the more intimate details of the Linnaean sexual system for plants and zoological anatomy. Whilst extremely conscious of his predicament, Smith also saw the humorous side. Referencing his appointment, he pointed Edmund Davall to a passage in *Flora Lapponica* in which Linnaeus describes "a particularly pleasant spectacle" relating to *Viola tricolor*:

> With the flower having just opened, you will see the maidenly womb—its shape a concave bowl and open on the side, white and beautiful, gaping lustfully ['vulva hians']. But as soon as the womb is ready to reproduce, her five neighbouring husbands discharge their reproductive dust onto the entire womb, which becomes swollen and soiled by dark colour, while her tube remains clear and translucent.[39]

"God knows what it will produce", he cheekily wrote to Davall, "I don't mean the vulva hians, but my attendance on the Royal family".[40] Thomas Woodward, meanwhile, revelled in Smith's dilemma, hoping that he had not "shocked their delicacy by any dissertations on the generation of animals, nor hazarded any opinions upon the physical causes which occasion why the boar to be so long, & the bull so short a time in performing the same natural operation".[41]

Smith, and his pupils, managed to survive the gauntlet unscathed, and made a considerable impression. A bemused and modest Smith informed Davall that his royal charges thought him a "wondrous learned philosopher ¡¡¡".[42] A month later he was able to give a better report of his 'conversational lectures'. "We all sit together at a round table," he wrote, "& my audience occasionally ask questions & make remarks, very much to the purpose". The Queen took notes throughout and would recite them back to Smith to check their veracity.[43]

With these recurring intimate settings, Woodward was quick to curtail any possible idea of Smith becoming enamoured with the Princess Elizabeth. He related an anecdote about the famous Dr Francis Willis, who having successfully treated George III's first bout of madness a few years previously, had reportedly fallen for her, and "was wise enough to fancy it was reciprocated". Woodward himself thought it odd that Elizabeth, whom he believed the "least handsome, has been most admired".[44] Smith, at first hand, could easily see the charms of Elizabeth; he admitted that her genteel personality and soulful glances made it easy for "any man who is a fool or a coxcomb" to believe she had fallen for him. He assured Woodward he was not "so vain" as that.[45]

As with the herbarium, there had been no discussion of recompense, but the greatly increased time commitment made Smith less sanguine this time. Woodward was particularly adamant on this point, reminding Smith that now was the time that he should be in receipt of "solid pudding from the higher powers".[46] Richard Pulteney hoped that this visit would financially reward Smith as much as it exalted him to "Fame & Honour".[47] Predictably, the one voice of disgruntlement came from the saturnine Sir Joseph Banks, who congratulated Smith but "faintly" on his occupations at Windsor.[48] Another botanist enjoying sustained royal favour presented a considerable transgression for the jealous Banks, who had been close to the King for many years, even managing the royal flock of merino sheep.

Shortly after Smith left Windsor it was rumoured that one of Smith's sisters had been offered Fanny Burney's recently vacated position as Second Keeper of the Queen's Robes, but had refused. The Queen would have certainly considered this ample repayment for Smith's troubles, but the report was without foundation, and an amused Smith wrote to Woodward, "you have no idea what tittle tattle there is at Windsor", promising a valuable crop of gossip for when they next met.[49] Smith left Frogmore just before Christmas, still without pecuniary reward, though the Queen did present him a copy of the three-volume *Hortus Kewensis*, and an invitation to return to Windsor again in the summer of 1793.

Smith's name was beginning to be celebrated, or at least known, outside scientific circles. In September 1792, Edmund Davall's botanical solitude in Switzerland was abruptly broken by the arrival of Margaret Spencer, Countess Spencer, and her daughters, Georgiana Cavendish, Duchess of Devonshire and Henrietta Ponsonby, Countess of Bessborough. Georgiana was in Europe on account of a pregnancy resulting from an affair with politician Charles Grey; her husband, William Cavendish, the 5th Duke of Devonshire, had given an ultimatum of a public divorce, or exile in Europe. Her mother and sister accompanied her, and they were now making a stately progress to Naples. Davall had all three women round his table, discussing the names of the various plants they had collected. Georgiana was "rather indifferent as she prefers minerals to plants!" but Davall thought that Lady Spencer and the "unfortunate & interesting" Henrietta (in an equally tempestuous marriage) could be inclined to seriously study botany. Davall made sure to put in a good word for Smith, and informed his visitors that he had a friend in England "infinitely better able" to assist and instruct them, partly on account of his possession of the Linnaean collections. The Duchess exclaimed: "Oh is it not Dr Smith of the Linnean Society?" "The very same", replied Davall, and on being asked, "do you think he would be disposed to give instruction", Davall made sure to relate all the important work Smith was engaged in, highlighting his tutoring of the Queen and Princesses; if time permitted "no one is so able".[50] For over a year every letter from Smith to Davall would contain a hopeful reference to the matter but none of the Spencer women ever took up the recommendation.

During 1793, Smith offered two series of lectures: zoology and botany. The zoology lectures began on 8 January, for which he had 16 subscribers, including Lord Stormont again.[51] His botanical lectures, which finished on 11 May, were more successful: 24 subscribers, including eight or nine ladies of "distinguished rank & elegance". Informing Davall, Smith ventured that another year would see them even better attended (though his request of "don't laugh" implies Smith had long been in expectation of this).[52]

In February 1793, he reported that his portrait was being painted. Commissioned by Sir Abraham Hume, the husband of Smith's patron Amelia Hume, it was to be exhibited in Summer Exhibition at the Royal Academy of Arts.[53] The artist was John Rising, a former assistant to the Academy's founder Sir Joshua Reynolds; his subjects including William Wilberforce and Admiral Lord Nelson. The portrait was clearly intended to show Smith, aged 33, as a distinguished and respected scientist. Anonymously titled 'Portrait of an eminent botanist', Smith is shown dressed in a frock coat against a backdrop of dark crimson fabric, with powdered hair. He sits at a table, holding open a book of botanical figures, turned towards the viewer as though interrupted in his studies; a knowledgeable observer could identify Smith by the figure of *Smithia sensitiva*. Opposite is a figure of *Woodwardia radicans*, a fern named in honour of Thomas Woodward in Smith's paper, 'Tentamen Botanicum de Filicum Generibus Dorsiferarum'.[54]

Smith continued to receive recognition from across Europe. At the end of 1792, he was elected to the Royal Swedish Academy of Sciences, founded by Carl Linnaeus in 1739, and in March 1793 was unanimously elected to the Royal Society of Sciences in Uppsala. Smith was particularly gratified by the latter, "as the Swedes can have no partiality to me", and therefore assumed the election was based entirely on his character.[55] Indeed, Swedish feelings towards Smith had remained mixed, and ambivalence clung to Smith's name; at the end of 1791 Carl Peter Thunberg remarked that few copies of Smith's works could be sold in Sweden, but requested Smith to send some anyway.[56] Others were less reactionary. Smith maintained an active correspondence with several eminent Swedish scientists, including Acrel, Thunberg, botanist Olof Swartz and astronomer Erik Prosperin. Informing him of his election to the Royal Swedish Academy of Sciences, physicist Johan Carl Wilcke praised Smith's work on the Linnaean collections and conceded that Smith and his base in London had increased their strength, which Sweden might have struggled to do on its own.[57] In 1791, Smith received a letter from the German Dietrich Stoever, who was engaged in writing a new biography of Linnaeus, with several questions on the Linnaean purchase and Smith's role in it, hoping to clarify the various rumours.[58] Smith seized the opportunity to give his version of events and to vindicate both himself and Acrel from any accusations of bribery or other wrongdoing. The biography was published in 1792, and Smith's response was presented in an epistolary format as an appendix.[59] For this reason, Smith actively encouraged support of the English translation (published 1794), undertaken by Joseph Trapp and dedicated to the Linnean Society. Its literary merits, however, left Smith bewildered. He described it as "odd, amusing, ridiculous, quackish, bombastic, german, queer—I don't know what to call it".[60]

The Country We are About to Illustrate

Smith's industry, skill, world-class collections and growing reputation made him an important authority for the determination of new plants and species. On 13 May 1787, 11 ships left England, loaded with convicts and stores, to establish a British penal colony at Botany Bay, New South Wales. Later known as the First fleet, much of the impetus for the new settlement came from Sir Joseph Banks. In 1788, Messrs Lee and Kennedy, nurserymen of Hammersmith, could claim "to have received exclusively the first lots of seeds from New Holland after the settlement was established", fuelling considerable interest amongst wealthy British collectors, including Smith's benefactress Lady Rockingham.[61] John White, surgeon to the settlement and one of the only scientifically inclined men in the fleet, became an important collector, sending many seeds and plant specimens to

Thomas Wilson, a Fellow of the Linnean Society who lived at Gower Street, London. Wilson, in turn passed them onto Smith, who eagerly received them: at the end of 1791, he reported having just opened a box of specimens from Botany Bay "so very new we can hardly settle the Nat[ura]l Orders of some of them".[62] Smith's first published accounts of the Australian flora appeared in White's *Journal of a Voyage to New South Wales*, published in 1790, which included 65 plates of birds, mammals, reptiles, plants and other 'productions' of the new colony. Smith provided the botanical descriptions for the seven new plants featured, including three new *Banksia* species, the genus named by Linnaeus the Younger in 1782 for Sir Joseph Banks.

The preserved specimens were often complemented by coloured drawings, making publication an attractive possibility. An obvious impediment lay in Sir Joseph Banks, the acknowledged British authority on Australian flora by dint of his having actually collected at Botany Bay in 1770. Banks was heavily invested in the new settlement, though by this point was more interested in ensuring its survival, arranging for the transportation of useful European crops and plants to the new colony. Nevertheless, he too received specimens from White, as well as the chaplain Richard Johnson. For years Banks had been delaying his own publication on the Australian flora, but Smith saw no reason not to produce his own. At any rate, he intended to talk the matter over fully with Banks.[63] In the end, the impetus came from Thomas Wilson. In October 1793, in conjunction with the esteemed zoologist George Shaw, the first part of *Zoology and Botany of New Holland* (1793) appeared. Each part was to consist of four plates, evenly split between plants and animals, with Shaw providing the zoological descriptions and Smith the botanical. The figures were all by James Sowerby, who achieved a remarkably fine execution considering that he was working solely from drawings and dried specimens for the plants, and skins for the animals. It was written in English, intended "to make the Public acquainted with some of the productions of a country of which they have lately heard so much, and in which they now as a nation are so deeply interested".[64]

Smith was uncomfortable with the joint botanical-zoological aspect, but as Wilson had settled the plan (in addition to providing the source material that now enriched Smith's herbarium), he had no say in the matter.[65] In the event, Smith did not have to endure long; after the second issue appeared by the end of the year, the work was split into *Zoology of New Holland* and *A Specimen of the Botany of New Holland*. These were the first works solely dedicated to the fauna and flora of Australia. Further parts of *A Specimen of the Botany of New Holland* appeared in July 1794 and January 1795, concluding the first volume, but neither the exotic contents nor Smith's status as author could sustain the work, and production came to an end. Through the work, Smith published 16 new plants, including the genera *Billardiera* (named for French botanist Jacques Julien Houton de Labillardière), *Goodenia* (named for Samuel Goodenough), *Pimelea, Styphelia, Platylobium* and *Pultenæa* (named for Richard Pulteney). Smith was particularly proud of his description of *Billardiera scandens*. Despite the extraordinary genera of the region, a plant had not yet been discovered that had a "degree of usefulness to mankind, at least with respect to food". As the common name he gave it, climbing apple-berry, suggested, this produced an edible fruit with "a very fine flavour, not unlike a roasted apple", and Smith claimed it was "almost the only wild eatable fruit of the country we are about to illustrate". His observations also included a penetrating passage on the inter-connectedness of the universe and man's place in it, inspired by the extraordinary discoveries being made in New Holland:

> It is the peculiar privilege of reasoning man, not only to extend his enquiries to a multiplicity of attainable benefits to himself and his species, […] but also to walk with God through the garden of creation, and be initiated into the different plans of his providence in the construction and œconomy of all these various beings; to study their dependencies upon one another in an infinitely complex chain, every link of which is essential; and to trace out all those various uses and benefits to every branch of the animal creation.[66]

Smith's name had spread across the Atlantic Ocean, too. Early in 1793, he received a letter from Gotthilf Heinrich Ernst Muhlenberg (otherwise known as 'Henry'), a Lutheran pastor residing in Lancaster, Pennsylvania,

Henry Muhlenberg (1753–1815), botanist and Lutheran pastor.

over 60 miles west of Philadelphia. The letter began: "Pardon a Stranger that intrudes upon your Studies. An enthusiastical Love of Botany and irresistible Desire to know the Plants of my native Country stimulate me to do it." He went on to explain that for a number of years he had been collecting specimens of the local flora, some 1,200 species from within a 10-mile radius of Lancaster by the time he wrote to Smith. He was now engaged in producing a local flora, but had come across so many specimens that defied identification that he was in dire need of assistance. Muhlenberg had seen Smith named as the possessor of the Linnaean herbarium and wrote to this "Oracle", convinced that Smith was his "greatest Prospect of Success". Muhlenberg proposed sending Smith all the unidentified plants to be compared with Linnaeus's, from which Smith could discern which ones were new to science. Smith's payment would be the specimens.[67]

Though the natural history of North America had been systematically studied for some 60 years by this time (Mark Catesby's *Natural History of Carolina, Florida and the Bahama Islands* [1729–1747] was the first published account of the flora and fauna of America), North American natural historians were few and far between. Even as late as 1813, Smith's old friend from his Tour days, José Francisco Corrêa de Serra, who had been in

America for the past five years, wrote: "Botany is still in her infancy in America; some amateurs are scattered through this continent".[68]

Muhlenberg had enjoyed some success corresponding with several German botanists, including Georg Franz Hoffmann of Göttingen University and Johann Hedwig, one of the leading authorities on cryptogams, but the "unhappy Troubles in the old Countries have broke up all my Correspondence with my German Friends", and he earnestly wished that he might find "a new and constant Correspondent" in Smith.[69] Smith leapt at the opportunity, replying as soon as he received Muhlenberg's letter in March 1794:

> You can hardly conceive how much pleasure your letter gave me, & how much I wish to deserve by actions the opinion you have formed of me. I want no other proof than your letter that you are worthy of my highest esteem, & I already reckon your correspondence, & (I hope) future friendship, among the choicest good things botany has procured me.

Smith assured his new correspondent, "you may depend on my accuracy & fidelity in my examination of y[ou]r plants—I do nothing in a hurry".[70] Muhlenberg duly despatched his first parcel of 234 plants across the Atlantic Ocean, Smith responding with his "pleasing and Instructive Remarks" in due course. As regular a correspondence as possible, not withstanding war, storm and plague, was established between the two, with 34 letters exchanging hands between 1792 and 1813, though there could be significant lapses. In 1798, not having heard from Smith for two years, Muhlenberg wrote enquiring of Smith's health: "O may the allmighty have preserved the good Doctor, may he still be alive and usefull to the admiring world".[71] Most disruptive was the War of 1812, a two-and-a-half year conflict between Britain and the United States, during which Muhlenberg was completely cut off from his European correspondents. Muhlenberg died on 23 May 1815, three months after the end of hostilities. Over the course of their long correspondence, Muhlenberg sent 803 numbered specimens to Smith, of which at least 351 entered

Smith's herbarium. Muhlenberg acknowledged the significant support he had received from Smith, "the learned, the candid, and ingenious possessor of the Herbarium of the two Linnaei", and his other European correspondents in the preface to his *Index Floræ Lancastriensis*, submitted to the American Philosophical Society in 1797.[72]

I Give Up Physic in My Own Mind

In his reply to Muhlenberg's first letter, Smith had felt himself beholden to explain a little of his situation, which provides a unique example of an unguarded Smith introducing himself to an entirely independent person, conveniently located on another continent:

> I am quite devoted to botany, & being happily enabled to support myself (though not rich) without the practice of medicine, I have at an early period of my life (being but now 33) set myself down as a man of science, for the sake of science, not in any hopes of any emolument—for though my taste have procured me a set of acquaintances even more choice in character, than extensive in number, many of them in the most elevated stations, yet I love independence & ask for nothing.[73]

This statement encapsulates Smith entirely. From the time of the purchase of the Linnaean collections, medicine was never really an option, but for the sake of appearances it was always an imminent prospect. Smith, however, was determined to make botany pay, on his own terms. It is true that he still received an allowance from his father, but he stretched it as far as possible and in the time it freed he worked tirelessly, committing himself to a relentless publication schedule, annual courses of lectures, private teaching (sometimes unpaid, as with the Queen) and a continual presence helming the Linnean Society. The only other person Smith confided in regarding his prospects was Edmund Davall, also conveniently placed from England. In February 1793 he wrote that his course of lectures had been so successful he soon hoped to "be able to live by my own means", and a few months later, in reference to a possible move to Kensington to escape the oppressive heat of London in the summer, confessed "I give up physic in my own mind".[74]

Alongside the lectures, the principal source for this newfound confidence came from *English Botany* (for which Smith was now receiving half a guinea per description). From the end of 1792 and through 1793, Smith and Sowerby instituted a raft of changes that further expanded its appeal to botanists. Though it had continued to sell well, the original plan of three figures for one shilling made it difficult for either Smith or Sowerby to make any money from it. At the end of 1792, the decision was made to enlarge it to six figures for 2 shillings and 6 pence. The remit of *English Botany* was also expanded to include cryptogams—plants without visible flowers, such as ferns, lichens and mosses. Thomas Woodward highly approved of this development, though he warned Smith not to include more than one or two in any issue, "for fear of disgusting the florists & the Ladies".[75] The public were unfazed, and by May 1793 Smith reported that it was selling upwards of 900 copies a month, an extraordinary circulation for the period.[76]

In March 1793, Smith finally claimed the text of *English Botany* as his own, after a letter in the February issue of *The Gentleman's Magazine* criticised the figure of *Geranium lucidum* in issue no. 25 of *English Botany*. The letter writer, 'R.G.', cited the differing shape of the leaves from Linnaeus's own specific character and a specimen the writer had collected from William Curtis's botanic garden, and claimed that the author had adjusted his own specific character to fit the figure.[77] Smith responded forcefully, immediately identifying himself as "answerable for any faults there may be in the letter-press". It was outrageous for Mr R.G. to have suggested that the specific character had been altered to fit the figure, and his "opposing a *garden* specimen to a declared wild one, to settle a doubtful point, is equally unwarrantable".[78] However, it was not until his signed preface to the fourth volume, published 1795, that Smith's name became attached to the work itself, and it would be another two years before his name appeared on the cover of every issue. Smith's initial decision for anonymity was a particularly poor judgement call that was to follow him for the rest of his life, and to this day the work is frequently referred to as 'Sowerby's *English Botany*'.

Smith's family are frustratingly distant throughout this conspicuously successful period of Smith's life, in large part due to the censorious efforts of Smith's widow. No family correspondence has survived, aside from occasional letters written by Smith's father. His brother John Frederick, who had never had the same business aptitude as brother Francis, had left the family business and established himself in Wakefield, Yorkshire. Francis, as far as is known, had remained in Norwich in the textile trade. Smith had always been particularly close to Francis, who had accompanied him home from Paris; they shared a similar scientific bent, Francis's passion being astronomy, but with a passing interest in botany. Richard, the youngest of the Smith brothers, was a very different proposition. Nine years younger than James Edward, he appears in sudden, troubling detail in several of his brother's letters in the early 1790s. Richard displayed an early proficiency at mathematics and drawing, to which a career in architecture or surveying was the obvious conclusion. According to Smith, sometime before 1784 Richard almost won a Royal Academy gold medal for his plan for a proposed church (the details do not survive).[79] In November 1784, James Snr apprenticed Richard to an unnamed "eminent" London architect, and though it was not what he would have chosen for his youngest son, an apparently weary father justified the decision by stating the world "says 'tis right to give way to a strong propensity in youth". The contrast between the eldest and youngest of the Smith boys are striking. Unfortunately, whilst James Edward thrived on such indulgence, Richard's life was to become blighted by wasted talent and opportunity. In December 1791, Smith reported that his brother was spending the winter in lodgings by himself, "doing nothing & burying good taste & abilities in meer sloth, to our great unhappiness".[80] The next April, James Snr was informed that Richard was "just in the same state", though by this time he was also in financial difficulties.[81] Whilst Smith was engaged at Frogmore, Richard had visited Robert Batty asking for money, which he implied would be repaid on Smith's return. Unwittingly, Batty lent Richard three guineas, which Smith repaid (without Richard's knowledge), and requested that Batty and Sowerby, amongst others, lend no more on any account.

Richard died suddenly at the beginning of September 1793, in Clerkenwell, London, aged just 25. There appears to have been a steady build up to this climax; his letter informing Lady Rockingham of the news was full of so much "grief of mind" that she felt almost wrong to even touch on the subject.[82] Mystery surrounds the circumstances of Richard's death: Thomas Woodward, a close family friend, hoped for Smith's sake, and that of his family, that it was "natural; but knowing his situation, & I may add perverseness, I had my doubts & fears".[83] Even with Davall, Smith was evasive. With striking unfeelingness, to modern sensibilities at least, he wrote: "poor fellow he is no loss to us or himself, having fallen into total indolence, w[hi]ch I really believe was mental disease not likely to be cured – & therefore his death is a happy release". From being "very industrious & very affectionate when young", later he had "cared for nobody".[84] Smith claimed Richard had no "vice or dissipation of any kind", but admitted that he was the only one of his siblings that ever gave the others "uneasiness". A modern diagnosis would certainly include depression, and suicide cannot be ruled out. Smith, betraying himself, wrote a touching epitaph for his brother's tombstone:

> Though genius fire the ardent mind,
> And early virtues flattering bloom,
> The Lord of Heav'n may send a cloud,
> And his last blessing be the tomb

In the end, Richard's life became little more than a cautionary tale, "strong proof, how little great abilities & splendid genius avail, when not under the guidance of judgement & how dangerous it is for a young man to give way to habits of indolence & inactivity"; everything that James Snr fully trusted his eldest son with whilst away in Edinburgh and London.[85] There was considerable resignation at the turn of events; even before Richard had died, Smith commented that for a "family of 7 we could hardly hope to avoid all trouble or anxiety. Thank God we have nothing but love & happiness besides".[86] Unfortunately, this was not to be the last time the Smith family would be touched by mental imbalances.

Smith returned to Frogmore for another round of royal lectures at the end of September, with an invitation to return again the following year, and the ever-dangling hint of reward. At the end of 1793, Smith finally published his account of his European tour, *A Sketch of a Tour on the Continent, in the years 1786 and 1787*, in three volumes. He had been intermittently working on this since at least 1790, using his journal and the letters he had sent home as his source material.[87] He had also written to his travelling companion William Younge, now a physician in Sheffield, for details missing from his own journal of the trip.[88] Smith worked on the manuscript during his long visit to Frogmore at the end of 1792; the first part went to the press in March 1793, whilst he was still working on the latter parts of the manuscript.[89] It became his chief priority during this period, with Smith committing himself to writing at least six pages each day.[90]

The Friend of Truth and Humanity

Since Smith and Younge's travels around the Continent, political events had irrevocably changed France. Smith's dissenting faith, professed love of Rousseau (he was also an admirer of Voltaire and the controversial Jonathan Shipley, Bishop of Llandaff and St Asaph, a supporter of the American Revolution) and his Norwich origins all identify Smith as a Jacobin (an English proponent of the French Revolution). In his own time, Smith rarely labelled himself as anything, particularly when it came to religion and politics, aware no doubt, of his increasingly public profile: non-Trinitarian (an unbeliever in the doctrine of the Holy Trinity) or monotheistic beliefs were technically illegal in Britain until the passing of the 1813 Doctrine of the Trinity Act. Claiming he was "no trinitarian", he explained: "I am no enthusiast. I believe no nonsense under the specious name of mystery. I look up to one God, & delight in referring all my hopes & wishes to him". He was further put on the spot when, in March 1790, Edmund Davall asked Smith to stand as godfather to his unborn first child. Smith was honoured by the suggestion, but he was candid with his friend in that he could not "conscientiously promise" to raise the child in the Church of England, thinking that church "too near popery", and left it to Davall to decide whether or not he was a suitable candidate.

Smith thought godparents an "unnecessary form, & even worse, as a religious form that means nothing cannot be innocent", and though he eventually consented, he insisted it should be without any ceremony.[91] Davall assured Smith that he only wished to ensure that the child would have Smith for its friend, and, moved by Smith's reasoning, decided the child would have no godparents at all. The child, a girl, was born 8 August, but died less than a year later.[92]

Norwich's strong tradition of religious dissent made it a natural supporter of the early stages of the French Revolution, and it was a "likely market for radical pamphlets", in time earning itself the nickname the "Jacobin city". Visiting her home county of Norfolk during this period, Fanny Burney noted how the local countryside was "filled with little revolution societies which transmit their notions to the large committee at Norwich which communicates the whole to the reformists in London. I am told there is scarce a village in Norfolk free from these meetings".[93] Indeed, Smith's employment by the Queen had caused him some moral qualms. On his ever being invited to "share some of the plunder of honest John Bull", he wryly commented that he should "be ever bound to pray that light & liberty may never make any progress in the world—but in the mean time I most heartily & fervently pray that they may."[94] Though the tour had been undertaken several years before the outbreak of the Revolution, there could be no question of ignoring it in his book. He was acutely aware of the sensitivities involved, and even confessed that he "feared getting into altercations—for I must & will show myself the friend of truth & humanity".[95] Even more contentious was Smith's support for Rousseau, whose writings provided a theory of popular sovereignty, and proclaimed that all men were created equal and rulers should be accountable to their citizens. This had an incendiary impact on the course of the Revolution. In *A Letter to the National Assembly* (1791), Edmund Burke, staunch opponent of the Revolution, launched a vicious attack against Rousseau, referring to him as the "mad *Socrates* of the National Assembly" and the "founder of the *philosophy of vanity* in England".[96] Smith was determined to offer a defence for Rousseau, in an attempt to rescue his reputation from both the "barbarians" who had used his work for their own ends, but also the "uncandid and the dishonest" who had falsely smeared his name by "not daring to declare the real cause of their aversion—his virtuous sincerity".[97]

As events deteriorated in France, they had a direct effect on public opinions at home. In August 1792, the Duke of Brunswick, commander of the Austrian and Prussian armies, had issued the 'Brunswick Manifesto', promising the total destruction of Paris should any harm come to the royal family, then under house arrest. Rather than cow the revolutionaries, it provoked them to greater resistance, and their decisive victory at Valmy (100 miles north-east of Paris) a few weeks later forced the Prussians to withdraw from French territory. In England, William Younge wrote to Smith of the strong republican feelings that had erupted in Sheffield on account of the Duke of Brunswick's defeat. Younge had returned home to the sound of celebratory cannon fire, and reports that several groups of workmen were planning a feast for the following week, with a sheep or two to be "roasted whole". A bookseller erected a sign depicting writer and American revolutionary Thomas Paine and several street corners bore the inscription "Death or Liberty". Adding fuel to the fire, a government commissioner had arrived in Sheffield a few days earlier, requesting sellers of luxuries to inform on any evasions of duties. This news was received "with a hiss, & the remark that it must be a poor government that cannot be supported without sowing Dissension among neighbours [...]. Where these things will end, God knows".[98] On 21 January 1793, Louis XVI was executed, and on 1 February, France declared war on Britain. Both of these acts adversely affected perceptions of the Revolution, turning many former friends against France. Smith was bitterly disappointed with the French response: "If they had but moral or religious principle—I should hope they would yet do well—while the poor king was alive I had hopes—but now I am much out of patience, though a sincere friend to genuine liberty. The idea here is that they must be crushed—but I say can they?"[99]

These tensions are more than evident in the preface to *A Sketch of a Tour*. Smith provided a disclaimer for the early part of the work (covering his time in France); it had been composed and printed some time before publication, and thus had "style and sentiments" that might now seem inappropriate in light of recent, tumultuous events.[100] Nevertheless, Smith had succeeded in producing a traditional, eminently readable tour, which was both a critical and commercial success. Written as a journal, his descriptions focused on the churches, institutions and galleries he visited, as well as the local customs and people he met. Where the botanical influence did show itself, it was to the work's advantage. *The Critical Review* noted that though the author was appearing under a new character, they had hardly "perused any book of travels with more satisfaction", and recommended it highly to their readers.[101] *The British Critic* observed that upon arrival at any metropolis, Smith's immediate business was to connect with most distinguished men of learning, leading the reviewer to declare: "we know more of the present state of science on the continent, from these, than from any modern volumes of travel".[102] At the beginning of March 1794, Smith reported the sales of 600 copies, and three months later the work was being translated into German, French and Italian, the latter "somewhat castrated".[103] Smith was genuinely surprised at its success; he confided to Davall that it had met with "unexpected commendation, & sells fast", and furthermore, the political part, which he had worried about, "seems to conciliate most people".[104] In fact, the only real criticism Smith received was from his "honest but bigotted friend" Thomas Marsham, Secretary to the Linnean Society. Marsham was, according to Smith, a "furious friend to the slave trade & an enemy of Dr Priestly". Joseph Priestley was a leading chemist, credited with discovery of oxygen, and instrumental in establishing Unitarianism in Britain. Marsham hated Priestley so much he reportedly rejoiced when Priestley's house was razed in the Birmingham riots of 1791. Smith referred to this unfortunate incident in the account of his visit to Ermenonville in the first volume.[105] Marsham claimed that Smith "had done wrong in mentioning Priestly", and accused him of a style so similar to his nemesis that Priestley himself may as well have written it. However, one more important opinion remained to be gauged: though Smith had received "great praise & approbation" from an unnamed Windsor friend, as yet he knew nothing of the reaction of that other important Windsor resident—the Queen.[106]

Though the entire work is suffused with Smith's professed love of liberty, his most contentious statements appeared in his apology for, and defence of, Rousseau. Addressing himself to those with only a partial understanding of Rousseau, who might not understand why such a controversial figure would be celebrated, he explained that he respected him as "a writer eminently favourable on the whole to the interests of humanity, reason, and religion" – precisely the things he was accused of targeting. Smith claimed that when any of Rousseau's writings ran counter to these, he could "as freely dissent from him; but do not on that account throw all his works into the fire". Nor did he believe that any of the personal woes in Rousseau's private life hindered "the refined moral and religious principles with which his works abound". Smith depicted Rousseau as a visionary persecuted by the reactionary elements of Europe, his ideas "too hostile to the prevailing opinions, or at least to the darling interests of those in authority among whom he lived". *A Sketch of a Tour* reminded readers that Rousseau had been driven from France and Switzerland, and sought refuge in England in the 1760s. Having been "received with open arms, being justly considered as the martyr of that spirit of investigation and liberty which is the basis of our constitution, and on which alone our reformed religion depends", Rousseau was even offered a pension by King George III. Opinion had turned since then. Smith identified Edmund Burke as "the calumniator of Rousseau!" by cryptically referring to several passages in Burke's anti-Revolution pamphlet, *Reflections on the Revolution in France* (1790). Smith attempted to discredit Burke's work, latching on to his statement that George III had come "to the crown in contempt of his people", and that in his outspoken support for Marie Antoinette, Burke had "held up a Messalina [an infamously promiscuous Roman empress] for public veneration".[107]

Unfortunately, though intended as an apology, some thought Smith was passionately defending a body of work that they viewed as an insidious and corrupting influence on society, and worried he would lead people astray. *The British Critic* took Smith to task. It strongly believed that Rousseau's work was "injurious to religion, his conduct equally so to morals; nor do we allow the arguments of Dr Smith, in his vindication, to be either strongly stated or happily introduced". They would not tolerate Smith's "sneer at Mr Burke, and insinuation against the unfortunate Queen of France" which they considered feeble and "unworthy of the respectable author".[108] This was certainly one of the several passages that Samuel Goodenough "fear'd would not be relish'd at Frogmore".[109] Indeed, Smith's comparison of Marie Antoinette to the notoriously debauched Roman Empress Messalina was spectacularly ill-timed: the French Queen had been executed by the Revolutionary Tribunal less than three months before the publication of *A Sketch of a Tour,* and Smith's comments appear to have caused a minor court scandal. The details are murky, but Smith was later told that Queen Charlotte, having read some of the first volume, "found so many bad things which she could never forgive, that she could not go on¡¡¡".[110] It seems clear that the Queen's reaction was encouraged and abetted by the Queen's reader, Jean André de Luc, who had had several run-ins with Rousseau. Smith was in a combative mood: informing a friend of the continued success of the work, he reported that whilst generally it was very well regarded, there were some who thought the "politics not courtly enough". Smith professed to care little about this, having written them "chiefly because I think them true". Smith reported that de Luc had found him "too partial to Rousseau", and that they had corresponded on the subject; the letters, unfortunately, do not survive.[111] Goodenough lamented the Queen's reaction and the misrepresentation of Smith's work. "I always fear'd that she might have ideas of the kind", he wrote to Smith, "Kings & Queens naturally like to have the cause of Kings & Queens beprais'd".[112]

At the end of 1794, just as Smith was expecting to depart for Frogmore, he received a letter from de Luc, politely withdrawing the invitation on the pretext of the house being "in disorder, & the Queen too busy at pres[en]t to study; she therefore postpones all such occupations till the next year". Smith was unimpressed by the Queen's reactionary response to his mild comments. He joked to Thomas Woodward that he intended to go to Windsor over the course of the winter "as an amusing experiment to see how the land lies".[113] He was franker with Davall, writing in March 1795, that the Queen's "forgiveness is as yet unasked, & her opinion not much regarded, but I am sorry she mistakes her own solid interest in these critical times, w[hi]ch is to make friends of all moderate people".[114]

Smith was an astute politician, and by quickly circulating an unpublished polemic he had first written in November 1792 to various Establishment figures, including Shute Barrington, Bishop of Salisbury, and Sir Joseph Banks, saw to it that his commitment to the British constitution was known. Entitled *People of England! Beware of Wolves in Sheep's cloathing!*, Smith urged the populace to ignore those advising the English to mirror the French: "we have already gone through what the French wanted, a revolution in government & a reformation in religion". He argued that the French court of Louis XVI had been administered by "a weak & besotted king, entirely governed by a woman, the most notorious of debauchees, & the most insolent of her sex", while, by contrast, the counterbalanced English institutions of crown, parliament and aristocracy admirably stood firm. The polemic was signed 'Common Sense', the title of Thomas Paine's 1776 pamphlet written in support of the American Revolution—a clear indication of Smith's political leanings and his commitment to liberty and freedom. Barrington reassured Smith that it contained "unequivocal proofs of his attachment to the constitution of his country".[115]

Regardless, Smith's brief moment in the royal gaze had ended: he received no further invitations to Frogmore and he was never compensated for the considerable time he had devoted to Her Majesty. In private, however, the Queen continued to maintain an interest in Smith's work. Following her death in 1820, her library was auctioned. At the auction, several Smith works were present within the collection; she had continued to collect *English Botany* and had acquired his later works *Flora Britannica* (1800–1804) and *Compendium Floræ Britannicæ* (1800).

CHAPTER EIGHT

The Bereaved and Betrothed

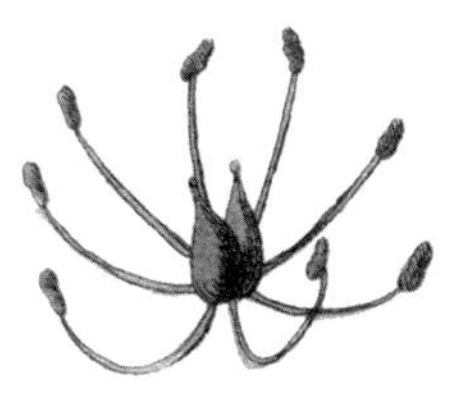

Preparing *A Sketch of a Tour* had distracted Smith for the greater part of 1793 from most of his scientific endeavours, except *English Botany*. It had even caused him to neglect correspondence with friends such as Davall. The following year saw a renewed sense of botanical purpose, beginning with the acquisition of three new private pupils: Germans Caspar Voght, a merchant and social reformer and his travelling companion Paul Christian Wattenbach, and an unnamed American. Smith taught them together; in addition to the usual botanical lectures they also took an additional course on the genera represented in the Linnaean herbarium.[1] Smith also gave his usual courses of zoological and botanical lectures at his home, and following "a very flattering invitation" he also gave a course of botanical lectures at Guy's Hospital.[2] The 18 lectures were probably modelled on the Great Marlborough Street series, giving "a summary view of the vegetable kingdom with respect to physiology and classification", but went further by elaborating on the medicinal uses of various plants.[3] The success of the course meant that Smith was able to publish *Syllabus of a Course of Lectures on Botany* (1795), an outline of his Guy's Hospital lectures. By his own admission, he had done so only because of the "mostly original" lecture plan, specifically the physiological part, had "scarcely been taught in any school" before, save the late Dr Hope's in Edinburgh.[4] Smith continued as lecturer in medical botany for several years, and in 1795 he even advertised his Great Marlborough Street series in conjunction with the series at Guy's. For seven weeks, every Monday, Wednesday and Friday, Smith lectured at his home from 1 o'clock in the afternoon, then dashed across the River Thames to Guy's Hospital where he would lecture again from half past five.[5]

By 6 June 1794, Smith had fulfilled his London lecture commitments for the year. Though a great demand on his time, they were now sufficiently profitable that he could "readily let other things give way to it".[6] Indeed, it seems as though his finances were now healthy enough to allow him to employ two maids. A few days later he decamped to Norwich for the summer, where he expected to see his cousin Nathaniel Kindersley and Kindersley's family, home on leave from India.[7]

Whilst Smith was away in Norwich he allowed Thomas Woodward not only to stay at Great Marlborough Street but also permitted him unprecedented access to his "sacred repository" – the Linnaean collections. It is probable that this was the first time Smith had ever allowed anyone access to the Linnaean collections outside of his direct supervision: Woodward promised to "handle the old & tender *Fuci* [seaweeds] with great care; & deposit them safely in the place where I shall find them". Nor would he "betray the secret of your permitting me to enter the Library in your absence, however proud I may be of the honour". And, perhaps remembering the unfortunate situation of the maid Molly Standard, Woodward jokingly assured Smith that neither he nor Mrs Woodward should be alarmed "at my being left with two damsels; my time will be too busily employed for Gallantry". In any case, added Woodward, if they were the same maids he had previously encountered at Smith's home "they were not chosen, as single mens maids sometimes are for their superior beauty".[8]

Smith's previous servant, Francesco Borone, had returned to Britain from Sierra Leone in September 1793 but could no longer be thought of as a mere valet. Early in 1794 Smith succeeded in obtaining Borone a position as botanical assistant to John Sibthorp, who was returning to Greece to gather further specimens for his *Flora Græca*. The unfortunate caveat: Borone would not be allowed to collect his own specimens.[9] Isolated in his Oxford world, Sibthorp always had an uneasy relationship with those in his employ. During his first expedition of 1786–1787 he was accompanied by the Austrian botanical artist Ferdinand Bauer, but treated him in such a servile way that Bauer refused to join the second expedition. By August,

Sibthorp and Borone had reached Cyprus. Sibthorp was impressed by Borone's industriousness and skill in collecting plants, commenting that he was "in action quite a Le Fleur". Sibthorp himself exhibited a typically 18th-century approach to collecting. Whilst bemoaning the Cypriot custom for burning the forests, "very unfriendly to the researches of the Cryptogamist [a studier of ferns, mosses and other plants without visible flowers]", he had no qualms when an Egyptian vulture alighted in the tree under which he was reading: "I could not resist [...] to shoot it".[10]

Events during the first half of 1795 were to prove graver. In early January, having received news that his father was seriously ill with a swollen leg, Smith was about to journey to Norwich when a follow-up letter indicated a resurgence of body and spirit. Smith's relief was palpable, though there was a sense of wilful ignorance; his father was "a counsellor & friend we [the family] could ill have spared, independent of the attachment we all have for him".[11] Others interpreted James Snr's disorder as "a symptom of a breaking constitution".[12] However, more immediately devastating news, contained in a letter from Sibthorp, soon distracted him: "I should have been happy to have sent you a pleasant letter from Athens, but from Athens I must write you a very mournful one.. poor Borone is no more!".

Sibthorp had written the letter on 1 November 1794; by the time Smith received the letter at the end of January Borone had already been in the ground for three months. Sibthorp related the whole sad, strange story. It was an archetypal dark and stormy night, but Borone was unusually happy, singing to a guitar played by Arakiel, the servant of Sibthorp's friend John Hawkins, who had joined them in Athens. A little after midnight, the house was awoken by the sound of Borone's cries—he had fallen some 18 feet onto the street below his window. A servant was the first to reach him, at which point Borone groaned "Ah! povero Francesco e morto!". Moving him into the house, Sibthorp attempted to bleed him but it was too late and he died shortly after. He was 25 years old. The window out of which he fell was extremely narrow; to reach he must have climbed on a box and squeezed himself through. Sibthorp assured Smith "we have every reason to think all this was done in his sleep". Borone was buried the next evening at the Church of the Madonna, under the shade of a mulberry tree. Sibthorp grieved with Smith at the untimely end of the intrepid youth who had "escaped from the thieves of Italy", and endured eight days with Sibthorp blockaded "by pirates at Mount Athos", only to leave the world by a miserable accident.[13] For Smith, the death of the "truly good & amiable" Borone, whom he affectionately called François, was a severe loss.[14] Smith wrote a flowery epitaph for "Ill-fated Youth! On whose unclouded brow/ Hope faithless gleam'd, to lure thee to thy doom". A much more fitting, and lasting, tribute, was his naming of *Boronia*, a new Australian genus, in his *Tracts Relating to Natural History* (1798).[15] The genus now contains over 90 species.

A few months later, Smith received a letter from Barnaba Oriani of Milan, writing on behalf of Borone's father, Luigi, too distressed to write himself. The Borone family had been "in a torrent of tears" since receiving the news. The family were grateful to Smith, who had ensured a mass was said for their son in a Catholic chapel in London. Luigi Borone also assured him that he did not hold him in any way responsible for his son's death, convinced that Smith had his best interests at heart. Smith was asked to sell Borone's pistol, books and mathematical instruments and send the money to Milan, together with any savings, to act as a dowry for Francesco's sister. Luigi managed to gather himself enough to add a short postscript, in which he asked Smith to send a copy of Borone's likeness as "not having had the joy of seeing him alive I might have the consolation of kissing his portrait".[16]

Smith's sadness for Borone was soon overwhelmed by an even greater sorrow. His father's health had been fluctuating all winter and early in March it became clear that the latest decline would be the last. Smith himself was bedridden, suffering from a "low fever, extreme weakness & a cough", but on 6 March 1795, wrapped in a blanket and accompanied by Robert Batty, managed to haul himself into a chaise and make for Norwich. By the time he arrived his father was "insensible". Smith "watched to the last in vain for a sign of recognition". On 8 March, at 9 o'clock in the evening, his father "ceased to breathe, without the least struggle or groan". He was 67 years old. Though Smith mourned "the loss of his usual affectionate welcome, & the wretched vacancy that now remains", by all accounts James Snr had made a good death. He had settled all his accounts, and was surrounded by "the perfect harmony & affection" of his family.[17] Indeed, Samuel Goodenough commented that such a peaceful exit "was enviable in the extreme, would I may go in such quiet!".[18] At James Snr's own request, his body was dissected, an unconventional last request for the time. The autopsy showed that the pain he had occasionally experienced in his left side since infancy was an ulcerated kidney. Smith suggested that this had arisen from "his nurse giving him drams [small amounts of whiskey] to keep him quiet". Smith was pleased that his father had been vindicated in his regime of "water-drinking & low living", admitting that "nothing but his temperance [despite his nurse] could have saved his life so long".

James Snr left his family in "easy circumstances", and provided his widow Frances with a "considerable & very proper independent provision".[19] Smith's second eldest brother, Francis, still resident in Norwich, received all his father's lands in the parish of St Peter Mancroft, whilst the remaining lands in Norwich's other parishes and elsewhere were sold, along with his goods and other effects. The proceeds of this paid his bequests: £4,500 to James Edward and £1,500 each to Francis, John Frederick, Sarah Maria, Esther Anne and Frances Julia.[20] James Snr was buried in the family vault inside the church of St Peter Mancroft, Norwich, for which his son wrote an epitaph:

Tears for the dead unprofitably ſlow .
  Their virtues yet a richer tribute claim .
Let emulation sanctify our woe .
  And raiſe a living trophy to their name .

Hither may ſtill each kindred mind retire ,
  If boiſterous paſsions urge , or vice allure ,
Muse o'er theſe sacred relics , and aſpire
  To keep their boſoms pure , as theſe were pure :

That , when to theſe their mouldering duſt ſhall come ,
  O'er their cold urn may fall the filial tear :
Still fond remembrance dwell upon their tomb :
  And virtue find a fair example here .

Samuel Goodenough approved, thinking it "beautiful", though he pedantically suggested several alterations and grammatical corrections, pointing out that "come" and "tomb" did not rhyme. Smith ignored his friend's advice.[21]

In August, Smith undertook a much-anticipated journey to Wales that was to provide great solace from the earlier sorrows of the year, travelling to Hafod, the Cardiganshire home of Thomas Johnes, located 14 miles from Aberystwyth. The friendship had been initiated entirely through the auspices of *A Sketch of a Tour*, of which Johnes was a great admirer. Smith informed Davall that by the acquisition of Johnes, "a man of taste, feeling, liberality & large fortune", he had been "richly repaid" for the loss of the Queen's patronage by the same engine. Johnes, an MP since 1775 and colonel of the Carmarthenshire Militia from 1779, was also an enormously wealthy landowner. Since inheriting the Hafod estate in 1780 he had dedicated his efforts to create a picturesque paradise, inspired by his cousin, Richard Payne Knight. Knight held that the "sophisticated artificiality" of Lancelot 'Capability' Brown's landscapes were akin to political despotism, whilst the picturesque offered a "spiritual liberation in some ways akin to political revolution".[22] Smith was suitably astonished by what he found at Hafod: "here is a most sumptuous modern house in a vale among rocks woods & cascades of the wildest kind & on the most magnificent scale".[23] The centrepiece of the house was a superb octagonal library, housing Johnes's extensive collection of books and invaluable Welsh and French manuscripts. A benevolent landowner, in the bitter winter of 1794/95 Johnes had averted a famine in the local area by importing, at his own expense, barley for the poor, and he was committed to supporting modern agricultural techniques on his estates.[24] Smith referred to Johnes and his wife, Jane, as "the guardian angels of the country". Such benevolent activity left them disliked by the neighbouring gentry, who, as Jane informed Smith, wanted "to keep up all the old tyrannic notions & never think of other people's starving". Also resident at Hafod was their charming daughter Mariamne, an only child. Mariamne, who "though not above 10 years of age has taken a wonderful turn for botany & entomology", delighted Smith; he was astonished to find that she had identified almost every plant in the local area. Until now she had no scientifically inclined companion, her parents only able to indulge her superficially; Smith concluded it was "a remarkable instance of early ardour". Ironically, the only disappointment at Hafod was the botanising, with Smith observing just the "common plants of hilly not alpine countries, & not great variety of them".[25] He found a valuable correspondent in Mariamne, who sent him many letters in her large, carefully spaced hand; some letters still charmingly bear the pencilled guidelines, visible below the inked script. A strictly scientific correspondence, Mariamne frequently sent Smith insects and plant specimens, whilst he sent a filled insect cabinet. She politely declined the live tortoise Smith offered, "a thing that I have not the least desire to have".[26]

Before leaving on his trip, Smith had set in motion his removal from Great Marlborough Street. Though he had previously hinted to Davall of his desire to move from the centre of town, his intentions seem to have taken his other friends by surprise. Samuel Goodenough's thoughts leapt straight to the Linnean Society, which would now be turned "adrift", though in the same letter he also offered to enquire about a house he had seen for let in Hammersmith.[27] Woodward was less sympathetic, replying that Smith's absence would be "unpropitious to the Society". Assuming that the Society was not yet rich enough to hire rooms for its purposes, Woodward considered Smith's quitting of Great Marlborough Street a "serious inconvenience".[28] Promisingly, just as the Linnean Society was looking for new rooms, so was the Westminster Library; together they leased 10 Panton Square (the London Trocadero now stands on the site). Westminster Library was to take the ground floor, the Linnean Society the first, and the Library's Secretary Benjamin Price was to live in the property as caretaker and clerk to both institutions. With the proposal agreed, the Linnean Society was in place in time for the first meeting of the new session in October.

Smith completed his own move in late September, taking a house in Hammersmith just 50 yards from Lee and Kennedy's famous Vineyard nursery (amongst other introductions, it was the first in Britain to sell fuchsia). The Linnaean collections also moved with him, severing the unique link between the Linnean Society and the collections of its namesake. It was an ideal location for Smith, who made numerous additions to his herbarium from the nursery during his time in Hammersmith. The move did not go unnoticed. At least two newspapers reported "Dr Smith, the celebrated botanist, has retired from London; as it is said upon a pension, with her usual magnificence, granted by his pupil the Queen". The source of this false report is unknown. Smith did not comment on it, though Thomas Marsham was dismayed, fearing a malicious explanation for its appearance.[29]

I Shall Certainly Never More Be As I Was

Immediately after moving, Smith returned to Norwich to settle up further items of business. One such 'item', the successful resolution of which seems to have been a surprise even to himself, was his engagement. His intended bride was Pleasance Reeve, the same girl he had confessed his fondness for to Davall in 1790. At the time of the engagement, Smith was 35 and Pleasance 22; by his own account he had been prepared to be a life-long bachelor. Though he desired marriage he had harboured only "faint hopes that my ideas of it could ever be realized". Smith credited the successful match to his sister, Esther Anne, admitting that without her assistance he would never have known if he had a place in Pleasance's affections "nor have scarcely presumed to look for it". Smith was enamoured: his bride-to-be possessed "a very fine person, & an angelic countenance, which is the true picture of her delicate, feeling, & very intelligent mind—her tastes exactly accord with mine, my way of life & pursuits are precisely what she most admires & approves". Furthermore, she stood to inherit a "very pretty fortune", though necessity dictated that to begin with they would need to live economically, and they could not marry until at least March the following year, "for pecuniary reasons".[30] A little of her character can be sensed in a portrait by Cornish artist John Opie painted the following year, which certainly corroborates Smith's opinion of her looks. She is depicted as a gypsy reading her own palm, sitting under a darkening autumnal sky with a campfire in the distance, wearing a vivid orange cloak and an arch smile, her hair tousled.

For Davall, the news of Smith's engagement only served to highlight his own disappointments; long years of a chronic bowel complaint and social isolation in Switzerland had left him increasingly unwell in "both body & mind". He envied Smith the "foresight & wisdom" with which he was entering matrimony, wishing that he had acted with "more mature consideration" and married an Englishwoman.[31] Considering himself permanently exiled from England and Smith, he was tormented by the idea that his children were strangers in both the country of their birth and the country of their father. By the time of Smith's engagement, Davall's wife Henriette had given birth to five children: a daughter in 1790, who died a year later, a premature son in 1792 who died shortly after birth, a son, Edmund in 1793, a daughter in 1794, name unknown, and another son, Charles Edward, in 1795, named in honour of both Linnaeus and Smith. Davall's botanical work, an illustrated flora of Switzerland, had completely stalled, owing to a combination of his parental duties, the hostility of the Swiss botanists—who felt that the English Davall was infringing on their flora—and a ruinous legal dispute with his wife's brother.[32] Smith continued to encourage his friend, urging him to cut his losses and publish what he had so far completed. Sensing that praise no longer had an effect on a despondent Davall, Smith now scolded, complaining that Davall was "as bad" as Sibthorp, whose *Flora Græca* had been in development since 1785. Smith admitted that he was in a "similar predicament" with *Species Plantarum*, a new edition of which he had been promising since acquiring the Linnaean collections. Yet his time had not gone unoccupied, as he told Davall, "I do other things". He announced that he was now "going hard to work on a Flora Brittanica in Latin", a project in gestation since even before the Linnaean purchase![33] Davall, though, had already given up. The final despair came in the summer of 1794, when he discovered extensive, irretrievable damp throughout his herbarium specimens—a disaster for a botanist. It was a blow that nearly unbalanced Davall as he stated, "I shall certainly never more be as I was".[34] Smith was deeply concerned for Davall's state of mind, and without indulging his melancholy attempted to reassure him: "all feeling people suffer more than others, but they also enjoy more [...] whatever you do I am fated to love you the more".[35] Such platitudes no longer drew effusive responses from Davall, who had been broken down by too many sorrows, of which there were more to come. In March 1796, his surviving daughter died, aged 20 months. Davall hoped that if Smith was also "doomed to lose a beloved child may it be previous to its first dawn of intelligence, to its first expressions of attachment to you & its Mother!!".[36]

Smith sealed his own happiness, on 1 March 1796, when he and Pleasance married in Lowestoft, Suffolk. They returned to Hammersmith shortly afterwards, intending to honeymoon at Hafod later in the year. In their absence, the Linnaean collections had lost one of their component parts; on the very same day as their marriage, in King Street, Covent Garden, an auction of the "genuine and entire" Linnaean cabinet of minerals had begun. Over the course of two days, 243 lots were sold, including the very cabinet in which the collection had been contained.[37] No clear reason was given for the sale, though Smith's interest in mineralogy was cursory at best. Perhaps the prospect of moving the 2,424 specimens across London for a third time was too much for him to bear. Indeed, it appears as though they never came to Hammersmith at all. Prior to the sale William Babington, apothecary to Guy's Hospital and lecturer in chemistry for the medical school, and Dr Mitchill (possibly Smith's Leiden acquaintance) arranged the collection according to the most recent edition of *Systema Naturæ* at Guy's; the first day's lot no. 43 "was left by mistake at the Hospital". This suggests that from their arrival in 1784, Smith had not so much as glanced at the minerals. The final amount raised, £71 8s, confirmed Babington's bleak prognosis of the value of the collection: "it was indeed scarcely possible that it should be otherwise considering the worthless chaos of which the Linnean Cabinet consisted". Babington claimed that there was just one valuable specimen within the whole, which had been "so concealed by dust that had not the collection undergone individual examination it would probably have been overlooked". This was probably the first day's lot 101, "a large specimen of very rich auriferous pyrites" which sold for £3 10s, by far the highest price for a single item. Babington apologised to Smith, convinced that had he and Mitchill not catalogued the collection for auction there would have been "many who for the chance of a valuable discovery would have given more for your part than it now amounts to".[38] Smith had clearly been determined to raise as much money as possible. On hearing of his intention to sell, several Fellows of the Linnean Society had reacted with concern. Prior to the auction, Marsham asked Smith if he had set a price for the mineral collection, and whether he would be willing to sell it to the Society (though he feared there would not be sufficient funds).[39] No further communication on this subject was made, and the collection was dispersed. Though an annotated catalogue survives in the Linnean Society Library, unfortunately it includes only the prices realised and not the names of the purchasers, making it almost impossible to today trace the Linnaean minerals.

Good Letter, Good Paper and Showy Plates

This was the only part of the Linnaean collections that Smith sold. In fact he considerably augmented the entomological collection; as many of two-thirds of the insects in the present 'Linnaean' collection were added after Linnaeus's death, and in such a way that it is very difficult to differentiate between Smith's and Linnaeus's specimens.[40] Almost the entirety of Smith's scientific life was devoted to botany; of the 52 papers he published in the Linnean Society's *Transactions*, the only one that included any nod to entomology was his 'Introductory Discourse'. In fact, had Smith not published *The Natural History of the Rarer Lepidopterous Insects of Georgia* (1797), Smith's continued collecting of insects could almost be attributed to his general 'collectors' mentality' (he also collected letter seals and coins, part of a network of numismatists which included Thomas Woodward and Sophia Banks, sister

Black and Blue Admirable Butterfly (*Papilio Ursula*) and Green-Wooded Whortle-Berry (*Vaccineum stamineum*). From *The Rarer Lepidopterous Insects of Georgia* (1797).

of Sir Joseph). The work had been inspired by a set of entomological drawings and notes by John Abbot, an Englishman who spent his adult life delineating the flora and fauna of eastern North America. Abbot's drawings were particularly informative, including figures of the larvae, pupae and adult life stages of each insect, as well as the host plant of each species; most other entomological works of the period depicted only the adult. Smith thought the original drawings "were the most perfect things I ever saw". The details of its genesis are unclear; it seems as though either the jeweller John Francillon, Abbot's literary agent in London, or James Edwards, the publisher, approached Smith to edit the work, who was engaged on it since at least the latter part of 1794.

Corn Emperor Moth (*Phalæna io*) and Maize (*Zea mays*). From *The Rarer Lepidopterous Insects of Georgia.*

Just before publication, Smith revealed to Richard Pulteney that some of the plates figured well-known plants, and though he would have "substituted rarer ones" to increase its appeal, that selection process had been completed before he was even engaged with the project. It may have been the plants that first attracted Smith's attention, for there were several that were "quite new", and a few from Kew that had not yet been figured. Smith also had little involvement in the production, admitting that it "was more splendid than I w[oul]d have made it".[41]

The Natural History of the Rarer Lepidopterous Insects of Georgia was a ground-breaking publication: the first extensively illustrated monograph devoted to North American insects. In the preface, Smith identified himself as the editor, rather than the author—for "all such facts recorded in these pages the public are entirely obliged to Mr Abbot"—Smith humbly stating that he had only put it "into some sort of style and order". He identified himself as a botanist, citing expertise "in the principles of scientific arrangement" and the transferable tenets of Linnaeus's *Philosophia Botanica* as his qualifications for directing his attention to entomology. Containing 104 Lepidoptera (24 butterflies and 80 moths) in its two volumes, Smith provided the scientific names and descriptions for the butterflies, moths and plants figured, and presented his own remarks in a separate paragraph and typeface. Fifty-seven of the Lepidoptera were new species, of which 43 are still recognised today. Naturalist Adrian Haworth recognised the dual nature of the work in 1807, commenting: "we never before beheld the sister sciences walk so closely, and so engagingly hand in hand, as in this interesting volume. —It is truly a Flora et Entomologica".[42]

Smith dedicated the work to Mariamne Johnes, in memory of the many hours they had "passed together, in the practical application of similar objects to those which it illustrates, amid some of the noblest scenes of Nature".[43]

TO

MISS JOHNES,

OF HAFOD.

MY DEAR YOUNG FRIEND,

THE tribute of a dedication, at least of an honest dedication, is usually paid to established worth or pre-eminent knowledge; yet, as it is also sometimes permitted to breathe the effusions of affection alone, it may surely be allowed to combine those effusions with hope. When you look over this book, it will remind you of many hours we have paſsed together, in the practical investigation of similar objects to those which it illustrates, amid some of the noblest scenes of Nature; hours equally delightful to you and to me. To you they unfolded the exquisite perfection and endleſs variety of the creation; to me they displayed a youthful mind, affected and improved by the contemplation of such objects as the God of Nature intended it should be. May that mind never be less ingenuous, leſs ardent in the pursuit of truth and virtue, nor leſs affectionate to all who endeavoured to inform and direct it, than I then beheld it! Such is the sincere, the ardent prayer of,

My dear young friend.

Your most affectionate,

And faithful servant,

LONDON,
May 29, 1797.

J. E. SMITH.

Dedication of Smith and John Abbot's *The Rarer Lepidoterous Insects of Georgia* to Mariamne Johnes.

On publication, William Jones, whose collections had assisted Smith with some of his identifications remarked that it had "the three great requisites to a modern publication—good letter, good paper and showy plates".[44] Others were less encouraging. Completing work on *Insects of Georgia* and his continued commitment to *English Botany* inevitably led to even further delays for his long projected works, particularly *Flora Britannica*. Since announcing this work it had been much looked for by his botanically inclined friends, who feared that Smith had "so many irons in the fire" it would never proceed to a conclusion. His progress was eagerly watched: in May 1796 Thomas Woodward reported to Dawson Turner, a Yarmouth banker and botanist, that Smith had now "got amongst the grasses" but was stuck "fast in the genus *Agrostis*", a labyrinth from which Smith was finding it difficult to emerge. Woodward speculated: "I do not suppose it can be completed in less than two or three years".[45]

A Perfect Lounge

The move from Great Marlborough Street, and the removal of the President and the Linnaean collections, precipitated one of the biggest crises yet encountered by the Linnean Society. From having presided at almost every meeting since its foundation, Smith was now an itinerant President at best. Of the ten Fellows' meetings during 1795–1796, he attended only five, with a similarly low attendance recorded at the General Meetings. Aware of the need to formalise a solution—he usually called on Jonas Dryander to preside in his absence—he proposed the appointment of four vice-presidents, the eldest present presiding if required. The motion was approved, and Smith selected Jonas Dryander, Aylmer Bourke Lambert, Thomas Martyn and George Shaw as his vice-presidents. At the same time, Dryander resigned as librarian, and was replaced by Alexander Macleay, an entomologist and Chief Clerk at the Prisoners of War Department.

Any security established by such a motion was nevertheless quickly dashed by Smith's decision in the summer of 1796 to leave Hammersmith, and London, altogether, and return to his hometown of Norwich.[46] Shocked, Goodenough rode straight to Smith's house, only to find that Smith and Pleasance had left for their 'honeymoon' trip to Hafod the previous day. He received all the confirmation needed from Smith's servant and the notice advertising that the house was to be let directly. Immediately, he mourned for both Smith and the Linnean Society, convinced that at such a distance Smith would be "buried alive", fatally absent from the interchange of ideas and information that had made the Society such a vital conduit of scientific exchange. Recognising Smith's eminent position as one of the principal botanists in the country, Goodenough reminded him "how necessary it is, that he who would reign over many, must be perpetually contending with many". At Norwich, Smith would have nobody to question his scientific authority, and if Smith "once settled in any error [...] you will continue in it".[47] In an attempt to subvert these oppositions, Smith had proposed spending nine months of the year in Norwich and three in London, in order to fulfil his Presidential duties and give his lectures at Guy's Hospital. Goodenough thought the ratio was ridiculously insufficient and begged him to reverse it, but the newly married Smith held fast—establishing a balanced public and private life, which was impossible in London, had to take precedence. The move was also imperative for his health, which was threatened every summer by the bad London air. Goodenough was personally upset at the prospect of losing one of his closest and most like-minded friends, an individual whom he credited with sparking a botanical revolution. He feared Smith's departure would begin a cooling down period in botanical study. He wrote imploringly, "it was the easiness & freedom of access to you which prompted many a tardy spirit to activity". Fearing the 'cooling' would extend to the scientific exchanges within the Society itself, he expounded, "I do not know any common event which would make me grieve so much as the failure of that".[48]

The announcement drove Thomas Marsham to despair; since the Society's foundation in 1788, he had provided the continuous stability that such a society, particularly in its fledgling years, desperately needed. Marsham had a considerable personal stake in the continued success of the Society, in an entirely different way to either Smith or Goodenough. They had established names and intellectual niches for themselves outside of the Society's meeting room, but for Marsham it was his only outlet from his decidedly unscientific work at the Exchequer Loan Office. Smith's departure also meant that Marsham would be the only principal officer and founding member still resident within London (Goodenough, despite his criticisms, lived in Ealing and could never guarantee regular attendance at the Society). In a raging letter to Smith, Marsham revealed that for the past eight years he had continuously put off his own private engagements in deference to Linnean Society business, which had entailed many "disagreeable things". By way of example, he outlined that at the final Fellows' meeting of 1795–1796, "neither President, Vice Presidents or Treasurer & but two Members" — besides Marsham himself — had been in attendance. The tirade continued:

> The Fellows are almost £100 in arrears, and when I apply [to them for payment] I give offence. The rules are not kept to, the Museum in a state of confusion, no one knows what is in it — the volume of Transactions, two years in the press when two months ought to finish it — in short the whole system is so completely relaxed that as a Society it is not worth attention. It is become a perfect lounge once a month for a few persons & I am now so fully persuaded that it will grow worse & worse on your quitting London, that I am determined not to witness its disgrace.[49]

Marsham considered the Society to be Smith's progeny (though both he and Goodenough had a good claim to its paternity), and "grieved to see the Father leave his Child to be supplanted by aliens & strangers".[50] With his usual clarity, Goodenough recognised that Marsham's continued "cordiality will be as necessary to the welfare of the Society as any one's", and took the helm in ensuring the continued support of the Society during the President's long absences in Norwich. It was agreed that Dryander would become a fixed Vice President, presiding whenever Smith was away, thus solving any issues of discontinuity whilst tempering Marsham's sense of betrayal.[51]

With the leadership crisis over, Smith and Pleasance moved to Norwich in November 1796, taking up residence in a house owned by Pleasance's father. 29 Surrey Street, with its three and a half storeys, possessed "great elbow room", and was considerably more spacious than the Hammersmith house.

No. 29 Surrey Street, Norwich; Smith and Pleasance's home from 1796 until his death.

It also included a sizeable garden. The large study had been arranged for maximum scholarly efficiency, with Smith's books, insect and shell cabinets lining the walls, and an adjoining "large light closet" for his plants.[52] Just over a year after moving, he told Davall "I every day rejoice that I am come here". His health had vastly improved, and he was also extremely content in his marriage, Pleasance providing the emotional support that he had previously relied on friends for. Indeed, from the date of his marriage, there was a marked reduction in the number of letters from Smith to Davall, with none at all being sent in 1797. Conversely, Davall's own marriage and growing family had only served to increase his attachment to Smith. Almost two years on from their wedding day, Smith and Pleasance as yet had no children, nor did he "anxiously wish for any".[53] This is surprising, as it is well documented that he enjoyed an easy familiarity with children, Mariamne Johnes being the most recent case in point. In 1799, a friend of Pleasance's, Lady Hannah East, having spent the day with Pleasance, observed "that Mrs Reeve will soon [...]

experience the joy of being a grandmother—is it not so?"[54] The answer was decidedly not so, with Pleasance informing her friend of their happily childless state, and pointedly preventing any further speculation.[55]

The uninterrupted hours at Norwich allowed Smith to go on rapidly with the two principal works that he now had in hand, the continuing *English Botany* and the considerably more complicated *Flora Britannica*. In March 1798, Smith was able to report that he had now emerged from the "very troublesome" grasses, and had also recently completed the fourth Linnaean class Tetandria though he could not describe more than five plants in a single day.[56] In April of the same year, Smith and Sowerby decided to double *English Botany* again and publish 12 plants every month. Smith was glad of the change: "it will double my profit & labour, but I run no risque".[57] His profit was to increase two-fold again the following year, when Sowerby proposed that Smith's payment per description be raised from half a guinea to a full guinea from plate 618 onwards, a sure indication of the continued financial success of the work, meaning that Smith was now paid 12 guineas per issue of contributions.[58] The move from London naturally had an impact upon their working relationship. Regular parcels were now sent between Norwich and Sowerby's London home at 2 Mead Place in Lambeth, containing specimens, drawings and the finished engravings for Smith's descriptions and final approval. It was not uncommon for these to be returned with the author's remarks scribbled in the margins. A temporarily misplaced parcel in early 1799 infuriated Smith: "your man deserves to be well scolded, for it was an abominably careless trick. Young people & servants cannot be made too careful about parcels & letters. It put me to no small anxiety & inconvenience".[59] Smith was also critical of some of Sowerby's production techniques. The partially colour printed plates (as opposed to fully hand-painted ones) for *Conferva villosa* and *Conferva byssoides* were "too pale a colour—I have a great dislike to printing in colours at all, or at least it ought to be done in a darker rather than paler hue than nature, because the eye is used to see[ing] black lines in a plate & to make allowance for it".[60] Smith could also be condescending; after multiple errors occurred in volume seven, he asked that everything Sowerby sent him in the future be looked over by at least two people beforehand.[61]

Smith returned to London for the first time in the spring of 1797, five months after leaving for Norwich. Having initially planned to attend the Linnean Society meetings of 7 and 21 March, at the end of February he requested Dryander to preside in his stead, and he eventually arrived for the General Meeting on 4 April.[62] More than a month later, at the Anniversary Meeting of 24 May, he received an incontrovertible sanction of his decision to leave London when he was again elected President. (Smith would continue to be elected annually until 1828.) He also gave his course of lectures at Guy's Hospital, and this, combined with his Linnean duties, provided ample proof that he had been right to leave. He complained to Richard Pulteney "the hurries & interruptions of this busy town are such that one has little time for study".[63] In fact, the lectures proved such a strain that at the end of the course he gave up the lectureship, to be succeeded by his physician friend Robert John Thornton.

Thornton was also a botanical author, who, in early 1797, announced a monumental, ultimately ill-fated, publication called *New Illustration of the Sexual System of Linnaeus* (1799–1807). The work was composed of three distinct sections: Linnaeus's 1759 prize dissertation on the sexes of plants; 'A full explanation of the classes, and orders, of the sexual system', with 91 botanical plates and 26 portraits of eminent botanists and patrons of the science; and the 'The Temple of Flora', with 31 plates of imaginatively realised plants, often placed in romantic settings. As well as an homage to Linnaeus, it was also to be a monument to British artistry and printing skill; Thornton hoped to "to surpass in his Plates and Type all botanical works which have hitherto appeared".[64] The final product was a curious mixture of science, poetry and art, and both the work and its author received an unfavourable reception.

At Smith's instigation, Thornton was proposed a Fellow of the Linnean Society. His election took place on 18 July (by which time Smith had returned to Norwich), at a particularly full meeting of 18 Fellows, on account of a controversial amendment to the rules for the appointment of Honorary Fellows. At the election, Thornton's name was rejected with three blackballs on the grounds of his being "a Quack in Botany as well as in medicine", as well as his audacious presumption in already listing himself as an FLS in an announcement for *New Illustration*, "as if his Election were a mere matter of course".[65] Thomas Martyn was mortified at having witnessed the rejection first hand, though he admitted that Thornton's scientific endeavours were not "exactly in the train" of either Smith's or his own. He also suspected the malign influence of Sir Joseph Banks, having observed "a strong tendency in Soho Square to throw a ridicule on all persons and proceedings except a certain set".[66] Smith was disappointed, and a little admonished, having "really believe[d] him to be a deserving man, or I w[oul]d not have promoted his recommendation—but I will never urge the Soc[iet]y on any such subject".[67] Jonas Dryander, out of respect for the President, had not voted against Thornton, but he did not hide his joy at the rejection of the "great Charlatan".[68] The feeling against Thornton was so strong that it was later revealed that had his nomination been more widely known even more would have attended solely to contribute further blackballs.[69]

Though he was not proposed again, Thornton remained grateful for Smith's patronage and support. In 1800 he featured Smith's portrait in an ostentatious segment of *New Illustration* titled: "Select Portraits of Living Botanists, or But Lately Deceased; —The Brightest Ornaments of their Respective Countries, and the Age in which we live", part of an illustrious roster that included Rousseau, Thomas Martyn, the Earl of Bute and Sir Joseph Banks. Smith sent a copy of the portrait to Dawson Turner, commenting, "some people think it a likeness, others not—it is smug & dapper enough".[70] Presented as President and Founder of the Linnean Society and looking considerably less than his 40 years, Smith's image appears above a fanciful depiction of the fictitious naval chase that supposedly followed the purchase of the Linnaean collections.[71]

In creating *New Illustration*, Thornton had spectacularly overreached himself. The work was chaotically produced and sold poorly, ruining its author. In 1811 a lottery was held in an attempt to recoup some of his losses, but even this failed. Nevertheless, he succeeded in producing some of the most extraordinary botanical prints ever created, though love of a dramatic composition often resulted in inaccuracies. It remains one of the most curious and impressive botanical productions ever created.

The Return of Smith the Physic

On their visit to Hafod in the summer of 1796, Smith and Pleasance had been shocked to find Mariamne Johnes a shadow of her former self, suffering from a "diseased spine", possibly scoliosis, which had left her lame.[72] The timing of their trip was fortuitous, with Smith recommending what he considered the best course of treatment. After reports of improving health throughout the winter, Mariamne relapsed in the spring of 1797. The family decamped to Bath in hopes of bringing respite, but by the autumn Johnes implored Smith to come to Hafod to personally attend to Mariamne.[73] Arriving in the pouring rain on the evening of 24 October, Smith was greeted by a grateful Johnes who immediately led him "by the hand" to Mariamne's dressing room, where he found his "dear little patient [...] much better" than expected. For the greater part of a year she had been strapped into a specially made spinal brace, referred to as the "machine", to apparently good effect.[74] His principle prescription seems to have been to "leave off much of the physic [medicinal drugs]" she had previously been taking, and by the end of November 1797 friends were congratulating him on having been the "means of restoring health to a beloved Daughter of a beloved Friend".[75] Smith was recalled to Hafod again the following spring, Mariamne experiencing another relapse. Though her spine was better she was still lame, and Smith diagnosed a "lumbar abcess [...] formed deep in the loins, the matter of which migrated its way down among the muscles of the thigh". Surprised that her regular physician had not identified it, Smith prescribed an incision to let out the 'matter'; such a course ran the risk of inflammation but he was confident she would walk "as well as ever" once recovered.[76] It is not recorded whether the operation took place, but Mariamne continued through the summer in discomfort, unable to walk even with the aid of her machine and stays. Towards the end of 1798 her father reported that she was doing "vastly well" and improving daily, and by mid-1799 she was walking without crutches and singing for the first time in two years.[77]

Smith revived his correspondence with Mariamne in 1804, when she was 19 years old. Though she was now attending operas and the usual round of amusements of London's social season, she still held her interest in botany. Mariamne was delighted by Smith's description of "the real study of Botany", having often regretted "that so many People have made that Charming science to consist in a long catalogue of names & Classes, instead of directing the mind to discover the affinity Plants bear to each other and their medicinal virtues".[78] Mariamne remained in good health as she entered her twenties, but the Johnes family had little to look forward to in the coming years. In 1807, the house at Hafod, including its library, was destroyed by fire. The house was rebuilt by 1810 but Johnes's extravagant habit of collecting had crippled his estate. On 10 June 1811, Johnes reported that Mariamne was "exceedingly ill", diagnosed with a strong nervous affliction that would require a long recovery. Mariamne died on 4 July, aged 27. Her death destroyed Johnes: he died of heart failure less than five years later, on 23 April 1816.

The Father They Have Lost

Further afield, but closer to Smith's heart, another friend lay in the throes of a debilitating condition. At the end of 1797 Smith received a letter from veterinarian Bracy Clark, then engaged in a tour of the continent, informing him that Edmund Davall had been suffering intensely from "a paralytic affliction".[79] Smith had not heard from Davall since his letter of 18 September 1796, and he himself had not written since 2 November that same year. He now wrote, full of apologies and anxiety, urging his friend to "unburthen your mind to me. Your communications shall be most sacred".[80] The receipt of Smith's letter had an extraordinary effect on Davall, kindling "a latent spark" in his old friend, who started writing about his litany of tribulations: "my health totally destroyed, my intellect in some degree affected & even my faculty of speech sensibly impaired at the premature age of 35 [...] afflicted with one of the most cruel disorders incident to humans". Davall was suffering from severe epilepsy.[81]

Smith was not to receive this missive till after Davall's death; his wife, Henriette, sent her own letter to Smith on the same day, informing him of Davall's letter but explaining that he had been too weak to finish it in one sitting, though was hoping to do so in stages. Henriette urgently requested Smith's medical advice. Davall's physician thought that his ills could be traced back to his persistent constipation and the taking of too many purgatives. Henriette thought that her husband had irretrievably exhausted himself from a combination of gruelling botanical expeditions in the mountains, establishing his garden and studying his herbarium. Preceded by crippling headaches, twice during the autumn of 1796 he had fits in his sleep, "which only became evident by the bite-marks on his tongue". After completing an exhausting two month project to put his mosses in order, on 2 February 1797 he suffered "three bouts of apoplexy in 24 hours", saved only by "severe bloodletting, violent purgatives, vesication [blistering] of his left arm and right leg", leaving him so weakened that his convulsions often left him unconscious. He was now on a self-imposed milk diet.[82]

Smith diagnosed "debility" as the prevailing feature of Davall's disorder, and, scorning the milk diet, instead advised "plain light meals" and prescribed Peruvian bark taken in peppermint tea. He prohibited any further bloodletting, suspecting that Davall had taken "too much physic [medicinal drugs]" from an overly enthusiastic doctor.[83] On 19 March 1798, Bracy Clark arrived back in Orbe, who reported that Davall's health was "on the whole greater than it has been", though still very changeable.[84] With growing optimism, by 10 July, Clark was able to report only one "partial attack" in the last 13 weeks, though Henriette, just a week later, gave a very different account.[85] The "partial attack" that Clark described had resulted in another round of bleeding, leaving Davall in a "state of nervous instability" and without the use of his right arm. Clark had prescribed opium to ease Davall's facial convulsions, but after 18 days Henriette forced him to stop. He was now weak, thin, and "absolutely demoralised"; he spoke only of Smith, it being his greatest wish to see his friend once more.[86]

On 26 September, at 9 o'clock in the evening, having been in an insensible sleep all day, Davall passed away, just as the apothecary was applying mustard plasters to his feet. He had been confined to his bed for the last three weeks, some days "extremely low & exhausted" and others so much better that they could almost hope for a recovery.[87] Henriette was devastated. She asked Smith, as soon as possible, to send her a specimen of *Davallia* (Smith named this fern genus for Davall in 1793), with a label written in his own hand, so as to have "the consolation of showing it to my children and thus introducing them soon to the father they have lost".

Davall left his herbarium to Smith; Henriette enclosed in the cabinet her husband's copy of Haller's *Nomenclator ex Historia Plantarum Indigenarum Helvetiæ* (1769), his principal guide to the Swiss flora. She also returned all the letters that Smith had ever sent him. Davall's extensive botanical library, formed at such ruinous expense to his patrimony, was also to be sold to help support the family. Bracy Clark made a catalogue before his departure, and Henriette asked Smith to be her adviser should anyone make an offer.[88]

Smith's reaction to Davall's death is entirely unknown; the correspondence is silent on the matter, which implies that only the two men, and latterly their wives, knew the true intensity of their friendship. Smith, sequestered in Norwich, could mourn in private for the loss of this very particular friend. Davall's bequest arrived several years later in November 1802, when the short-lived Treaty of Amiens allowed the bulky cargo to be safely transported from Switzerland. On receiving the plants, Smith recorded how his heart sank to see "the relicks of my beloved friend Davall, who languished to see me in Switzerland".[89] The library followed in its wake, to be sold at auction in London across three days, beginning on 17 June 1803.[90] Smith attended and spent £70, though was sorry to see it go "very cheap" on the whole, the books generally selling for half their full price. He feared that Henriette would "hardly save £480", even after he had done his best to give "a lift to many books to prevent them going too cheap". He bought the exceedingly rare *Plantarum Historia* (1592) and *Lyncei Minus Cognitarum Stirpium et Purpura* (1616) of Fabius Columna for just 17s 6d, confident he could get 5 guineas for the pair for the family's benefit.[91]

Smith incorporated Davall's herbarium into his own, enriching it by around 4,400 specimens. A new moss was found among the many unidentified plants, which, in a further tribute, Smith named *Gymnostomum davallianum* (now *Microbryum davallianum*).[92] *Davallia,* also named for his friend, has lived on and now comprises 40 species.

CHAPTER NINE

The *Floras*

Despite the concerns of Samuel Goodenough and Thomas Marsham over the future of the Linnean Society following Smith's departure from London, it in fact enjoyed a modest revival of fortunes. By the end of 1798, Thomas Marsham happily reported that General Meetings now never met with fewer than 30 Fellows. The end of his service as Linnean Society Secretary at that year's Anniversary Meeting may have also helped to boost his mood.[1] Marsham replaced Samuel Goodenough as Treasurer, who had resigned following his appointment as a canon of St George's Chapel, Windsor, and Alexander Macleay became the new Secretary. Publication of the *Transactions* had also been brought under a certain degree of control, though Macleay was convinced that they needed to give up the idea of publishing every year, and there were still occasional lapses in the provision of new papers for meetings.[2] By the turn of the century, a volume was appearing every two to three years. At the same time, it had become clear that the Society's constitution needed to be formalised to ensure its longevity. It was decided at the Anniversary Meeting of 1800 that "it would be desirable to obtain a [Royal] Charter", for which purpose Smith was dispatched to consult Sir Joseph Banks on the matter.[3] Banks confirmed that the Society's application for a charter would not only be "proper, [...] [but] in all probabilities would be favourably received".[4] The cost, projected at £300, was to be raised by a Fellows' subscription.[5] Macleay was confident that the Fellowship would help them reach the requisite sum, but admitted there were "many perverse souls among us who will not give a farthing", including Erasmus Darwin, who, living so far from London, was "in no ways interested about the Society". Much to Macleay's surprise, George Shaw (one of the Vice Presidents), also objected, on the grounds that there were "as respectable Societies without Charters as any that have them". The reality, however, was that without a Charter and the accompanying Deed of Trust, the bonds that Fellows signed on admission guaranteeing payment of dues were worthless.[6] Macleay appears to have been the driving influence in this arduous endeavour. By March 1802, with only the final endorsement of the King's Great Seal remaining, he remarked to Smith "the trouble which has attended it is inconceivable".[7] In faraway Norwich, with intermittent good health, there was little Smith could contribute, and in fact he almost became a hindrance in proceedings. Early during the process for gaining the charter, several unnamed Fellows, and possibly even Sir Joseph Banks, expressed fears that the King would refuse to sanction it if he observed Smith's name and recollected the offence *A Sketch of a Tour* had given at Frogmore. Macleay was moved to reassure Smith that this suggestion was "so absurd that no attention was paid to it" and that he stood "as high in the opinion of the Society at large as you ever did".[8] Smith wrote to Macleay at Christmas 1801, thanking him for his dedication and warning him "to expect a visit from a countryman of mine on Sunday the 20th. I hope he will prove a jolly fellow". Smith's 'countryman' was a Norfolk turkey, and Macleay joined an exclusive list of other friends so honoured, including Sir Joseph Banks and James Sowerby.[9]

The charter was granted on 26 March 1802, beginning a new epoch in the Society's history. In a succession of nine meetings in as many days, the Society was completely overhauled, with the introduction of official byelaws to replace the rules. Amongst other introductions such as limiting the number of Foreign Members to 50, perhaps the most significant change was the appointment of the first Linnean Society Council. This was formed of the 15 Fellows listed on the charter, who from now on would represent the interests of the Fellows, with a turnover of five at each Anniversary Meeting election. The Society also acquired a crest, based on Linnaeus's own from his ennoblement in 1761, and the motto *Naturæ discere mores* ("to learn the ways of Nature").

An Additional Leaf to Your Wreath

Following the death of Francesco Borone in Athens in October 1794, John Sibthorp continued his botanical expedition across the Hellenic region, accompanied part of the way by John Hawkins. Sibthorp departed for England in May 1795 but endured an arduous journey by sea from Greece to Italy and thereafter by land, arriving back home in July. His health was shattered. Writing to Smith in October, he stated that he had been very ill, suffering from a low fever and cough that hinted of "some affectation of the lungs". "The unconquerable disease", possibly tuberculosis, continued to advance unchecked, and Sibthorp died at Bath on 8 February 1796, and was buried at the Abbey, leaving his great work, *Flora Græca*, unfinished.[10]

Frontispiece for volume three of John Sibthorp's *Flora Græca* (1806–1840), depicting Mount Olympus. Published 1819.

Flora Græca, a stunning reference work encompassing all the then-known botanical species of the Hellenic region, would go on to become one of the most magnificent botanical productions ever undertaken, but its appearance before the public was tortuously slow. In full expectation of his untimely death, Sibthorp had drawn up his will specifically to ensure its publication after his decease, bequeathing one of his Oxfordshire estates to Oxford University, the revenues of which were to pay for the remaining work. Once the work was complete, the receipts from the estate were to be used to establish a Professorship of Rural Economy.[11] *Flora Græca* (1806–1840) was to comprise 10 folio (12″ x 19″) volumes, each containing 100 hand coloured plates, limited to 50 sets. There was also to be a *Prodromus Floræ Græcæ* (1806-1816), a smaller octavo (6″ x 9″) without plates. The huge scale of the operation meant that each volume of *Flora Græca* was split into two parts of 50 plates each, to reduce the time interval between appearances and to bring in a little more money to fund the remainder.

The executors, charged with overseeing the production and administration of the publication, were Sibthorp's travelling companion John Hawkins, solicitor Thomas Platt and Francis Wenman, Regius Professor of Civil Law at Oxford, who survived Sibthorp by only two months. Hawkins was still travelling in the Levant when Sibthorp died in early 1796, and did not return to Britain until the end of 1798; nearly three years passed before any work was undertaken to enact Sibthorpe's will. In early 1799, Smith was selected for the prestigious task of editing the work. The choice was an obvious one: Smith had not just been a personal friend of Sibthorp, but was also one of the most visible and prolific young botanists then working in Britain. Furthermore, with *English Botany* he had proven his stamina in committing to a long running serial. His skill and patience in identifying, clarifying and correcting synonyms from pre-Linnaean sources would prove to be essential in navigating the chaos in which Sibthorp had left his materials. Furthermore, Smith's own travels through the south of France and Italy had acquainted him with the aspects and habitats of the Mediterranean flora. For Smith, editing such a work would bring great recognition, in addition to an annual salary of £150. Combined with his earnings from *English Botany*, this gave him a guaranteed income of around £300 a year, not including any fees from other publications or lectures he might choose to produce.

Smith's appointment was well received in the botanical community. Thomas Woodward commented that through his capable hands the work would "come out with more credit to Sibthorpe, than it could have done in the hands of any other editor […] as to yourself it will only add an additional leaf to your wreath already sufficiently full".[12] The engineer Davies Giddy—later to become President of the Royal Society as Davies Gilbert—was a more impartial observer and a friend of Sibthorp's, who claimed to be "extremely happy" about the selection.[13] On 16 May 1799, executors Hawkins and Platt authorised Smith to take possession of "all the materials which he requires for the completion & publication of Dr. John Sibthorp's Flora Graeca".[14] Consisting of Sibthorp's herbarium specimens, his diaries, field notes and an incomplete manuscript for the *Prodromus*, Smith also received Ferdinand Bauer's line drawings and watercolours of the collected plants and other materials relating to the Greek expeditions. It was immediately obvious that Sibthorp's collections had been left in a greater state of disarray than first feared. The biggest obstacle to overcome was also the most essential: identifying the very plants that were to be the basis of the work. Sibthorp had not affixed any names to his specimens, having preferred to rely on his "perfect knowledge of them", but Hawkins was confident that Smith would have little difficulty in identifying them. Hawkins offered his own assistance in deciphering the "vulgar Greek names" for plants and locations, and provided information on the parts of the collection he had assisted Sibthorp in gathering.[15]

By early 1800, Smith had finished organising the plants, though he had become convinced that specimens were missing; Hawkins believed that the specimens had rather been mislaid than lost. Sibthorp usually collected up to four specimens each of uncommon species, and Sir Joseph Banks had also received duplicates. The issue appeared to be the garbled manner of the journals and field notes. Owing to the profusion of new and rare plants being described, confusion lay in "supposed new Species prov[ing] perhaps on farther investigation to be old and some of the supposed old, new, while the old too are mistaken one for the other".[16] In a letter to Dryander, Smith confirmed that the greatest difficulty was to "decypher & digest" Sibthorp's manuscripts and a further update almost a year later showed little improvement.[17] Smith revealed that Sibthorp's writing, having proved "so execrable & his manuscripts […] so confused", had forced him to rework everything into his own wording before he could even begin work on the publication proper. "I am sometimes out of patience", he sighed, "at such unnecessary impediments".[18] Time was of the essence, even in such a grand and extensive project as the *Flora Græca*. The University of Oxford was eager for funds to be freed up in order to appoint a professor of rural economy, and for Sibthorp's new plants to have any taxonomic authority they needed to be published. In the 14 years since Sibthorp's first expedition other botanical authors had since published many of his discoveries. Smith received considerable support from Soho Square; early in 1800, Dryander pulled out all of Sibthorp's duplicate specimens from Banks's herbarium in order to assist identification.[19]

As editor, Smith was able to exert a limited, but effective, amount of pressure on the executors regarding various aspects of the works. Only with difficulty did Smith receive permission to call it *Flora Græca* rather than the incorrect *Flora Græcia*, as it was spelt in the will.[20] Of much more import was the influence Smith exerted in having James Sowerby chosen as the engraver and colourer for *Flora Græca*. With an anticipated print run of 50 sets (each set containing 10 volumes and 1,000 plates) a potential 50,000 engravings would need to be hand coloured, an endeavour both time consuming and costly. The executors initially wanted to offer the position to Ferdinand Bauer, the artist who had accompanied Sibthorp on the first Greek expedition. However, a combination of dithering on the part of the executors and the project's huge time commitment eventually dissuaded Bauer, who did not want to sacrifice his "liberty" for what he felt was "so tedious a work".[21] The project was proposed to Sowerby in January 1800, who immediately declined, but by October Smith had convinced both the executors and Sowerby to accept a trial period. Sowerby was an ideal choice: the continued success of *English Botany*, proved that he already had the skills, experience and, most importantly, the capacity to commit to such an audacious enterprise. However, as Smith remarked on receiving the results of the trial, there were some important differences: "you know I shall not flatter, but on the contrary it is my business in this stage of the business between you & I to find all the fault I can". He was "highly pleased with the Greek plants", but warned against too strongly engraving or etching the outline as there were to be so few impressions, something he had sometimes "found fault with in E[nglish] Bot[any]". On the whole he thought "the performance admirable & worthy" of Sowerby, and did not doubt the executors' approving.[22] Smith sincerely thought that Sowerby "would execute it better than any one else", but with Hawkins and Platt suspicious of Smith's partiality to his long-time collaborator, he later revealed that he felt it better to be cautious.[23] Needless to say, Sowerby was given the commission, though tensions were evident between Sowerby and the executors. On receipt of the first parcel of Bauer's original drawings back into his care, Smith was alarmed to see "many of these drawings dirtied, wafers at the back, &c—the exec[uto]rs will not like it—I hope you can clean and furbish them up when you have quite done with them".[24] As predicted, Hawkins leapt on the perceived damage, complaining to Smith of "the miserable state" in which Bauer's drawings had been returned: "Surely there is no occasion for this negligence and it may be avoided! Does Mr S[owerby] think that when the flora is published the drawings will be of no further use?".[25] Platt, who administered the foundation's money, also had concerns, believing that Sowerby was not progressing quickly enough.[26] For Smith, too, time was an issue. Even with the luxury of his relative isolation in Norwich, the work soon became a burden. His letters frequently contained references to the work; often it delayed his coming to London. There are also many hints of exasperation at the difficulty of the project, which Smith blamed on "Sibthorp's want of care & regularity".[27] Yet, in her *Memoir and Correspondence*, Pleasance Smith claimed that the compilation of this work afforded her husband a "peculiar pleasure", a work "to which he returned with impatience after any pause in its progress".[28] Once finally underway, Smith does seem to have derived a certain satisfaction from bringing order out of chaos. In 1805, as work on the first part of *Prodromus Floræ Græcæ* drew to a close, he revealed that he was now devoting every morning to it. "It is indeed, though a labour, so pleasant", he wrote, "that I sit down to it with eagerness by about 9 o'clock, & am sorry when I am called to dinner at 3".[29]

On 23 February 1801, Smith confidently reported to Linnean Society secretary Alexander Macleay that he would have the first half volume, or

Sempervivum arboretum, a synonym of *Aeonium arboretum*, the tree aeonium, or Irish rose. From John Sibthorp's *Flora Græca*.

perhaps even the entire first volume of *Flora Græca*, ready for the press by the end of April.[30] As it turned out, even the first half alone was not to appear to the public for another five years, until 1806 – a considerable lapse. The issue, again, was the huge scale of the endeavour. The physical production of the book was entirely dependent on the rents received from Sibthorp's estate. The production was so lavish that it cost £620 to produce each set, with the shortfall from the £254 subscription made up from the estate. At such a high price, it was only able to attract the wealthiest and most privileged subscribers, 25 in total, just half of the anticipated 50. Fluctuating receipts from the Oxfordshire estate resulted in a decidedly inconsistent publication schedule for both *Flora Græca* and *Prodromus Floræ Græcæ*. Significantly, this also had an impact on Smith and Sowerby's salaries; at the beginning of 1805 Smith complained that Platt had been unable to pay him the £75 then due, and at the end of that same year Platt again deferred payment. Smith could have no more until the work was published and began bringing in money.[31] By also delaying payment to Sowerby, Smith was doubly deprived of his dues, Sowerby in theory using a proportion of the money to pay Smith for his *English Botany* descriptions.[32]

Flora Britannica

That *Flora Græca* was produced at all came down to providential timing. The materials arrived just as Smith was finishing the first two volumes of his other masterwork, *Flora Britannica*. Interest in this highly anticipated work was high. Smith, through announcements in his paper 'Observations on the British Species of Bromus, with Introductory Remarks on the Composition of a Flora Britannica' (published in the fourth volume of *Linnean Transactions* in 1798) gave a potted history of English botanical writing. Starting with John Ray, whom he referred to as "the fountain-head of authority", he continued through to William Hudson, author of the first Linnaean flora of England. From the work of these pioneers descended the regional and national floras of men such as John Lightfoot, John Sibthorp and William Withering. Yet, despite this heritage, Smith identified that "a great mass of error" had been accumulating. Hudson, wrote Smith, had often applied "a Linnaean name to a plant, because Linnaeus has quoted Ray for it, or because Haller, or Scopoli perhaps, has referred to Ray and Linnaeus, while [in reality] all three may chance to have intended a different species". Through intensive study of the Linnaean, Banksian, Oxford and British Museum herbaria, and an exhaustive bibliographic search, Smith's intention was to "bring the synonyms nearer to perfection". His work, and subsequent paper on the grass genus *Bromus,* would support the need for this "careful investigation of the old herbariums, the errors in authors being so great and unaccountable as could not be believed".[33] In other words, for the British botanical community, *Flora Britannica* was an overdue and essential undertaking.

Four unillustrated volumes were planned, in which Smith was to delineate the entirety of the known British flora. Printing of the first two volumes, covering the first 19 of Linnaeus's 24 classes, commenced around October 1799. The descriptions, including details of flowering time, were written in simple Latin, whilst concise details of the species distribution were given in English. The simplicity of the work was reflected in the title; as opposed to many botanical works of the period, *Flora Britannica* was not part of a much longer title. The work's motto, taken from Horace, was abundantly clear: "*Nullius addictus jurare in verba magistri*"; "I am not bound to swear allegiance to the word of any master". Though Smith was intent on correcting the repeated errors of the past, he belied his motto in his almost total commitment "to follow in the footsteps of Linnaeus". Smith had "not yet felt that today's changes to botanical science have contributed anything to Linnaeus's perfect system, so clearly a work of art", but did include certain "reforms to the genera of mosses, which overbearing necessity has demanded".[34]

The first two volumes were published early in May 1800 and dedicated to Sir Joseph Banks, the second time Smith had so honored his early patron.

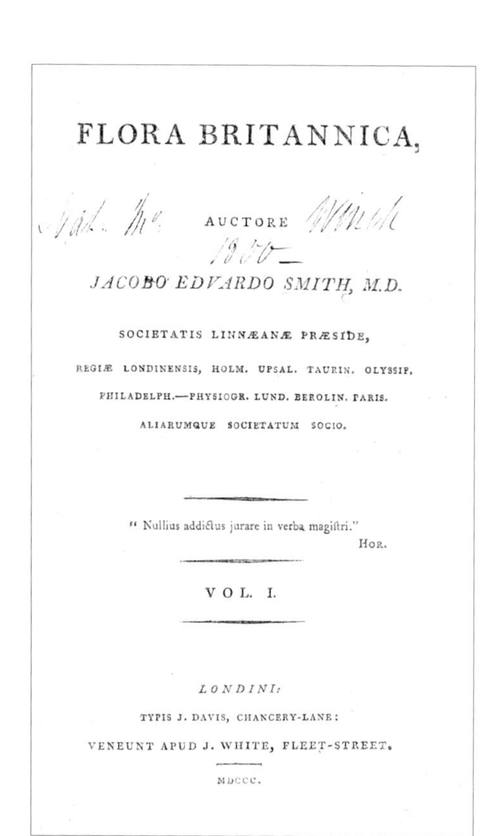

FLORA BRITANNICA,

AUCTORE

JACOBO EDVARDO SMITH, M.D.

SOCIETATIS LINNÆANÆ PRÆSIDE,

REGIÆ LONDINENSIS, HOLM. UPSAL. TAURIN. OLYSSIP. PHILADELPH.—PHYSIOGR. LUND. BEROLIN. PARIS. ALIARUMQUE SOCIETATUM SOCIO.

"Nullius addictus jurare in verba magistri." HOR.

VOL. I.

LONDINI:

TYPIS J. DAVIS, CHANCERY-LANE:

VENEUNT APUD J. WHITE, FLEET-STREET.

MDCCC.

Title page of Smith's *Flora Britannica* (1800–1804).

On the advice of his publisher, John White (the son of Benjamin White, who died in 1794), Smith had opted to delay publication of the concluding two volumes until the high price of paper had lowered, a circumstance he frankly communicated at the end of his preface.[35] The initial publication met with great approval, both at home and on the Continent. Sir Thomas Frankland was the first to congratulate Smith, remarking that his descriptions had "lessen[ed] the Botanist's labour tenfold".[36] Concurrently with *Flora Britannica*, Smith also issued a single volume *Compendium Floræ Britannicæ*, intended as a pocket field-guide, in which he had endeavoured to include as much information as possible without sacrificing portability. Descriptions were limited to a single line, and a system of symbols and numbers was used to indicate whether the plants were annual, biennial or perennial, and the months the flowers were in bloom. The synonyms were simply omitted, Smith describing them as "superfluous to ramblers".[37] At the end of a long critique on *Flora Britannica, The Monthly Review* had "no hesitation in asserting that these islands are now in possession of the best *Flora* yet published".[38] After sending a copy of both *Flora Britannica* and the *Compendium* to the library of the *Museum National d'Histoire Naturelle* in Paris, he received a letter of thanks signed by five of France's foremost naturalists: his erstwhile sparring partner Lamarck, Thouin, Jussieu, Desfontaines and geologist Barthélemy Faujas de Saint-Fond, with the acknowledgement that "these works, worthy of their author's reputation, by contributing to the progress of science, have already acquired him the gratitude of all naturalists".[39] The only grievances to be heard were from those regretting its incomplete appearance; Samuel Goodenough informed Smith that the publication coming out "imperfectly is not much relished at Oxford".[40]

Less than a year later, "several new motives" had since presented themselves and persuaded Smith to further delay publication of the concluding volumes, which were to cover the final four classes, the Monoecia[41], Dioecia[42], Polygamia[43] and the most difficult, and vaguest, of all, Cryptogamia. Within this last, vast class were placed all plants without visible flowers or seeds: ferns, mosses and liverworts, as well as algae, lichens and fungi. It seemed that Smith was not as confident in dealing with the cryptogams as he was with flowering plants. To aid his work, he was now awaiting the imminent publication of both volume four of James Dickson's *Fasciculus Plantarum Cryptogamicarum Britanniæ* (1785–1801) and Christiaan Hendrik Persoon's *Synopsis Fungorum* (1801). He was also hoping to seize the opportunity to exchange specimens with lichen expert Erik Acharius, whose *Lichenographiæ Svecicæ Prodromus* (1798) Smith described as having taken "the lead [...] in that department". The subsequent delay gave Smith two more springs for working on the notoriously difficult genus *Salix*, or willows, of the Dioecia class. (Willows are dioecious—with male and female reproductive structures appearing on separate plants, rather than on the same one—and easily hybridise both naturally and in cultivation.) Smith believed that, though it would still be "an imperfect sketch of the subject", it was with *Salix* that *Flora Britannica* would be "likely to merit the praise of labour and originality than perhaps in any other part".[44] For much of his *Salix* material, Smith was indebted to James Crowe, one of the Norwich school of botanists, who, for many years had assiduously collected indigenous and exotic willows, "distinguishing the truly wild from the naturalized, or merely cultivated kinds; and watching them with a most discriminating eye through all their stages of growth in his garden".[45]

Smith also received advice and support from Dawson Turner who at this time was also engaged on Cryptogamia, writing the two-volume *A Synopsis of British Fuci* (1802) and *Muscologia Hibernica* (1804). Smith and Turner had first met in the latter's native Yarmouth, before Smith's return to Norwich, and communicated regularly, lending each other books and specimens. Turner maintained an extensive correspondence with the cryptogamic botanists of Germany, the results of which Turner freely shared with Smith, leading Smith to term him "Flora's Secretary of State for the german department".[46] Turner read and commented on at least half of the manuscript of the third volume of *Flora Britannica*, with Smith doing the same for Turner's *A Synopsis of British Fuci*.

Over time, their botanical communications developed into a close and enduring friendship that became one of the mainstays of Smith's later life. Smith relished Turner's letters, and in this busy period thanked him for having been "an excel[en]t correspondent of late. I mean it not ironically—

yet think not that I always reckon you so for writing little, but I certainly think others the reverse (whose letters I will shew you) for writing a great deal".[47]

Smith was performing a careful balancing act at this time, with his precarious health bearing the brunt of his hectic schedule. Alongside his work on *English Botany*, *Flora Britannica* and *Flora Græca*, he was also still committed to his duties as president of the Linnean Society. In November 1800 he made a whirlwind visit to London; travelling by mail coach on Monday evening meant he would be able attend the Linnean Society on Tuesday, be present at a printing committee on the Wednesday, meet with Sibthorp's executors to discuss plates, and hope to be home again within four days so as to "sit down close" with *Flora Græca*.[48] Such interruptions clearly concerned his friends, impatient for the remainder of *Flora Britannica*. In October 1801, Goodenough asked Turner if he knew when Smith was to complete the Cryptogamia, and hoped he was not terrified by the "arduousness" of it: "If it terrif[ies] him, who will have boldness to undertake it?"[49] By the end of May 1802, Turner confidently wrote "the remainder of the Flora Britannica is expected about the end of the year".[50] Just as Turner was writing these words, Smith's health entered a dramatic decline that was to delay the third volume for almost another two years.

Early in 1802, Smith had been invited to give a course of botanical lectures at Liverpool to coincide with the opening of a new botanic garden in the Mount Pleasant area of the town. First envisaged in 1800, the funds for its establishment and maintenance were entirely derived from shares sold to members of the public.[51] The new institution quickly garnered wider support, with Sir Joseph Banks presenting books to the incipient library.[52] Early in May, before its public opening, William Roscoe, the incumbent President of the Liverpool Botanic Garden and one of the prime movers in its creation, gave a speech in which he passionately described the need for such a facility, and for the science of botany itself. He touted their luck, having secured a visit from the "very learned and eminent Dr Smith" for a first-hand display of that "genius, opportunity, and application, which has deservedly placed this illustrious disciple of Linnaeus at the head of the first Botanical institution in the kingdom".[53] Shortly before leaving Norwich on 21 May, Smith had suffered one of his periodic lung inflammations; even as he set out he reported that he still had "much strength to recover".[54] Intending to travel to Liverpool via London to attend the Linnean Society, he had just completed his presidential duties before he suffered a significant relapse, and, with difficulty, made it to his friend Richard Salisbury's house at Mill Hill in Middlesex (Salisbury had moved here from Chapel Allerton in 1800). Arriving on 30 May, he was completely bedridden for several days, laid low with a fever and a flare-up of erysipelas (an acute infection resulting in large, painful rashes) that completely covered one side of his face, leaving him almost blind in one eye. Unable even to write, he was forced to rely on his botanical pupil and secretary, the 16-year-old William Fitt Drake, an orphan who had first come under Smith's tutelage the year before, to communicate the news to his family and friends.

By 3 June, having endured exhausting rounds of "bleeding, blistering, and large doses of James's powders", Smith hoped he would soon be able to return home—the Liverpool lectures, of course, having been entirely given up.[55] Smith was not to leave Mill Hill until 12 June, and spent two days travelling back in post-chaises, but even this slightly gentler mode of travel brought back both the inflammation and violent pain in both his eye and head.[56] In one of the most serious bouts of ill-health Smith had experienced, it is interesting to note that he had not sent "so full an account of his illness" to Pleasance, who, after his return home, appears to have been daunted by the responsibilities as nurse to her ailing husband. Her friend Lady East combatively bolstered her confidence, certain that "good sense, joined to affection, will produce a good nurse at any time; therefore pray never let me hear you <u>abuse</u> yourself in such a manner again".[57] Thanks to her administrations, the pupil Drake, still writing on Smith's behalf, was soon able to report that his eye was "a great deal better, & there is no fear of the sight being impaired".[58] However, it was an extremely long recovery. By the end of July, the fever and underlying lung inflammation had cleared, but the erysipelas had left "so tedious a chronic inflammation" in his eye that he was confined to a darkened room, occasionally managing a walk about the garden of just a few minutes duration, rendering him, much to his distress, useless to botany.[59] News of Smith's indisposition, and in particular the threat to his eyesight, generated considerable concern amongst his friends. Andrew Caldwell, an amateur botanist based in Ireland, hoped that Smith's friends would join in imploring him to spare his eyes and not "attempt minute Botanic examinations, or the use of microscope Glasses 'till next summer".[60] Unfortunately, this was exactly the kind of study required to finish his investigations into the cryptogams. Tentative recovery only came following a visit to Lowestoft, where the sea air benefited him greatly and in the middle of September he rejoiced at being able to write to his friend Aylmer Bourke Lambert "with my own hand & eyes!".[61]

For all his medical training, Smith could exhibit surprisingly little regard for his delicate health. At the beginning of 1803, Dawson Turner received a letter again in Drake's hand from Smith, who had caught a cold from walking in a sharp wind that he initially thought would benefit his bad eye. Smith was mortified to find a return of the painful sensations in his forehead and a corresponding inflammation and dimness in his eye. Even more frustrating, he had been in hopes of finishing the mosses for *Flora Britannica* by the end of January. It was to be almost two months before he was sufficiently recovered again.[62] Similarly, in 1806, William Jackson Hooker recounted to Dawson Turner how he had called upon Smith one morning but "could not see him as he was just retired to his couch to seek relief, in the arms of sleep, from a violent head-ache, caused by having eaten, without considering the weakness of his stomach, too many oysters the preceding evening".[63]

In May 1803, Smith left East Anglia for the first time in a year, in order to consult several books in Oxford, followed by a visit to London. He was again accompanied by Drake; Pleasance generally did not accompany her husband on such visits, unless guaranteed a comfortable carriage.[64] He also visited Lady Rockingham, on his way to London, for the first time in several years. The ailing Marchioness clearly appreciated the visit; following Smith's arrival in London she sent a suckling pig for Aylmer Bourke Lambert's table, where Smith was staying, to be roasted whole, not with "the limbs cut off, as is the fashion of some cooks".[65] Despite his recent illness, Smith was as frenetic as usual whilst in London, on this occasion witnessing the long delayed sale of Davall's library.

To the Great Joy of All Good Men

Smith intended to go on to Liverpool and finally give his course of lectures, though he did not confirm with the organisers until he was certain of his continued good health. Even after setting off on 27 June, Smith came close to repenting of his decision, the "east wind, vile atmosphere, & my many occupations & hurries" having brought on a headache and loss of strength lasting several days. Revived by the clean air outside of London, Smith and Drake travelled by mail coaches, a quick, albeit uncomfortable form of transport. Upon arrival at Liverpool, Smith lodged with a childhood friend, Thomas Taylor. He was particularly "struck with the pleasantness of the Liverpool air", thanks to its proximity of the sea and the high tides, and credited it with a beneficial effect on his eye. Smith's first lecture commenced on Wednesday 6 July and was "most numerously & brilliantly attended, & seem to stir up a great taste & ardour for botany".[66] Drake, who had not heard Smith lecture before, was surprised to find Smith "so much of an orator, as he says", though Smith humbly claimed that he "never aim[ed] at more than plainness". William Roscoe had procured Smith a room for free, and with a final list of 120 subscribers paying 2 guineas each for the series, Smith ended up making at least 200 guineas.[67] He would return to Liverpool for another successful series of lectures in 1805 (this time accompanied by Pleasance), where Prince William Frederick, Duke of Gloucester and Edinburgh, headed the list of subscribers. Smith also committed to preparing a duplicate of his own herbarium for Roscoe, beginning work in 1804. (Smith particularly wished for it to be purchased by the Liverpool Botanic Garden, and in October 1806 sent a first parcel of 2,000 plants as a specimen of their quality, and committed to increasing the amount to up to 10,000 species, "a respectable herbarium, especially with Linnaean authority".[68]) An arduous job, it was not to be completed until 1817.

Though the whole trip far exceeded his expectations, for Smith the most rewarding aspect of the visit was his introduction to William Roscoe. Six years older than Smith, Roscoe was the son of a former butler and innkeeper, born and bred in Liverpool. By the turn of the century he had already enjoyed a full career as a lawyer. After a brief dalliance with being called to the bar, he eventually became a partner in a local banking firm. For almost 50 years he had a huge impact on the town's artistic, social, scientific and political life, in addition to being an internationally famous historian and author. His *Life of Lorenzo de' Medici* (1796) was enormously popular, going through many editions and leading Horace Walpole to describe him as "by far the best of our historians, both for beauty and style, and for deep reflections".[69] On Roscoe's finishing the second volume, Andrew Caldwell commented to Smith his surprise that such an elegant work could issue from "the dross of such a place as Liverpool".[70] Smith related his first impressions on meeting Roscoe to Pleasance, describing him as a "tall, active, lively man, with all the taste & intelligence one would expect, & not a grain of reserve of hauteur, nor any sort of affectation".[71] Heavily involved in the abolition movement, he was also a Unitarian, and in Smith's words a surprisingly good "practical botanist"; in short, he was Smith's kind of man.[72] The two quickly hit it off, seeing each other at least once or twice a day throughout his stay and Smith visited Roscoe's villa, Allerton Hall ("a perfect paradise"), six miles south of Liverpool, multiple times.[73] It was on one of these visits that Smith excitedly wrote a letter with the "very pen which has just been correcting his manuscript of Leo 10th [Roscoe's forthcoming 'sequel' to *Lorenzo de' Medici*]".[74]

After Smith returned to Norwich, the two men began a correspondence that was to fuel a friendship which lasted until Smith's death. In many ways, Roscoe filled the void left by the death of Edmund Davall. As with Davall, Smith's friendship with Roscoe developed very quickly in its intensity (within days of Smith's return, Roscoe referred to Smith as a "friend of very early days, but lately found"[75]). Unlike his friendship with Davall, Smith and Roscoe met as equals, both men having risen to the tops of their respective fields. As a result there were none of the extravagant, florid outpourings that characterise sections of the Smith-Davall correspondence.

Roscoe also had an impact on the young Drake, effecting a "revolution in his mind as to politics, for he had been biased to the illiberal side"; Drake had been "in tears" at leaving Roscoe on their return journey home. "I know not whether to regret that age", wrote Smith, "when <u>tears of the mind</u> so easily find vent at the eyes, but I love to contemplate it in others".[76]

Since joining the Society for Effecting the Abolition of the Slave Trade in the late 1780s, Roscoe had become a leading abolitionist, publishing several pamphlets and the long abolitionist poem *The Wrongs of Africa* (1787–1788). In November 1806, during one of the most remarkable elections in Liverpool's parliamentary history, Roscoe was elected as MP for Liverpool. This was an astonishing outcome for an abolitionist in a town "still wedded to the slave trade" and a dissenter in a community "dominated by Anglicans and Tories".[77] The implications were immediately clear; on hearing the news an elated Smith informed Sowerby that Roscoe's election would be "to the great joy of all good men".[78] Congratulating Roscoe, Smith was sure of the positive "effect of this blessed event upon the fate of thousands, nay millions, of happy africans!"[79] In January 1807, a Bill for the Abolition of the Slave Trade was introduced to Parliament; with no small amount of pressure, Smith informed Roscoe:

> I think you are not aware how much <u>you</u> are looked up to by the nation on this subject. It is I believe a very popular one. People of all parties, clergy & dissenters, quakers [sic], aristocrats & democrats, if good people, all agree in this. I have heard from various unexpected quarters expressions of some fear lest you should be inclined to compromise.[80]

Smith favoured the immediate abolition of the trade itself, but felt a more gradual abolition of the institution of slavery would guarantee the safety of "the unfortunate objects of the trade".[81] Smith advised Roscoe to seize any opportunity when he could stand "forth as the independent champion of the Abolition of the Africa Slave trade [...] All the nation would support & applaud you". On 23 February 1807, during the second reading of the Bill, Roscoe fully vindicated his supporters with a rousing speech:

> I have long resided in the town of Liverpool; for 30 years I have never ceased to condemn this inhuman traffic; and I consider it the greatest happiness of my existence to lift up my voice on this occasion against it, with the friends of justice and humanity.[82]

The Bill was passed in the House of Commons. Smith ecstatically wrote to Roscoe, congratulating him on the "glorious majority in favour of the abolition", but the same joy was not felt everywhere.[83] Roscoe's triumphant return to Liverpool in May was marred by the appearance of a mob, orchestrated by local slavers, and after beating a hasty retreat, Roscoe resolved never to stand for Parliament again.[84]

After the success of the Liverpool lectures, Smith accepted an invitation to lecture at the Royal Institution, founded 1799, in Albemarle Street, London, which was to become an annual event for many years, health permitting.[85] The first run was for just ten lectures, but with each season Smith tried to push for either more lectures or more money, emboldened by the report that his series had been universally well received.[86] For the first series, Smith was accompanied by Pleasance, Drake and his youngest sister Fanny (Frances Julia). Showing their reluctance for such journeys (they travelled by mail coach), by the time of their arrival in Cavendish Square, Fanny and Pleasance were both so "vapoured" that they wished that they had not left Norwich. They were soon revived by the fact that William Roscoe was unexpectedly in town. The diary Pleasance kept of this trip gives a good indication of her own interests and preoccupations; she had a passion for the theatre (on this trip she saw Sarah Siddons as Desdemona in *Othello*), and a love of music, dogs and food. She was again forced to act as nurse to Smith in May, her husband fatigued and feverish. At Salisbury's persuasion, Smith retreated alone to Mill Hill for a day or two and returned refreshed. He faced another setback just a few days later—when they found a dead rat in the bath. Pleasance recorded the event in her diary, with a distinct hint of exasperation: "James afraid of it."[87] His squeamishness aside, Pleasance wholeheartedly supported her husband in his scientific endeavours. Unlike his father, she never pressured him to go into medicine, despite the financial comfort it might bring, and was quick to reassure him that she felt such "veneration for the 'chair of the great Linné'" that he should never give up his bounty just to "exchange it for a coach".[88]

Smith's own health seemingly restored, in September he was summoned by "the printer's devil" to resume work on *Flora Britannica*. Despite the delays and frustrations that had accompanied work on the cryptogamic specimens (Smith said Roscoe "could hardly be aware how much labour these little plants cost me") Smith's methodical approach had opened up this mysterious class of plants to him: "when carefully studied they amply repay our care by their beauty, the precision of most of their characters, & the admirable exercize they afford to a systematic mind". Though he dreaded the variability of liverworts and lichens that were to fill the fourth volume, he consoled himself with the thought that once finished, all other botanical endeavours would be comparatively simple.[89] The third volume of *Flora Britannica* finally appeared at the end of March. *The Monthly Review* praised "the author's unwearied diligence and acuteness of research", particularly in his treatment of *Salix* and the cryptogams.[90] *Flora Britannica* was well regarded, both during Smith's lifetime and after his death. *The Edinburgh Journal of Science*, in its obituary of Smith, said that *Flora Britannica* was "perhaps the most perfect specimen [of a *Flora*] existing".[91] In another obituary, *The Philosophical Magazine* commented that *Flora Britannica* was "remarkable [...] for accuracy in observing, accuracy in recording, and unusually accuracy in printing".[92]

At the end of December 1804, Smith committed his friendship with Roscoe to the public sphere in the dedication to a new Smith-Sowerby part-work entitled *Exotic Botany* (1804–1805). As with the majority of their collaborations, the impetus for the project came from James Sowerby. Initially, a very busy Smith dodged the idea, but, despite several previous attempts (and failures) at producing a popular work on exotics, within a year Smith had fully entered into the enterprise. Emboldened by the continued success of William Curtis's *Botanical Magazine* (flourishing even after the proprietor's death) they were convinced that the abundance of exotic species arriving from distant colonies could amply support a rival publication.[93] Though executed with the usual scientific and artistic rigour, both the working title for the new publication, *Exotic Garden*, the preface and presentation made clear that this was a commercially-minded publication aimed at the botanically inclined upper echelons and aspirational middle classes of society. Written exclusively in English, the impressive plants featured were shown to full advantage, including the occasional fold-out. Smith's rich seam of correspondents provided the majority of the plants and drawings, including Aylmer Bourke Lambert, who owned the sketches of John White's Australian specimens in Smith's possession, Captain Thomas Hardwicke, who had provided 1,500 sketches of plants from his time in India, and Sir Joseph Banks, who was "so perfectly friendly" about the publication that Smith was pleased to inform Sowerby he "should not scruple asking him for any thing".[94]

Smith and Sowerby were so confident that this new endeavour would succeed that they had already agreed that once a total of 500 copies were sold Smith would be paid an additional 2 and a half guineas for his contributions.[95] Smith in particular thought that having so many new genera early on (named in large part after his aristocratic patrons) would make it particularly valuable, and passed an exacting eye over Sowerby's proofs. Shortly before publication of the first issue, he lamented that the very first plate, *Humea elegans* (a new genus named in honour of Lady Amelia Hume, but preceded by *Calomeria amaranthoides*, its correct name) was not very effectively shaded: "'tis as flat as a board – is it too late?".[96] On seeing the coloured versions of two of the *Tetratheca* species featured he bluntly stated that there was "such a want of effect, & such a dawbing about them that I am quite out of heart. They might be made very pretty things".[97] Unfortunately, despite the celebrated names and a host of new Australian plants, it quickly became apparent that *Exotic Botany* was in danger of following *Icones Pictæ* and *Spicilegium Botanicum*. Roscoe, flattered by the dedication, took a strong interest in the work and immediately identified that it needed better marketing.[98] Smith was convinced there was "no doubt that such a work ought to be exceedingly successful", and in September 1805 arranged to have it advertised in Liverpool and Norwich, giving Sowerby £5 for it to go into the London papers.[99] A month later, with 10 extra sets ordered from the Liverpool advertisement alone, *Exotic Botany* managed to obtain a temporary stay of execution.

CHAPTER TEN

Smith vs. Salisbury

At the beginning of 1805, in a reflective frame of mind, Smith commented in a letter to William Roscoe: "how happy I am in having so few literary quarrels—indeed none but with Lamarck & Curtis—& a private quarrel I never knew".[1] By the autumn of the same year, the longstanding friendship between Smith and Richard Salisbury, originating from their student days in Edinburgh (where Salisbury went by his original name of Richard Markham), had been terminated following a bitter and acrimonious quarrel, both personal and scientific, that dwarfed any previous altercation.

Though Salisbury had only briefly attended Edinburgh (he never took an MD), his and Smith's shared love of natural history led to a close and productive bond; Salisbury was a founding member of both the Natural History Society of Edinburgh and the Linnean Society, and several plants from Salisbury's extensive gardens at Chapel Allerton, near Leeds, featured in Smith's *Icones Pictæ*. In December 1796, in honour of Salisbury's "acuteness and indefatigable zeal in the service of botany", Smith renamed the tree *Ginkgo biloba* (an "equally uncouth and barbarous name") as *Salisburia adiantifolia* (a procedure now reversed).[2] Others, however, were less enamoured. Salisbury was an early British follower of Antoine Laurent de Jussieu, and arranged the catalogue of his plants at Chapel Allerton, the self-published *Prodromus Stirpium in Horto ad Chapel Allerton Vigentium* (1796), according to the natural system. More controversially, he also commenced a sweeping, unjustifiable revision of botanical nomenclature; writing a new arrangement of heaths in 1797, he determined to give each a new name, expressive of its difference: *Erica tetralix* (cross-leaved heath) became *Erica botuliformis* (sausage-shaped heath).[3] This resulted in several "very warm" discussions between Salisbury, Samuel Goodenough and Banks's librarian, Jonas Dryander. The latter exclaimed: "If this is to be the case with every body, what the Devil is to become of Botany?", whilst Goodenough "laboured in vain" to persuade Salisbury to revert the order, and keep the Linnaean names with his own suggestions appended beneath. An infuriated Goodenough stated that Salisbury possessed "a happy firmness which some people will call obstinacy, which makes him rise superior to every opponent", and refused to engage in botanical debate with him again.[4] About this time Salisbury was also busy alienating his wife, Caroline, whom he had married at the end of 1796. A daughter quickly followed, but by early 1798 Caroline had returned to her parents, taking the baby with her; Salisbury reported to Sir Joseph Banks that Caroline was "disappointed at not finding me so rich as she expected", and that he had returned her dowry and "settled handsomely" on their daughter. Salisbury warned Banks "you will hear a 1000 Lies and Reports", particularly that his benefactress, Mrs Salisbury (on whose account Salisbury changed his name from Markham, as condition for receiving a substantial bequest), had never existed. Salisbury insisted that she had, but that all the money left him by her was now spent.[5] Replying, Banks confirmed that he "had indeed heard very unpleasant stories", and whilst reassuring Salisbury that he, Smith and Dryander were doing their "utmost [...] to keep back our belief of them" pending a full explanation, continued support was not a given. Until they received "full and incontrovertible proofs" that Mrs Salisbury had existed, "we shall not be able to make defence for you when we hear you attacked as we all of us wish to do." Salisbury's reply, if he ever sent one, does not survive, and the true facts remain as murky today as they were in 1798.[6]

Smith, at least, seems to have been sufficiently satisfied with Salisbury's explanations, for he remained a core member of the Linnean Society, being named in the Society's 1802 charter as one of the first 15 Fellows – the same year Smith made him a vice-president. It was shortly after the Anniversary Meeting of that charter year that Smith, suffering from a debilitating attack of erysipelas, sought refuge at Salisbury's house in Mill Hill in Middlesex,

Richard Salisbury (1761–1829), Smith's erstwhile friend and botanical foe.

the former home of botanist Peter Collinson, to which Salisbury had moved after his separation. Smith was accompanied by his botanical student, the 16-year-old William Fitt Drake. Smith later recounted that whilst Salisbury was "nursing him like a brother", he was "throwing out the most strange, oblique or direct remarks, about me, my works, or the Linn[ean] Soc[iet]y", with Salisbury even claiming he had been offered the editorship of *Flora Græca* before Smith.[7] Worse still, each night, after Smith had gone to bed, Salisbury continued the attacks *tête-à-tête* with Drake, belittling Smith by criticising his botanical teaching methods and cautioning him "against being corrupted" by Smith's principles, whilst simultaneously attempting to debase Drake's morals himself. On finding that the boy was still a virgin, Salisbury proposed taking him to "a girl of his acquaintance in London, saying 'it would be good for him, manly'". Smith swiftly quashed this scheme after a naïve Drake had asked for Smith's consent. No longer able to proffer "practical instructions", Salisbury instead offered to lend Drake the sexually explicit plates from Pietro Aretino's notorious *I Modi* (*The Ways*) (1527).[8]

Smith was not to learn the full extent of Salisbury's salacious conversations with Drake until after their return to Norwich. Combining this behaviour with "obscure & strange passages" in some of Salisbury's recent letters, Smith began to suspect that "envy & jealousy were rankling in his mind". Smith immediately sought to "recall his former affection & disarm his jealousy", and the pair reconciled, with a flurry of visits between Mill Hill and Norwich exchanged.[9]

The spring of 1805 passed with "much cordiality [...] with now & then a little sparring" over the preface of a recently published work, the botanical artist William Hooker's *Paradisus Londinensis* (1805–1808). Like *Exotic Botany*, it was an attempt to cash-in on the craze for exotics, though *Paradisus Londinensis* focused on plants already in cultivation in the London area. Hooker was assisted anonymously in the scientific descriptions "by a Botanist more learned than himself". Arranged according to Jussieu's natural system, the anonymous botanist further expressed his disdain for the Linnaean system by stating:

> In all similar publications which have hitherto appeared, not even excepting the most respectable, a considerable portion of each page has been filled with useless repetitions of the classes, orders, and generic characters of the sexual system.[10]

Smith interpreted this as an attack on *Exotic Botany* and particularly *English Botany*, which did indeed repeat the classes and orders of the sexual system, for the benefit of the amateur botanist who may not have the benefit of an extensive library to refer to. All decorum vanished on 4 June, when, at a meeting of the Linnean Society, Salisbury interrupted a conversation between Smith and Lambert about the recently published figure of the Indian lotus, *Cyamus nelumbo* (*Nelumbo nucifera*), in *Exotic Botany* with "such a torrent of contemptuous abuse" that Smith could no longer control himself. Still smarting from their earlier 'sparring', Smith accused *Paradisus Londinensis* of "misrepresentation", at which point Salisbury revealed himself as the author, leading his shocked friend to exclaim it was no "less false for that". They parted without reconciling.[11]

The Quarrel Has Assumed a Most Inveterate and Virulent Appearance

As with their previous falling-out, Smith expected a rapprochement in time, but it soon became apparent that there were much darker undertones present—by the end of July he began to fear that Salisbury was becoming "really malevolent".[12] Smith publicly responded to the *Paradisus Londinensis* preface in the August 1805 issue of *Exotic Botany* by mischievously acknowledging Salisbury's botanical skills whilst stating that "the science will be benefited by our friend's talents, in whatever way they are directed. The more moderate he is in his triumphs over us poor Linnaeans, the more resplendent and unsullied will be his own fame".[13] Smith later admitted that there was "a little malice" in the comment.[14] Salisbury responded in the October fascicle of *Paradisus Londinensis*, in which he criticised James Sowerby's figure of *Nymphæa alba* in *English Botany* and attacked Smith directly: "had I not known him to be very *sensitive*, even before I named a genus after him in the Hortus Kewensis [*Smithia*], I should have said much more upon the subject".[15] Unknown to all but Smith's immediate circle, Salisbury further compounded the insult by arranging for a copy to be anonymously delivered to Smith. Smith affected indifference, but he was franker in a letter to William Roscoe, providing a full transcription and commentary on the offending passage, particularly regarding the naming of *Smithia sensitiva*, which Smith had always believed Jonas Dryander had named for him in recognition of his paper on *Berberis*.[16]

Smith returned the offending issue of *Paradisus Londinensis* in a parcel conspicuously addressed to Salisbury as 'Vice President of the Linnean Society', hoping to goad him into resigning, and thereafter followed an exchange of increasingly acrimonious letters (three survive, only as copies).[17] Salisbury affected complete astonishment on hearing of the anonymous delivery: "Who has played you this trick, and thus blown the coal between us I call God to witness I know not." Salisbury defended his conduct by claiming that he was only responding to Smith's accusations that he had asserted a "falsehood" (harking back to the original slight of Smith response to the *Paradisus Londinensis* preface), adding that he expected a full retraction from Smith. Should this not be forthcoming, he had taken it upon himself to scrutinise the scientific validity of Smith's publications, the results of which had "not only completely justified my preface, but afforded me so easy a victory, that I shall disdain to use it". Smith's "boasted corrections" of Linnaeus's generic characters were like "drops of water scattered at a mile's distance in the wide ocean", and Smith's own original generic characters "would disgrace a botanical scholar, much more a botanical pedagogue". He concluded with a stinging attack on Smith's character:

> Be then what you pretend: in Botany really eminent, studying the science more and whist (if I may credit vulgar fame) less: in friendship truly disinterested, not suspicious, less ready to take offence or give it, if it falls to the lot of your friend to censure either your botany or abusive pen.[18]

Smith was unfazed by Salisbury's threats, replying "they prove how little you have to say against me on that subject [...]. My corrections of Linnaeus [...] are indeed not many, but certainly all that, to my judgement, & to his honour, he wanted. I did not aim at celebrity by altering without absolute necessity. You know we have always differed about changing names". Smith was not particularly concerned with maintaining the moral superiority, and referred to the most controversial of all Salisbury's changing of names: "perhaps I might have expected more gentleness of expression from Mr Markham, an amiable friend whom I now consider as dead to me ever since Mr Salisbury came upon the stage". Hoping to decisively end the dispute, and the friendship, Smith was determined that any future intercourse between the two "must be purely botanical".[19]

Two days later he informed Dawson Turner that he felt like a character in "some German novel, who had been bound by enchant[men]t to something indescribably horrible, & who has just burst his chains, ridding himself at once of a nuisance & an opprobrium". Smith continued to pretend that he was unhurt, laughing that aside from his supposed botanical ignorance, Salisbury's only other charge was that he apparently played too much whist: "I fear I am so wicked that he can find nothing else to say that is false, for he disdains truth!"[20]

The wished-for resignation of Salisbury's vice-presidentship came in early January 1806, though any satisfaction was tempered by the accompanying letter's sneering attack on Smith for daring to earn money through botany. Salisbury insinuated Smith had only been appointed editor of *Flora Græca* through the agency of Sir Joseph Banks, and that Smith would have wasted his "brains for mucor" [mould] before earning £150 a year by any other botanical publication. Claiming that Smith was as much to blame as himself for their disagreement, he ended with the declamation: "if a certain muscle on your left side had not been more cankered than the oldest of the apple trees I saw the other day, you would have esteemed [me] instead of quarrelling with me".[21] Despite the indifference displayed to his friends, Smith, who had always placed so much stock in the virtue and value of friendship, was shaken by the whole affair. Turner wrote to a friend that Smith was "worried in mind by his quarrel with Mr Salisbury, into which so much matter of personal animosity has now crept, that the quarrel has assumed a most inveterate & virulent appearance".[22]

So unseemly had things become that in early January Sir Joseph Banks attempted to intervene, hoping to effect reconciliation between his two former protégés. Smith was fully compliant, sending his interpretation of events and copies of their three most recent letters (by which means they survive today), the perusal of which horrified Banks; he declared that both had been "so ungentle" in their prose it was impossible to determine whose letters were the worse.[23] In less than two weeks he abandoned his self-assumed role as mediator: had he known "the quarrel had taken so deep a seat in both your minds" he would never have become involved. Nevertheless, though Salisbury had dropped in Banks's esteem, he still could not fault his "indefatigable industry".[24] Smith, who was already hurt that many of his colleagues supposed that their quarrel was "merely botanical", was particularly upset by this response from Banks, and believed it showed "a want of heart & principle", as well as confirming his long-held opinion of "queernesses in this great man".[25]

At the beginning of March 1806, Salisbury fulfilled his threat against Smith and published a pamphlet entitled *The Generic Characters in the English Botany, collated with those of Linné*. In this he listed the almost 800

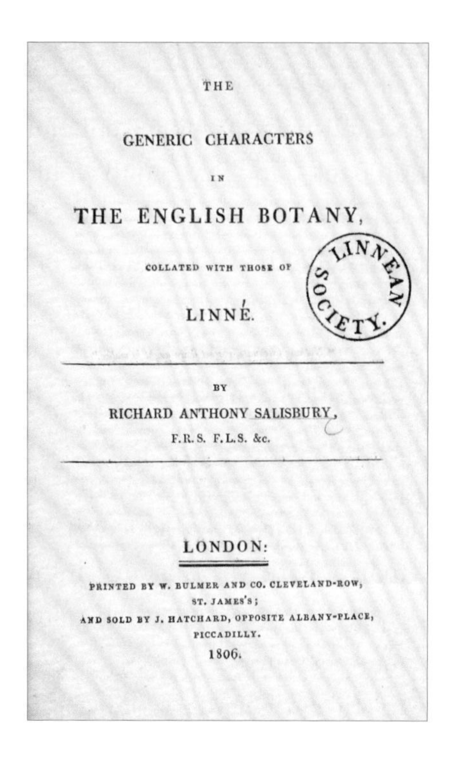
THE
GENERIC CHARACTERS
IN
THE ENGLISH BOTANY,
COLLATED WITH THOSE OF
LINNÉ.

BY
RICHARD ANTHONY SALISBURY,
F.R.S. F.L.S. &c.

LONDON:
PRINTED BY W. BULMER AND CO. CLEVELAND-ROW,
ST. JAMES'S;
AND SOLD BY J. HATCHARD, OPPOSITE ALBANY-PLACE,
PICCADILLY.
1806.

Title-page of Richard Salisbury's pamphlet, *The Generic Characters in The English Botany* (1806).

instances in which, he claimed, Smith had "copied verbatim" the generic characters in *English Botany* from Linnaeus's works.[26] He personally presented the pamphlet to the Linnean Society at a meeting on 4 March (Smith was not in attendance). Samuel Goodenough, who was present, later assured Smith that had he been in the Chair (occupied that evening by William George Maton) he would have recommended that Salisbury "keep it to himself", and after the meeting defended Smith by elucidating on the "weakness & impotency of the attack".[27] Trusting that Smith would not hear of the event until several days later, Salisbury had deviously sent Smith a copy of the pamphlet on 6 March, offering to delay its release if Smith made "concessions". Smith, having long expected such an attack, did not respond: "how like a fool I should have looked if I had been frightened or wheedled into any concession!".[28] Though he termed it a "most abusive & lying pamphlet", he was confident in his botanical integrity.[29] He reassured Sowerby that they should not fear any negative influence on *English Botany*:

> The ground of his attack is as futile as can be, Hudson, Lightfoot, Curtis all did really copy Linn[aeu]s without correction, or nearly so. I am the first English writer who undertook to examine the char[acte]rs of Linn[aeu]s, & to correct them where I found an error. All therefore that I can be blamed for is that I have not brought them at once to perfection.[30]

The official Linnean Society response to Salisbury's pamphlet was lacklustre at best, and though Goodenough spearheaded an attempt to have the document expelled from the library there was little sense of urgency. (In fact, the pamphlet still remains in the library today.) Smith would have been happy to see it "burnt at a meeting by order from the chair", though he was quick to add it was only "as far as the honour of the Soc[iet]y is concerned".[31]

Several of Smith's friends were glad that Salisbury had so publicly shown his vindictive nature. Turner had worried that Smith's "moral character w[oul]d suffer by a reconciliation" after such a public spat.[32] He was urged by all not to respond, a measure Smith reluctantly agreed to, though he found it "provoking that I must not answer what I could so easily".[33] He made one exception for his Royal Institution lectures, where his new introductory lecture would "refute Salisb[ur]y & yet not honour him with apparent notice".[34]

Aside from his personal woes, 1806 was in fact a propitious year for Smith. The calls of both the Linnean Society and the Royal Institution compelled Smith to spend three months in London that year, the longest he had stayed in a single sitting since moving to Norwich. For the first time ever the Society's finances were in a healthy state, even with the expenses incurred by the previous year's move to larger premises at 9 Gerrard Street (in the same year they had also acquired a new librarian, Robert Brown, fresh from his circumnavigation of Australia on board HMS *Investigator*).[35] With the publication of the initial parts of the first volumes of *Flora Græca* and *Prodromus Floræ Græcæ*, Smith was, for the first time in years, able to properly consider his own publications. Ensconced back in Norwich, he set himself an ambitious writing schedule for the winter, namely, to finish work on volume four of *Flora Britannica*, to start (and finish) a popular 'introduction to botany', and continue work on *Flora Græca*, *English Botany* and *Exotic Botany* (the latter having received a significant boost by way of Nepalese plants and drawings from Smith's old Edinburgh friend, Francis Buchanan).[36]

Despite its starring role in Smith and Salisbury's feud, *Exotic Botany* had struggled to find an audience. Sowerby almost suspended production in March 1806, but Smith, convinced that an upturn in sales was imminent, prevailed upon him to continue, even offering to wait for payment for his own contributions.[37] Publication eventually came to a halt in October, with just two issues remaining to complete the second volume. A possible lifeline was offered by the publishers Longman, Rees & Co., who had tentatively agreed to take a share of the work, only for it to be withdrawn after discovering the chaotic state of Sowerby's accounts. Smith, though annoyed, was not surprised: he described Sowerby as a "perfectly good & honest man, but a bad man of business – & sometimes apt to despond".[38] Hoping to motivate Sowerby, Smith sent a scolding letter in which he blamed him for failing to produce a publication that "might have been of great pecuniary benefit & credit to both of us". Smith was anxious that the final two issues at least be published, without which the work would be "ruined".[39] Smith's anger was at least partly fuelled by the "trumpery" of *The Botanical Repository*, *Botanical Magazine* and *Paradisus Londinensis*, which, to his mortification, had all consistently outsold *Exotic Botany*.[40] Despite strong hints that Longman would be willing to begin negotiations for a third volume, Sowerby had given up. The remaining two issues finally appeared in October 1807 and in January 1808.

He Has Certainly Tied Himself to Linnaeus's Tail

After so many years honing his botanical lectures, the writing of *An Introduction to Physiological and Systematical Botany* caused Smith little pain. Published in November 1807, it was an introductory publication "on an original plan, easy, comprehensive, and fit for general use", but that could also lead the student "into the depths of botanical philosophy".[41] Smith was also responding to a demand from the botanical public "to remove the objections which are often made to the admission of females into this part of the temple of science".[42] These objections centred on that perennial bugbear of the Linnaean system of botany: its presentation of plant sexuality. Samuel Goodenough believed that "a literal translation of the first principles of Linnean Botany is enough to shock female modesty".[43] Such accusations had only been exacerbated by the likes of Erasmus Darwin, "tickled with the idea, that he had caught two anthers belonging to neighbouring flowers in the very act of adultery".[44] Even Pleasance Smith blamed Darwin for the opprobrium botany lay under, and eagerly awaited the time when by her husband's pen "this beautiful & innocent study [will be] rescued from all objection".[45] Smith was more than aware of the incongruities. At the beginning of 1807 Smith was asked to take over writing the botanical segments of Abraham Rees's *Cyclopædia* (1802–1819) after the initial contributor, the Revd William Wood, fell ill. Smith considered it a "pleasant & easy" job, even though one of his first articles was on the genus *Clitoria* (a legume) – as the name suggests, it had an uncomfortable etymology.[46] Speaking to Goodenough, the clergyman raged at the "gross prurience of Linnaeus's mind" and called *Clitoria* "a singular piece of vulgar lasciviousness".[47] He gladly accepted Smith's alternative explanation that that name derived from the Greek for "*claudo, includo* [closed, enclosed], expressing the manner in which the essential organs of fructification are enclosed or shut up in the keel and wings of the corolla". In the *Cyclopædia* entry, Smith protested "against every attempt to associate it directly with an anatomical term, to which, though derived from the same Greek theme, it has in fact only a remote, factitious analogy".[48]

Smith used the preface of *Introduction to Botany* to expound further on the purity of botany, and the physical, mental and spiritual satisfaction to be gained from its study:

> None but the most foolish or depraved could derive any thing from it but what is beautiful, or pollute its lovely scenery with unamiable or unhallowed images. Those who do so, either from corrupt taste or malicious design, can be compared only to the fiend entering into the garden of Eden.[49]

Aylmer Bourke Lambeth, one of Smith's most steadfast friends during the Salisbury debacle, thought that 'the fiend' was a reference to Smith's antagonist. Smith assured Lambert that this section had been written before the quarrel, "but how well it hits!".[50] The remainder of the work, however, did contain several veiled messages to Salisbury. When discussing the propriety of naming plants after botanists, Smith conspicuously used the example of *Smithia sensitiva*, crediting the name to Jonas Dryander.[51] In the matter of generic characters, he quoted his private response to Salisbury's pamphlet almost verbatim:

> For my own part I profess to retain, not only the plan, but the very words of Linnaeus, unless I find them erroneous, copying nothing without examination, but altering with a very sparing hand, and leaving much for future examination.[52]

Unfortunately, this was seized upon by Patrick Neill, an occasional reviewer for the *Edinburgh Review*, in one of the few criticisms the work received. Neill wrote that Smith "did right to leave out his favourite Horatian motto Nullius addictus &c [Smith's motto for *Flora Britannica*, "I am not bound to swear allegiance to the word of any master"] in this work; for he has certainly tied himself to Linnaeus's tail in it".[53]

Nevertheless, *Introduction to Botany* enjoyed considerable popular and critical success. *The Annual Review* praised Smith for having clearly, yet wholesomely, explained Linnaeus's system, so "that the most modest and timid may freely enter into the temple Flora without fear of being insulted with the unhallowed mysteries of a licentious Venus".[54] By February 1808, only three months after publication, more than half of the initial 1,500 print-run had been sold.[55] A second edition was published in 1809, with four more produced in Smith's lifetime, and a further two posthumously.

Smith's comments in *Introduction to Botany* served only to inflame the dispute. Prior to publication, the dispute had almost mellowed, even allowing for "a few words of distant civility" to be exchanged when they unexpectedly met at Soho Square.[56] In response to Smith's *Introduction to Botany* comments, Salisbury published a figure of the contentious *Smithia*

Fig. 14 'The Pantheon, the morning after the fire'. Described as "the most elegant structure in Europe", the Pantheon spectacularly burst into flames in the early hours of 14 January 1792. For a time the inferno threatened both Smith's home, which backed onto the assembly rooms, and the Linnaean collections. By JMW Turner.

Fig. 15 The 'Gypsy' portrait of Pleasance Smith by John Opie, painted the year after her marriage.

Fig. 16 'Portrait of an eminent botanist'. Aged 33 at the time of painting, this is the only oil portrait of Smith. It was exhibited at the Royal Academy in 1793. By John Rising.

Fig. 17 Thomas Johnes created a picturesque paradise at Hafod, Cardiganshire; Smith was a frequent visitor. By John 'Warwick' Smith, for Smith's *Tour to Hafod* (1810).

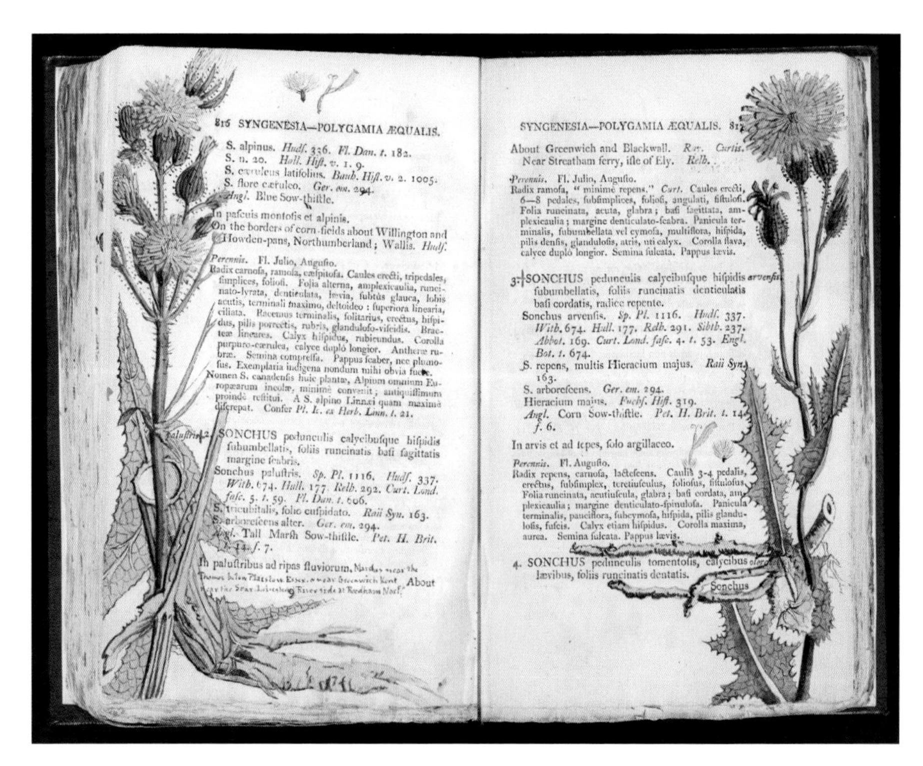

816 SYNGENESIA—POLYGAMIA ÆQUALIS.

S. alpinus. *Hudſ.* 336. *Fl. Dan. t.* 182.
S. n. 20. *Hall. Hiſt. v.* 1. 9.
S. cæruleus latifolius. *Bauh. Hiſt. v.* 2. 1005.
S. flore cæruleo. *Ger. em.* 294.
Angl. Blue Sow-thiſtle.

In paſcuis montoſis et alpinis.
On the borders of corn-fields about Willington and Howden-pans, Northumberland; Wallis. *Hudſ.*

Perennis. Fl. Julio, Auguſto.
Radix carnoſa, ramoſa, cæſpitoſa. Caules erecti, tripedales, ſimplices, folioſi. Folia alterna, amplexicaulia, runcinato-lyrata, denticulata, lævia, ſubtùs glauca, lobis acutis, terminali maximo, deltoideo : ſuperiora linearia, ciliata. Racemus terminalis, ſolitarius, erectus, hiſpidus, pilis porrectis, rubris, glanduloſo-viſcidis. Bracteæ lineares. Calyx hiſpidus, rubicundus. Corolla purpureo-cærulea, calyce duplò longior. Antheræ rubræ. Semina compreſſa. Pappus ſcaber, nec plumoſus. Exemplaria indigena nondum mihi obvia fuere.
Nomen S. canadenſis huic plantæ, Alpium omnium Europæarum incolæ, minimè convenit; antiquiſſimum proindè reſtitui. A S. alpino Linnæi quam maximè diſcrepat. Confer *Pl. Ic. ex Herb. Linn. t.* 21.

palustris 2. SONCHUS pedunculis calycibuſque hiſpidis ſubumbellatis, foliis runcinatis baſi ſagittatis margine ſcabris.
Sonchus paluſtris. *Sp. Pl.* 1116. *Hudſ.* 337. *With.* 674. *Hull.* 177. *Relh.* 292. *Curt. Lond. faſc.* 5. *t.* 59. *Fl. Dan. t.* 606.
S. tricubitalis, folio cuſpidato. *Raii Syn.* 163.
S. arboreſcens alter. *Ger. em.* 294.
Angl. Tall Marſh Sow-thiſtle. *Pet. H. Brit. t.* 14. *f.* 7.

In paluſtribus ad ripas fluviorum. Marshes near the Thames below Plaistow Essex. & near Greenwich Kent. About near the Star Inn... River side at Reedham Norf.

SYNGENESIA—POLYGAMIA ÆQUALIS. 817

About Greenwich and Blackwall. *Rev.* *Curtis.* Near Streatham ferry, iſle of Ely. *Relh.*

Perennis. Fl. Julio, Auguſto.
Radix ramoſa, "minimè repens." *Curt.* Caules erecti, 6—8 pedales, ſubſimplices, folioſi, angulati, fiſtuloſi. Folia runcinata, acuta, glabra; baſi ſagittata, amplexicaulia; margine denticulato-ſcabra. Panicula terminalis, ſubumbellata vel cymoſa, multiflora, hiſpida, pilis denſis, glanduloſis, atris, uti calyx. Corolla flava, calyce duplò longior. Semina ſulcata. Pappus lævis.

3. SONCHUS pedunculis calycibuſque hiſpidis ſubumbellatis, foliis runcinatis denticulatis baſi cordatis, radice repente. arvensis
Sonchus arvenſis. *Sp. Pl.* 1116. *Hudſ.* 337. *With.* 674. *Hull.* 177. *Relh.* 291. *Sibth.* 237. *Abbot.* 169. *Curt. Lond. faſc.* 4. *t.* 53. *Engl. Bot. t.* 674.
S. repens, multis Hieracium majus. *Raii Syn.* 163.
S. arboreſcens. *Ger. em.* 294.
Hieracium majus. *Fuchſ. Hiſt.* 319.
Angl. Corn Sow-thiſtle. *Pet. H. Brit. t.* 14. *f.* 6.

In arvis et ad ſepes, ſolo argillaceo.

Perennis. Fl. Auguſto.
Radix repens, carnoſa, lacteſcens. Caulis 3-4 pedalis, erectus, ſubſimplex, teretiuſculus, folioſus, fiſtuloſus. Folia runcinata, acutiuſcula, glabra; baſi cordata, amplexicaulia; margine denticulato-ſpinuloſa. Panicula terminalis, pauciflora, ſubcymoſa, hiſpida, pilis glanduloſis, fuſcis. Calyx etiam hiſpidus. Corolla maxima, aurea. Semina ſulcata. Pappus lævis.

4. SONCHUS pedunculis tomentoſis, calycibus lævibus, foliis runcinatis dentatis.

Fig. 18 Hand-illustrated copy of Smith's *Flora Britannica*, once owned by the Revd Richard Dreyer FLS (1763–1838). The botanically accurate figures were painted by Dreyer both from nature and from figures in Smith and Sowerby's *English Botany* and William Curtis's *Flora Londinensis*.

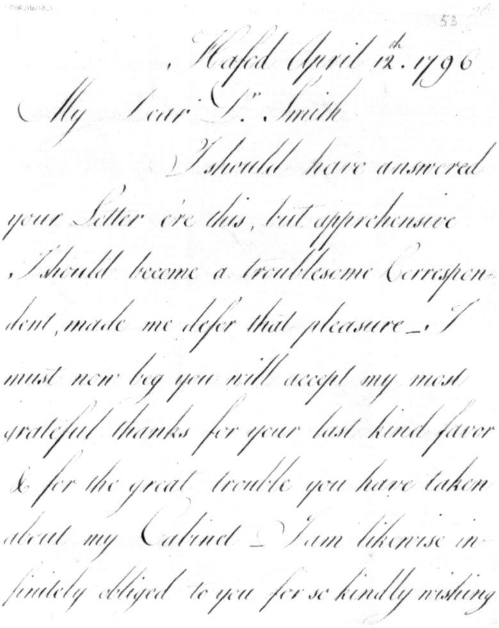

Hafod April 12th 1796

My Dear Dr Smith

I should have answered your Letter ere this, but apprehensive I should become a troublesome Correspondent, made me defer that pleasure — I must now beg you will accept my most grateful thanks for your last kind favor & for the great trouble you have taken about my Cabinet — I am likewise infinitely obliged to you for so kindly wishing

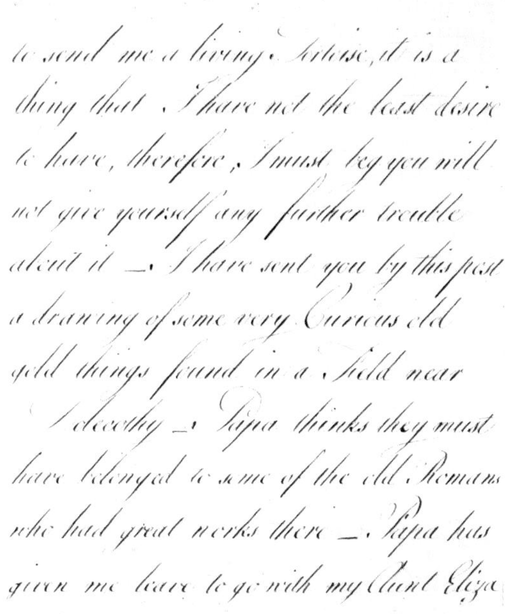

to send me a living Tortoise, it is a thing that I have not the least desire to have, therefore, I must beg you will not give yourself any further trouble about it — I have sent you by this post a drawing of some very Curious old gold things found in a field near Dolecothy — Papa thinks they must have belonged to some of the old Romans who had great works there — Papa has given me leave to go with my Aunt Eliza

Fig. 19 "It is a thing that I have not the least desire to have". A 12-year-old Mariamne Johnes turns down Smith's offer to send a live tortoise, 12 April 1796.

Fig. 20 Long-tailed skipper butterfly (*Urbanus proteus*) and Atlantic pigeonwings (*Clitoria mariana* L.). From Smith and John Abbot's *The Rarer Lepidopterous Insects of Georgia* (1797): the first illustrated work on American moths and butterflies. Samuel Goodenough described the name for the controversial genus *Clitoria* as "a singular piece of vulgar lasciviousness".

Fig. 21 Frontispiece by Ferdinand Bauer for volume six of John Sibthorp's *Flora Græca* (1806–1840), depicting Athens. Published in 1826, this was the last volume to be completed solely by Smith.

Fig. 22 Wild carnation (*Dianthus fruticosus* L.). From John Sibthorp's *Flora Græca* (1806–1840).

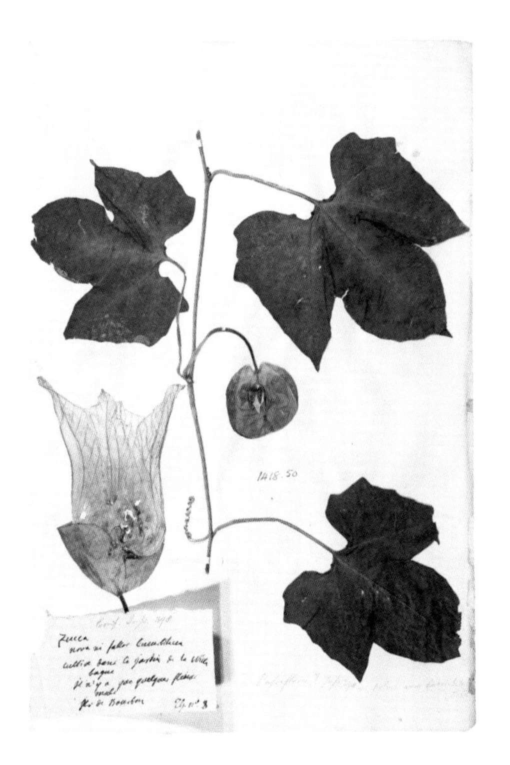

Fig. 23

Gathered from Réunion Island in the Indian Ocean, this undetermined specimen of the genus *Passiflora* entered Smith's herbarium via the herbarium of Carl Linnaeus the Younger.

Fig. 24

"With the flower having just opened, you will see the maidenly womb". Finding a way to delicately describe the 'lustfully gaping' female parts of *Viola tricolor* L. caused Smith much consternation when teaching Queen Charlotte. Specimen from Smith's herbarium.

Fig. 25

Commissioned by a grateful Linnean Society from sculptor Francis Leggatt Chantrey in 1825, Pleasance Smith later described this as "the only representation of him which retains the expression of his mind".

Fig. 26

The Meeting Room of the Linnean Society of London at Burlington House, Piccadilly, its home since 1873.

sensitiva in *Paradisus Londinensis*, using the text to give his version of its naming, raging at Smith for having "thought fit to quote *me* against *myself*". In a spectacular tirade he continued:

> Not that I ever thought the plant at all adequate to commemorate his botanical merits, for it is a low mean-looking hispid annual; and such is still my opinion of *some* of his labours, that if, like NAPOLEON the great, I had kingdoms instead of genera to bestow, he should wear one of the most brilliant diadems in my gift.[57]

Salisbury claimed that it was actually Smith who had selected this plant to bear his name and that Dryander had "permitted this child of pure friendship and solid merit, to pass for his till the real father owned it", thereby to lend the honour more gravitas.[58] The dispute was now picked up by *The Monthly Magazine's* 'Botanical Report', which, whilst conceding that Salisbury's account of the naming of *Smithia* "was very satisfactorily explained", reprimanded him for having perniciously revealed a secret of little public interest. The anonymous writer summarised the tensions of the last two years:

> Unfortunately for the science, Dr Smith and Mr Salisbury [...] are become such inveterate enemies, that while the one refuses to acknowledge even honours received from the hands of the other, the latter has declared war against the Linnaean system apparently for no other reason, but through it, to wound the sides of his former friend, the professed admirer and champion of that system.[59]

Unable to restrain his pen, Smith wrote to the editor to publicly refute Salisbury "in a decisive style" without having to stoop to his level, the letter appearing on the front page of the April issue.[60] Giving his own account of the naming of *Smithia sensitiva,* Smith made their formerly close bond perfectly apparent, revealing that Salisbury "was often projecting to name a plant after me". It was in "high spirits" that Salisbury called on Smith to inform him that Dryander was examining "a curious new sensitive genus from Bengal" and had announced, "let it be *Smithia*". Smith was clear that up until Salisbury's recent claims there had never been "any doubt or mystery about the matter", and attributed Salisbury's recent behaviour to that of a "lost friend", who, chagrined at their split, had wished to humiliate him. Smith invoked the support of the wider botanical community by claiming that Salisbury's infamous pamphlet had been barred entry to the library at Soho Square, implying that Salisbury was becoming increasingly isolated and ostracised by his contemporaries.[61]

Smith's friends had reacted with dismay to the publication of his letter. Turner wished Smith had "regarded the whole below his consequence to answer".[62] James Brodie was much more explicit:

> Dr Smith forgets—That the more you tread on a T[ur]d the more it stinks, he will deserve to be besmear'd. I have ventured to dissuade him from entering into a litterary contest with such a reptile, who wishes by such means to procure notice.[63]

Salisbury lost little time in penning his own response to Smith, but the editor of *The Monthly Magazine* refused to print it, declaring Salisbury had "outraged public decency by his personal rancour, private malice and bad manners".[64] Undeterred, Salisbury published it himself as a pamphlet. One by one Salisbury refuted the claims in Smith's own letter, and stated that Smith was now reneging on an earlier promise to acknowledge Salisbury's part in the naming. Salisbury concluded by denying accusations that he had caused the quarrel through envy of Smith's popular success: "For what could I possibly envy him? for his abuse of Adanson? for his difference with Curtis? […] for reproaching Lamarck […]? for being puffed by Thornton?"[65] This pamphlet appears to have had a very limited circulation (I can only trace two surviving copies, one of which was Smith's copy, at the Linnean Society Library, the other in the University of Cambridge Library), and there no surviving references to it in his correspondence.

Paradisus Londinensis continued as Salisbury's primary vehicle for attacking Smith, as well as the Linnaean system, describing it as so useless that it "now retards the progress of botany".[66] In March 1808 he published a new genus of North American plants first mentioned (but not named) in

Smith's *Introduction to Botany*; Salisbury named this new genus *Hookera* in honour of his botanical artist William Hooker.[67] A "sad grievance" for Smith, he had been preparing to name the same genus *Brodiæa*, after his Scottish patron James Brodie. He had also been intending to bestow the name *Hookeria* on a new genus of mosses, after botanist William Jackson Hooker, but would not now be able to do so due to the similarity of the names. Though he considered forging ahead with his *Brodiæa*, he instead resolved to "never let S[alisbury] know how he has plagued us".[68]

In less than a month, Smith had changed his mind, compelled by the discovery of "an infamous fraud" perpetuated on Sir Joseph Banks. Salisbury claimed as his source for the Australian plants *Corybas aconitiflorus* and *Byblis liniflora*, published in *Paradisus Londinensis* in October 1807 and February 1808, respectively, the gardens at Cassiobury, the 5th Earl of Essex's estate near Watford. A suspicious Robert Brown, an expert on the Australian flora, and Aylmer Bourke Lambert soon identified them as having been illicitly acquired from Sir Joseph Banks's own unpublished figures, leading Lambert to comment that he "might as well have quoted old Mrs S[alisbury]."[69]

Smith struggled to contain his glee, informing Turner that he was "malicious enough to rejoice at this 10 times more than if he had stolen it elsewhere".[70] Smith was determined that the unworthy Hooker, Salisbury's accomplice, should not have a plant named in his honour, and quickly moved to establish the priority of his own names, though it contravened taxonomic decorum. In April 1808, he sent papers to the Linnean Society establishing the genera *Brodiæa* and *Hookeria*, but affected botanical innocence, stating that his establishment of the latter was not an attack on Salisbury.[71] Dawson Turner, however, knew it was "calculated to make quite a stir in the Society" and feared retaliation.[72] Indeed, after the reading of the first paper Salisbury commented, "privately it was an attack on him, but nothing was said publickly".[73]

Salisbury waited until September, and the final issue of *Paradisus Londinensis*, to comment, within his observations for *Hookera pulchella*. Salisbury claimed that Smith had knowingly misled the Fellows of the Linnean Society by wording his *Brodiæa* paper so particularly that those in attendance would have no reason not to think it a new genus. Salisbury was surprisingly pragmatic, stating that it was of "little importance which of these names is adopted by future botanists"; he was confident that if his ideas respecting the genus were correct, "they will be confirmed in spite of all Dr J E Smith's opposition, whose multiplied acts of injustice to me whether open or concealed, I sincerely forgive".[74]

Undeterred, Smith forged ahead in his quest to have his own names accepted, and exerted gentle pressure on the Linnean Society to have them printed in the next volume of its *Transactions*, by which they would become established. Smith was confident that the Council would fully vindicate his course of action, relying on the fact that neither paper explicitly referenced the dispute. *Hookeria*, the least contentious of the pair, quickly proceed to publication in November 1808, but *Brodiæa* was held back in a reportedly acrimonious Council meeting. A bruised Smith informed Alexander Macleay that "all think it an undue deference to a villain who is our disgrace", and that some Council members had been disappointed to see Smith "yield to such opposition, not to mention the brutality" with which the decision was informed.[75] Smith maintained that the *Brodiæa* paper was not an attack, merely an attempt to "establish a good name in preference to a bad one". He forced the Society's hand by pointing out that in publishing *Hookeria* they were also committed to do the same for *Brodiæa* to avoid causing further confusion—"for there cannot be 2 Hookerias".[76] This was followed by the announcement of *Brodiæa* in the second edition of *Introduction to Botany* (1809) and in his description of *Fucus brodiæi* (also named by Smith for Brodie) in *English Botany*.[77] Smith's paper 'Characters of a new Liliaceous Genus called Brodiaea' was eventually published in March 1810, in which Salisbury's prior *Hookera* was acknowledged as a synonym by way of a footnote.[78] Despite the underhand way in which Smith had gone about securing his own names he received full sanction at the 1808 anniversary dinner, where his merits to the Society were praised and a toast was drunk "with all standing! & followed by 3 great rounds of applause!!".[79] This was to prove the final battle in the war between Smith and Salisbury, and Smith had emerged triumphant, albeit under dubious circumstances. Within a year Salisbury had squandered any sympathy this particular episode may have garnered him.

He Stands Between a Rogue and a Fool

In early 1809, Robert Brown's paper 'On the Proteaceae of Jussieu' was read across four meetings at the Linnean Society. In it, Brown introduced many new genera and species of this large family of plants, as a result of his investigations into Australian flora. Before it was published in the Society's *Transactions*, Joseph Knight, the gardener of Linnean Fellow George Hibbert, published a pamphlet entitled *On the cultivation of the plants belonging to the natural order of Proteeæ*. In part, it plagiarised Brown's paper, repeating many of the new names that Brown had coined, even though neither Knight nor Hibbert had been present at the meetings. The botanical community howled in indignation, and immediately pointed the finger at Salisbury (a known associate of Knight's), who *had* been present. Smith finally felt vindicated, and it appears that this, more than anything, finally gave him closure on the controversy. Smith informed Brown that he had received the pamphlet but had no intentions of keeping it, and resolved to give only a cursory glance to any of Salisbury's future output. He wrote, "He is now taken off my hands by the enemies he makes on all sides, & is a striking proof how much bad principles & feelings not only pervert, but absolutely sink, good natural talents. I am happy to say my resentment has become extinct much faster than my friendship did".[80] Brown, confident in his superior botanical talents, dismissed Salisbury, stating to Smith that he "scarce kn[e]w what to think of him except that in affinity he stands between a rogue & a fool" and that he found him "wholly destitute of judgement, the little that he has being chiefly expended in grafting his lies upon a stock of truth".[81] Salisbury had ostracised himself, at least within the Linnean Society, though he had been retreating from that body since his resignation as vice-president. Instead, he turned his attentions to the Horticultural Society of London, which he played a central role in founding in 1804 (the Society rented its rooms from the Linnean Society until 1819), and for which body he acted as Secretary. From this point on, the Linnean community ignored him; though he had established priority with his *Hookera*, Smith's name of *Brodiæa* became the preferred choice and is the conserved name for the genus.[82] Other than papers for the Horticultural Society, Salisbury published little else in his own lifetime, pinning his hopes instead on a vast 'Genera Plantarum' that was only to be published as a fragment in 1866. His death in 1829 went unnoticed in the papers and both of the Societies he had played such instrumental roles in, so that in 1835 a contributor to *The Gardener's Magazine* "had the greatest difficulty finding the time of his death", revealed only by tracking down the landlord of the house in which he had lived.[83] *Salisburia adiantifolia*, the plant Smith had named in his honour in happier days, has since reverted to *Ginkgo biloba.*

She Might Well Have Married an East India Captain!

The dispute had a profound effect upon Smith, most clearly displayed by his partial withdrawal from the botanical scene. Since the publication of the third volume of *Flora Britannica* in 1804, the fourth and concluding volume had been eagerly anticipated. In February 1808 he announced that it was to become his main objective for the year, only for Smith to again be diverted when he learnt of the death of William Wood, botanical contributor for Abraham Rees's *Cyclopædia* (and for whom Smith had filled in during an earlier indisposition). Smith offered his help, asking Rees for "the whole bot[anica]l department" of the *Cyclopædia.* To Turner, Smith implied that his involvement was to be a temporary measure until he could "arrange matters some other way", believing it "important to have in good & sound hands a botanical work of which 5000 sell".[84] In the event, Smith remained the principal botanical contributor until the *Cyclopædia* concluded in 1820, writing some 3,348 articles on botany and 57 biographies of botanists, receiving the handsome sum of 10 guineas per printed sheet. Yet certain friends recognised it as a diversion of Smith's botanical genius. Some also saw the on-going lectures at the Royal Institution as another fruitless distraction. In late 1808, Lewis Weston Dillwyn, a friend of Dawson Turner's, registered his surprise that Smith was again "speculating" at the Institution—"it surprizes me because I cannot suppose that empty Benches are productive, & I heard that he had little else last season. Lectures on Botany must in my opinion be dry".[85]

It became a frequent refrain of Smith's that *Flora Britannica* was to be finished "next winter".[86] As with the third volume, a hesitant Smith was awaiting the publication of several other works before proceeding with his own. Some of Smith's friends were more understanding than others. Goodenough exerted an unwavering pressure, constantly asking when the new volume might appear, but to little avail, and as the years wore on the requests for updates became less frequent. James Brodie was less sanguine, informing Smith in January 1809 that he was "nearly angry" with him on account of the delays: "where you have already done so much good, & consequently the publick [...] are so justly in expectation, how can you stop? Waiting for other publications! if so, you must leave it to the next generations".[87] He was even more outspoken with Turner, "accusing Dr Smith of lazyness, I must now give him up". It was, he wrote, "unjust, not to proceed in a work his country is so much interested in, & if we are to judge by what is published, is more likely to render him immortal, than any other work he can engage in—I mean the Flora Britannica".[88]

There is certainly listlessness evident in this period of Smith's life, in which he increasingly gave himself over to the trappings of the gentleman's lifestyle. Turner, geographically the closest of Smith's inner circle, witnessed much of Smith's unusual behaviour at this time. In 1809, Dillwyn, George Sowerby (a son of James Sowerby) and their friend named Leach, who has never been successfully identified, visited Norwich. Smith declined seeing Leach "because he said, it was such a bore to shew the Linnaean Collection!".[89] It was about this time that his long-standing acquaintance with Thomas William Coke, later 1st Earl of Leicester (of the seventh creation), developed into a fully-fledged friendship. Coke was a famous agricultural reformer and a long-standing MP for Norfolk, as well as being a staunch defender of personal and political freedom. During the American War of Independence, Coke claimed to have drunk George Washington's health every evening, and described him as "the greatest man on earth".[90] Smith and his wife soon became regular features at Coke's home, Holkham Hall, Norfolk, where he entertained his guests "right royally". Turner, another frequent visitor, described it as a household that consumed "365 hogs, 500 sheep, 52 bullocks, & 1200 barrels of beer annually", its vast size rendering it an easy place in which to become lost.[91] The mornings were spent "looking at pictures, & turning over books & drawings, or walking & talking with pleasant women, & our evenings in playing cards". Though Turner acknowledged that Smith seemed happy at the functions, they were not aiding the production of his publications. Even faithful Pleasance began to feel the strain. In 1811 his London commitments kept him from home for three months, terminated only by the onset of a sudden ailment. Pleasance had spent the time at her father's house in Lowestoft complaining "she might well have married an East India Captain!".[92] Smith's social aspirations were given a check in 1811, when his nomination to join the Society of Dilettanti was blackballed, along with all the other nominees for that year, a not uncommon occurrence in elections at this most exclusive of London clubs. The blow was softened with the knowledge that he received fewer blackballs than anyone else.[93]

In faraway Norwich, Smith appeared unaware, or uninterested, in the subtle shifts that were beginning to shake the botanical world. The harbinger of this was the death, on 19 October 1810, of Jonas Dryander. Sir Joseph Banks's "rough diamond" and "walking dictionary" of a librarian had been a constant presence at Soho Square since 1782.[94] His bluntness had a "great effect with innovators, impertinents & Popinjays".[95] Though it was feared the loss would have an adverse effect on Soho Square, Banks found an eminently able successor in the Linnean Society's librarian, Robert Brown. A staunch student of the Linnaean school of botany, Dryander had consistently clashed with Richard Salisbury and his innovations. Brown was through and through a proponent of Jussieu's natural system, and it was he who now did "the honors at breakfast and—does not blow in the teapot".[96]

Smith's apathy was also apparent in his publications, with which he was taking few risks, even indulging in non-botanical works. In March 1808, a curious tale entitled 'Fanaticism: A Vision', from an anonymous pen, appeared in *The Monthly Magazine*. Smith revealed his authorship of the piece to Aylmer Bourke Lambert: "no one suspects me, but as it is dated Norwich, every body's curiosity is agog. I beg you will keep it secret". His purpose was to show "the evil of setting up any one speculative point of faith in preference to the general tenour & doctrines of the gospel, & to prove that any thing may be made a subject of dispute by fanatics. I had the evangelical or methodistical people chiefly in view—the pest of the church & of all true Christianity".[97] Smith depicts himself awaking in a dystopian future, in which the once proud city of Norwich has been ruined by the fanatical pursuit of producing a seamless garment, inspired by a discussion over St John 19:23: "the coat of Christ was without seam, woven from the top throughout". Two camps formed: those who believed it had been "literally woven in a loom, so as to be of one piece, without a seam", and those who thought that as such a loom had never been heard of, the coat "might probably have been knitted". The leaders of the dispute treated the latter explanation as "heretical", and quickly gained the ascendency, burning all dissenters. Norwich's industry was given over to the production of seamless garments, the cathedral filled with looms and strange chants of "blessed by the holy garment, thrice blessed by the holy seamless garment, which endureth for ever and ever!". After being denounced as an "infidel, heretic, deist, and atheist" for unknowingly querying the inferior quality of the textiles now produced, Smith escapes into the country with an old friend he recognised, who relates all that has passed. The narrative ends with Smith's companion felled by a mace-wielding fanatic: "all attempts to escape were in vain. He levelled his weapon at me, and as it was falling to crush me, I started with horror and awoke".[98] According to Smith, the piece was "much liked, even by the most orthodox, the clergy of the Cathedral &c.".[99]

In 1810 Smith published *A Tour to Hafod*, an homage to Thomas Johnes's picturesque Welsh paradise. In development since his honeymoon visit of 1796, it consisted of 15 extraordinarily beautiful views of Hafod, delineated by John 'Warwick' Smith, accompanied by brief, explanatory text. Lavishly produced in a limited edition of just 100, it cost £12 12s. *The Eclectic Review* praised the work for its "typical elegance and correctness, as well as for the masterly execution of its plates",[100] though others saw it as further vacillating; William Jackson Hooker described it as "a sadly trumpery book".[101] While many were still waiting for the conclusion of Smith's great work, another tour journal followed in late 1811 instead. *Lachesis Lapponica, or a Tour in Lapland*, was a translation of Linnaeus's journal from his 1732 expedition to Lapland. The first new edition of a Linnaean work since 1792's *Flora Lapponica*, this was also the first publication of the journal in any form whatsoever, and as such had been highly anticipated by the botanical community. In the preface, Smith claimed that the manuscript was so valuable that on the sale of the collections "it was remarked that these papers at least ought to have been retained in Sweden, as a national property". An awkward manuscript consisting of both Swedish and Latin, Smith had commissioned Charles Troilius, a London merchant, to translate the Swedish as early as 1803. Smith warned that it was "such a journal as a man would write for his own use, without the slightest thought of its ever being seen by any other person" in defence of its rather unaffected composition.[102] Though Dawson Turner was initially sceptical, he soon retracted his words after reading the published version, commenting that it had "afforded me a pleasure very far beyond what I had expected" and that nothing has surprised him more than "the wonderful acuteness of Linnaeus's mind at that early age".[103]

Of course, throughout this period Smith was still working at *Flora Græca* and *English Botany*, as well as the *Cyclopædia*. The concluding part of the first volume of the Greek flora appeared in 1808. A much more significant milestone was achieved in the spring of 1814, with the publication of the final issue of *English Botany*. In total, 36 volumes and 2,592 coloured plates, issued in 267 individual parts, were produced, constituting a record for an on-going botanical publication at that time. On sending Sowerby the last four drawings in February that year, a sentimental Smith remarked that it was "not without a melancholy feeling that I put the last stroke to a work w[hi]ch has kept us, my dear friend, long together!".[104] They unofficially committed to future supplementary volumes to allow for new discoveries, though promised nothing at this time. Smith dissuaded Sowerby from dedicating the indexes to the Prince Regent, as to seek royal approval would not only delay publication, but would cost them handsomely as the prince would expect a gift of the entire run. Instead it was dedicated to the Linnean Society. In the advertisement announcing its completion, Sowerby wrote of his satisfaction in having produced and completed a "National Flora" ahead of Peter Simon Pallas's *Flora Rossica* (1784–1815), Nicolaus Host's *Flora Austriaca* (1761–1831) and Georg

Christian Oeder's *Flora Danica* (1761–1883). It had also bookended the French Revolutionary and Napoleonic wars. Commencing in 1790, the year after the outbreak of the French Revolution, and terminating in 1814, the year of Napoleon's short-lived exile to Elba, Sowerby hoped that the peace "will long promote the intercourse of British Botanists with their continental Friends".[105] *English Botany* also concluded to propitious advantage for Smith's own ambitions, highlighting the commencement of a bid to become the next Professor of Botany at Cambridge, as well as royal recognition of Smith's contributions to the nation's scientific life.

CHAPTER ELEVEN

The Lord Treasurer of Botany

In June 1813, Thomas Martyn, the Professor of Botany at Cambridge, wrote to the antiquarian and botanist Sir Thomas Gery Cullum that he was "standing [...] on the verge of both worlds, [...] looking forward to 'the meads of asphodel and amaranthine bowers'".[1] He had been in post since 1762, appointed after the resignation of the previous post holder, his father John Martyn. He was now aged 78, and was thinking of his successor.

The professorship was formed of three distinct strands: (1) the University Professorship, an unpaid position voted for by the University's Senate; (2) Dr Walker's Reader or Lecturer, appointed by the five governors of the botanic garden, also unpaid but entailing the right to read an annual course of botanical lectures, as well as control of said garden and use of the plants therein; and (3) the Regius Professorship, appointed by the Crown and commanding a salary of £200 per annum. Over the course of his long career, Martyn had become one of the most popular botanists working in Britain, but increasingly frail health had prevented him from lecturing since 1796. In Cambridge his absence became even more noticeable after he moved to Pertenhall, Bedfordshire, in 1798. He attempted to revive the study of botany in 1804, when he recommended local botanist and King's College Fellow Richard Relhan as lecturer in his stead, but there was not "Botanical spirit enough in the University" and the idea was abandoned.[2]

At least three possible contenders had already signified some kind of interest by the time Smith became involved, including Relhan. Smith proposed delivering a series of botany lectures, by which he could establish a

Cambridge presence in preparation for the contest. Martyn, one of the earliest Fellows of the Linnean Society, and both a long-standing vice-president and a friend of Smith, suffered no professional jealousy. Martyn felt that he would be "like the dog in the manger" were he to deny anyone else the role of teacher when he was unable to continue himself.[3] However, he was realistic about the other barriers in Smith's way: the current lack of interest in the subject at the university, the loss of his lecture room to the Professor of Mineralogy, Edward Daniel Clarke, and the more problematic issue that Smith was neither a member of the University nor the Church of England.

Martyn immediately suggested a plan of action: if he could gain the support of three of the five trustees of the University Botanic Garden, Martyn would offer to resign Dr Walker's Lectureship in favour of Smith. Once a foothold in the University was secured, Smith would be well-positioned for the Regius professorship, and to canvas for the University Professorship when the time came (Martyn indicated that he would also resign these posts once enough support was established). The two men placed their trust in the terms of the Walkerian bequest, which stated that the lecturer did not have to be a member of the university and could even be a foreigner (thus also negating the need to be an Anglican), whilst the Crown was perfectly entitled to appoint a stranger to the Regius professorship. As for the University post, Martyn cited the example of the first holder of that post, Richard Bradley, appointed in 1724, whose academic qualifications extended no further than being a Fellow of the Royal Society (although he was also a prolific botanical and horticultural author), and Martyn's own father, John, who never took a degree. Despite this, Martyn warned that Smith would meet with "a powerful opposition for the Professorship".[4]

Smith immediately started canvassing for the lectureship, visiting Cambridge in early June 1813 to sound out the trustees. With little effort he secured the support of two: the Master of Trinity College (and Bishop of Bristol), William Mansel, and the University's Vice-Chancellor, John Davie. Of the remaining trustees, he knew that the Professor of Physic, Sir Isaac Pennington was hostile on account of Smith not being a member of the University, but felt confident that the undecided Provost of King's College,

Humphrey Sumner, and Master of St John's College, William Craven, could be swayed.[5] However, when the trustees met in mid-June to appoint a new curator for the botanic garden, Martyn's recommendation that Smith be appointed the Walkerian Lecturer was rejected. The trustees sensed their hand might be forced once the professorship itself became vacant. Smith had attempted to forestall such an outcome by indicating that he would hold the post conditionally, resigning if he was not subsequently chosen professor, but to no avail.

Undeterred, Smith set his sights on the goal of the professorship itself. He planned to enter himself as a Fellow Commoner (a rank of student above pensioners—students who paid their own tuition—but below noblemen) at Trinity College and obtain a knighthood. Ennobled, he would then be entitled to apply for an MA in two years' time without having to subscribe to the 39 Articles of the Church of England (though he later discovered that subscription was required for all degrees). Moreover, Smith had already secured the promise of the Regius professorship from the Prime Minister, Lord Liverpool, whenever it should become vacant. Smith was prepared for both outcomes: "If I am not chosen I am but where I was; if I succeed they shall find me desirous of justifying their choice". Smith's rivals were a Mr Brooke (though "a man of honour", Smith expected him to swiftly withdraw, only wanting the position for a residence); George Leathes (whom the Vice-Chancellor supported); and Richard Relhan ("quite out of the question"). Despite having been rebuffed once already, and the warnings from Martyn, Smith was confident that the University would choose "an efficient professor, & not an idle one".[6]

Warm and Weighty Friends

This was not the first time that the idea of a knighthood had been mentioned, though until this point Smith had declined the honour. In April 1811 the Prince Regent (appointed in February, following his father King George III's final descent into madness) confirmed his position as a supporter of the Arts in a speech at London's Somerset House, then home of the Royal Society and the Royal Academy of Arts. Smith was in attendance and reported how the Prince had declared the work of those in attendance had proven "our eminence above other nations in so many things".[7] The Linnean Society actively sought the Prince's patronage and dispatched its president to the Prince's levée (a formal gathering at which attendees could court influence and curry favour) of 22 April 1812. After a gracious reception the Prince agreed to become Patron of the Linnean Society, though Smith's intermittent ill-health prevented the Society from presenting the Charter-Book for the Prince's signature until 15 June 1813. This began an unbroken line of royal patronage that continues to the present day. With this royal boost, the Linnean Society's Council insisted that Smith put himself forward for a knighthood, a move he initially resisted.[8] Pressed, Smith wrote to Alexander Macleay to determine the correct procedures when applying for such an honour. He made it clear that, should the honour be given, it should be for his role as President of the Linnean Society "out of due respect to the Society".[9]

Smith returned to Cambridge in July 1813 and began canvassing anew, quickly attracting a wide cross-section of support; Sir Joseph Banks was particularly desirous of his former protégé's success. Smith's assiduous courting of the upper classes throughout his scientific career now became useful. Specifically, he needed the support of the college heads, who would nominate two candidates to the Senate.

Thomas William Coke and other "warm & weighty friends" including the vice-chancellor; William Mansel, Bishop of Bristol and Master of Trinity; Martin Davy, William Frere and Joseph Turner, respectively the Masters of Caius, Downing, and Pembroke; the Provost of King's, Humphrey Sumner, and "others of less note". Coke was obtaining the interests of John Russell, 6th Duke of Bedford and Philip Yorke, 3rd Earl of Hardwicke. In this battle of "whiggism & science, against mere old-fashioned espirit de corps", Smith resolutely refused to hide his Unitarianism, also enlisting fellow dissenter and abolitionist hero William Roscoe. He implored Roscoe to mention his cause to Prince William Frederick, Duke of Gloucester and Edinburgh, and Chancellor of Cambridge, to help convince the ditherers amongst the college heads. Unfortunately, the Duke could offer little support, having committed himself to neutrality. By the end of August Smith had gained the support of eight college heads, plus that of the vice-chancellor, at which point he needed just one more to obtain the crucial majority.[10]

Smith named the genus *Roscœa* for abolitionist William Roscoe (1753–1831). This unpublished plate for *Roscœa falcata* appears in Smith's copy of *Icones Pictæ*.

Meanwhile, a strong Church and University contingent was amassing in the university. The same month, Martyn informed Smith of the true reasons why he had been previously turned down for the Lectureship. Sir Isaac Pennington, the hostile Professor of Physic, had protested on the grounds that "as Dr Smith is not a member of the University, nor of the Church of England, this makes a difficulty in granting any appointment here".[11] Smith identified conspiracy on the part of Pennington, whom he claimed was "unfavourably disposed towards a person, whose only pretensions were founded in a desire to be useful". The President of St John's College, mathematician James Wood, was also hostile, and Smith believed that Wood had unduly influenced the Master of St John's, William Craven, by stoking fears of the corrupting influence of outsiders. Whilst both Martyn and Smith were confident that current support would be sufficient to surpass such objections, the dispersal of the trustees during the summer vacation put everything on hold.[12] Despite this, Smith ended the year convinced he had made "considerable progress" that would lead to eventual success.[13]

Smith's confidence was to prove misplaced, and throughout his campaign he consistently failed to act upon the advice of his friends, several of who had first-hand knowledge of Cambridge politics. Sir Thomas Gery Cullum, admitted to Trinity College in 1786, begged Smith to become a member of the university "before it is too late", which would remove one of the principal objections to his candidacy, and suggested he try to obtain the knighthood at the same time.[14] Smith stalled, claiming that the knighthood should be delayed until the situation was more certain.[15] Instead, he placed his faith in the idea of progress, due process and the righteousness of his candidacy. Even Roscoe, a fellow stranger to Cambridge, questioned Smith's obstinacy on this point, but Smith justified his actions by citing the precedent of the first two professors of botany—respectively a stranger and a member who never took a degree.[16]

This block to his advancement caused Smith to lose patience, and by the summer he decided to forge ahead, changing his plans yet again. He now intended to be "dubbed" at the Prince Regent's next Levée and to enter Cambridge at the start of the next academic year.[17] The Home Secretary, Henry Addington, 1st Viscount Sidmouth made the necessary arrangements, and on 28 July 1814, the last Levée of the season, Smith attended and presented the Prince Regent with the first volume of the Linnean Society's *Transactions*, which:

> His R[oyal] Highness received most graciously & thanked me. L[or]d Sidmouth stood next him, & asked him to confer on me the honour of knighthood. The Prince asked him my Christian name—laid the sword on my shoulder & said "rise Sir Ja[me]s Edw[ar]d"—after which I passed on, having kissed his hand. I took care to be among the first who got in, w[hi]ch I think is always best—he being tired after a while, & hurried.[18]

Smith was the first person to be knighted specifically for his services to science. Writing to Pleasance (now Lady Smith) a few days later at her father's in Lowestoft, he hoped that she had "allowed her light to shine before men, & women too". As was the convention, Smith had entered a paragraph into the London and Norwich papers announcing the news, as well as having new cards made up for himself and Pleasance. Despite his heavy schedule—he was in London to work on the *Cyclopædia*—he was now obliged to drop his card in at many places, which he admitted he would rather not do, "but I must be careful on such an occasion".[19] His friends reacted with joy at the news of the knighthood: Lambert congratulated Smith on his "increasing Honors".[20] Samuel Goodenough advised Smith to "notice the concomitant effects" of gaining a title (Goodenough had been elevated to Bishop of Carlisle in 1808), and that Lady Smith now had to assume "a new rank in Society". By Goodenough's own estimation, she now stood at the pinnacle of Norwich society, not even surpassed by the Bishop of Norwich's wife.[21] Nevertheless, despite his appreciation of the honour, Smith hoped to make the title "as little inconvenience as possible by thinking little about it", and was mortified when Sowerby addressed a parcel to him as baronet—"Sir Jas Edd Smith Norwich is sufficient for my address".[22]

You Cannot Be Allowed to Sleep at Your Post

On 1 August 1814 a Grand Jubilee was held in Hyde Park to celebrate both the end of the war with France (following Napoleon's abdication in April) and the centenary of Hanoverian rule. Smith witnessed the festivities from the roof of William Smith's, the dissenting MP for Norwich, house at 16 Queen Anne's Gate, on the south side of St James's Park, including a hot-air balloon flight, which passed directly overhead, and a re-enactment of the Battle of the Nile on the Serpentine. As the evening wore on Smith grew cold, and spying that the park did not look too crowded decided to "set forth alone to see what I could". Sir James Edward Smith, his new title still fresh, cut a lonely figure; as he "passed through thousands of people" he "regretted that I had no one with me". He stayed and watched the fireworks and festivities in Green Park until half past one in the morning.[23]

With the start of a new academic year, and a new vice-chancellor, this time George Thackeray (a new one was elected each year), Smith once again changed his mind respecting Cambridge and now intended to focus purely on obtaining the Lectureship. Persuaded by Joseph Turner, the Dean of Norwich and Master of Pembroke College, and seconded by the Bishop of Bristol, they were confident that the university could not avoid choosing Smith as next professor, and furthermore that he should be given an MA without entering the university at all.[24] However, Smith's vacillating was beginning to have a detrimental effect on his campaign. In December, the previously supportive Bishop of Bristol informed Smith that owing to a prior promise, he must "with infinite Reluctance" publicly back Richard Relhan, though he felt Smith the better qualified by far.[25] Smith received another blow in the same month when vice-chancellor Thackeray refused to assist Smith in obtaining the Lectureship; "so the matter must rest", as it did for the greater part of 1815, whilst Smith awaited the appointment of a more sympathetic vice-chancellor.[26]

In July 1815, Pleasance's father, Robert Reeve, died; several months later Samuel Goodenough wrote regarding rumours that Smith "had lately a considerable accession of fortune".[27] Whilst not leaving the Smiths completely independent, Reeve's bequests (the annual dividend from £8,157 13s 7d of government bonds, £100 per annum for Smith's own use, plus the Surrey Street house) allowed Sir James Edward and Lady Smith to make the most of their new titles, and further freed Smith from the onerous task of making a living by writing.[28]

On 8 September Smith set out for a five-week tour of England and Wales with one of his "best-loved friends", Thomas William Coke. The tour had two principal objectives: to attend the Wynnstay Agricultural Meeting, near Wrexham, hosted by Sir Watkin Williams-Wynn, and to visit as many of Smith's far-flung friends as possible, including Thomas Johnes at Hafod, William Roscoe at Allerton and Samuel Goodenough at Rose Castle, Cumberland. The trip would also allow Smith to forge new alliances with some of Coke's influential friends: as they passed through the Midlands they stayed at the respective homes of Francis Russell, Marquess of Tavistock, Russell's father the Duke of Bedford and the Viscount Anson, Thomas Anson. Smith considered the acquaintance of the Russells in particular "a great acquisition".[29] However, on 14 September, Smith received a letter from Norwich imparting dreadful and unexpected news: the death of his younger brother, Francis, who had suddenly died of "water in the chest"—or pleural effusion—three days previously, leaving a widow and six children.[30] Francis had been Smith's closest sibling in both age and temperament, and in recent years the two brothers had been closer than at any time since childhood. Smith was left reeling; Francis's death was "a blow I never felt before—I can perceive no ray of comfort [...], the greatest loss (except one) that I could have had".[31] His first instinct was to return to Norwich, but Coke "absolutely forbad it"; even with the utmost haste he would arrive too late "to be of material use, nor to share in the sad scenes now probably at hand". Nevertheless, he felt isolated, and wrote to his wife longing for her company as "one word from you, who know how I feel, w[oul]d be worth a thous[an]d".[32]

The trip to Wynnstay was cancelled, and the party instead moved north to Shugborough, the Staffordshire home of Viscount Anson. Though surrounded by compassionate friends, paintings and sculpture, his grief remained raw: he described his previous encounters with mourning as "mere 'tickling of the fancy' compared to this. This is bitterness without alloy".[33] The only consolations were that Francis had not been "conscious of his end approaching, so he was spared the pangs of parting", and that he had left his affairs in such a way that his family would not be entirely destitute (though it later appeared that this was not the case at all).[34] Smith's main support at this time was his youngest sister Frances Julia, or Fanny, who lived in Liverpool with her merchant husband Thomas Martin and their children. After spending a week with them at the end of September, he met with Coke at William Roscoe's home at Allerton Hall for the abridged end of the tour. Journeys to Hafod and Rose Castle were now out of the question, though even in his grief he was able to make the best of his proximity to the upper classes. The Duke of Bedford became a Fellow, and the highly regarded Edward Smith Stanley, later 13th Earl of Derby, agreed to become a new vice-president with the next vacancy. Smith returned home to Norwich on 23 October with mixed feelings, desirous of being amongst his family but dreading the reminders of his departed brother. "I think of things", he wrote, "to say or do with poor Fra[nci]s as if he were still alive".[35]

Dawson Turner, geographically the closest of Smith's intimate friends, watched with considerable unease as Smith's previously famous industry began to be overwhelmed by a series of competing interests. Family concerns, increasingly regular bouts of ill health and the interminable Cambridge campaign all dominated Smith's attention. Smith revelled in the social privileges granted to him as a knight bachelor, having finally attained a rank to justify the long years of hard graft in the lecture hall, study and drawing room. On his first annual trip to London following his knighthood, Lady Smith, at home in Norwich, received frequent letters detailing his exploits, including attendance at Royal Society Club dinner with "the Duke of Somerset, 5 baronets, 6 esquires, [the astronomer] Dr [William] Herschell & your devoted knight!".[36]

Turner complained to a friend that Smith was sleeping "upon his laurels, or employs himself only in what I wish he did not do, writing for the Encyclopedia. Hooker says that his name is miserably low at Paris, whilst Robert Brown is extolled to the skies & deservedly so".[37] Since the completion of *English Botany* Smith had not taken up any new writing projects, focusing his attentions on *Flora Græca* and the *Cyclopædia*, in addition to producing new editions of popular works *Introduction to Botany* in 1814 and 1819 and *Compendium Floræ Britannicæ* in 1816 and 1818. Other prospects, including the long-awaited conclusion to *Flora Britannica* lay unfulfilled, though not entirely forgotten by Smith and his public. Goodenough took up the gauntlet again at the end of 1814, enquiring after the fourth volume and telling Smith, "you cannot be allowed to sleep at your Post".[38] Smith was fully aware of Turner's hostility towards the *Cyclopædia*. On concluding his work on *Cyclopædia* in 1819, he stated to Turner that he "could do nothing more extensively useful".[39] Over the course of 11 years, Smith had contributed 3,291 botanical articles and 57 biographies of botanists. Turner, however, was in the minority amongst Smith's friends, who generally reacted with enthusiasm to Smith's contributions and saw the value of his scientific input into such a work. Aylmer Bourke Lambert was so delighted with Smith's biography of John Ray that he exclaimed it "ought for men of science to be written in letters of gold & put up".[40] There were also complimentary messages from

Joseph Franz von Jacquin in Vienna, applauding Smith's insertions "of botanical notice", and Olof Swartz in Stockholm, who was willing to obtain it "at any prize or rate".[41]

Francis's death was just the first of a series of sorrows to overwhelm the Smith family at this time. Owing to Pleasance Smith's destruction of the family correspondence, we possess only the most tantalising of hints, contained in a letter from Dawson Turner to William Borrer sent in December 1815:

> Of Sir James Smith I hear an unfavourable report: it is believed that his lungs, which never were strong, are now diseased, & Lady Smith writes to her family full of alarm. Since he came to his fortune he has had nothing but vexation. His sister deranged & her husband threatening him with a chancery suit, one brother a bankrupt, & another just dead, leaving a large family in low circumstances, not to say in penury. It is a twelvemonth since I saw him except for a minute.[42]

Whilst Smith's lungs soon recovered, the same could not be said for the Smith family. John Frederick, the last surviving of Smith's brothers, had declared bankruptcy that November. The 'deranged' sister was Sarah Maria, the eldest of the Smith girls, who had married Charles Lloyd, a cantankerous and volatile Presbyterian minister (it is not known what came of the chancery suit). In 1811 she gave birth to a son, and appears to have descended into madness shortly afterwards. Only the most obtuse references remain in the surviving correspondence, but confirmation of her continued affliction emerges many years later, in 1838, when she appears in the admissions register of the Heigham Hall Asylum, located just outside Norwich. No particulars are given, but in 1843 a Commission and Inquisition of Lunacy found that she "is a lunatic of curious lucid intervals so that she is not sufficient for the government of herself". The commission had no details of her nearest heir. Sarah Maria died at the asylum in September 1850, the last surviving of Smith's siblings.[43]

He Has Nothing Left But a Collection of Black Beetles

Not long after Robert Reeve's death, Smith received news of the apparently mortal illness of Thomas Marsham, one of the three institutors of the Linnean Society and Treasurer since 1798. Earlier that year, Marsham had moved with his wife and three daughters from their home in Baker Street to Winchmore Hill, 10 miles north of London. The move had been accompanied by considerable gossip, not least as they were moving into the house previously occupied by his son William and his "chere ami".[44] Marsham's justification for the move was that it was both "prudent & convenient", the latter claim undermined by the 20-mile round commute Marsham now had to undertake to attend his job at the West India Dock House. By August it was reported that he was so ill with dropsy that death was expected at any moment. Though concerned for his friend, a pragmatic Smith acknowledged that "time & infirmity" were beginning to make "inroads among those friends who are a little before me on the stage of life". However, the accompanying revelation that Marsham, as Treasurer, had been unable to pay James Sowerby money owed to him by the Society led Smith to fear that financially all was not right—"perhaps his health suffers in consequence!".[45]

In December 1815, Samuel Goodenough was informed by letter "that the Linn[ean] Society is ruined & cannot publish their Volume, in consequence of the Treasurer having appropriated the funds of the Soc[iet]y to his own use (£600) & which he has nothing left but a Collection of black beetles to replace the deficit".[46] Smith's premonition about Marsham's financial woes was proven correct. In dire financial straits for some years, in March 1815 Marsham used the balance of his account as a tax collector at the West India Dock office to fund his daughter's wedding, hoping to recover the monies before anyone noticed. He was caught out when the Commissioners called in the funds early, and so he had emptied the Linnean Society's coffers to supply the shortfall.[47]

Goodenough, a longstanding friend of Marsham's, initially refused to believe the reports, though other members of the Society soon confirmed them. Seeing imminent disaster for the Society, an astonished and appalled Goodenough thundered: "what can be more dishonourable, perhaps, I ought to say, more rascally?". Confusion over the exact sums made others less judgemental, especially upon learning that Marsham had already tried to make amends: out of a total £728 4s appropriated, he had already paid back £300 in renewing the lease on the Society's home. Goodenough was infuriated by Lambert's attitude, who was "rather laughing over the story", and he lamented Smith's absence from London, in that Lambert (the most senior of the Vice-Presidents) was completely out of his depth. He complained that Lambert merely executed "the most trifling part of the President's office" — sitting in the chair at meetings.[48] Goodenough was unforgiving of financial strife: in 1826, when his eldest son fell into debt, Goodenough refused to help, stating that he "never would have any thing to do with his money concerns".[49] Smith was much more understanding. His own family, including brother John Frederick who had declared bankruptcy, had experienced their own financial troubles of varying severity. On hearing the full details of Marsham's predicament he wrote to Macleay saying he was "far more sorry than surprized. I grieve for him most sincerely. He is not a man of this world [...] If you see him, & think proper, pray assure him of my high regard, & my concern for his having any troubles whatever".[50] The Society's immediate response was to sell its government bonds, amounting to £400, so that the outstanding bills could be paid, whilst Marsham resigned both the Treasurership and Vice-Presidentship at the next Anniversary Meeting. After the accounts were audited in May, Marsham was devastated to find that he still owed £428 4s 0d, significantly more than he had anticipated.[51] The situation placed Smith, and the Council, in an awkward position. They agreed to Marsham's proposal to settle the remaining balance in three equal payments, but time and time again he failed to send the promised notes; by the time of the 1817 Anniversary Meeting he had repaid only £78 4s. After the Council requested some form of collateral for the remainder, Marsham reacted with fury, considering himself:

> The Father of the Linnean Society, and for some years was the only one, that gave a constant and steady attention to its welfare, I performed the duties of Secretary, Treasurer, Clerk and Librarian,

> without any assistance; Judge then of my surprize to find; that after Eight and Twenty years zealous labor and faithful service, my Character invaded and my actions stigmatised in so ungracious and underserved a manner.[52]

Indeed, Marsham's contributions had not gone unrecognised by others in the Society, and at the end of 1817 a frustrated Goodenough reported that there was a faction in the Society that felt "that no man would do what he has done without expecting to be paid for it".[53] Smith and Macleay privately agreed with this view, but President and Secretary had to be seen to be taking an interest in recovering the money. Unfortunately, by this point, there were few options left, other than prison. Were they really to repay the services of the Society's most valuable members "by throwing an old man of 70 into Prison, and keeping him there for the year or two that he may have yet to live?".[54] The sorry affair concluded only on 26 November 1819, with the death of Thomas Marsham. He had not repaid any more of the debt. Goodenough, relentless in his calls to recover the debt in any way possible, later accused Macleay of conspiracy. By holding Council meetings so late at night it had been impossible for Goodenough to attend, through which Marsham had been allowed to "escape repaying his shameful fraud".[55]

The Interests of Science, of Education and of a Great University

Smith's Cambridge campaign suddenly revived again in January 1816, when premature reports emerged of Thomas Martyn's death. Smith refuted the rumours with some satisfaction, announcing that Martyn was "'alive again'! very well, & all alive" in his cause. The news also brought new rivals, including an unexpected Linnean colleague; the entomologist and country priest William Kirby. Kirby opposed Smith's candidacy on the grounds that he was a dissenter, whilst Smith thought Kirby was a "priest in the worst sense; [...] it is not worth enquiring whether hypocrisy or bigottry be the uppermost quality, as they go very lovingly together".[56] With the backing of the Dean of Norwich, who promised to fight all of Smith's "political & religious" battles for him, Smith was now ready to ask

Martyn to stand down and "try the fate of the election".[57] Unfortunately the news of Martyn's death had also caused a stir amongst the college heads as to the proper mode of electing a successor, and the remainder of the campaign in 1816 was given over to debates between lawyers. It was confirmed that according to Martyn's original appointment authority lay with the Crown alone, the Walkerian lectureship being the only position decided by a university election. Smith was exhorted to apply to the government and to enrol immediately in one of the colleges.[58]

Smith continued to receive promises of support and was further encouraged by changes in Cambridge: in February 1817 the hostile Sir Isaac Pennington died, replaced as Professor of Physic by the more amenable John Haviland. The current vice-chancellor, James Wood, now Master of St John's, remained unsympathetic, but he would soon be replaced by William Webb, Master of Clare College and a supporter of Smith's campaign since 1813.[59] He moved another step closer to the final goal in March 1818, when an ailing Martyn, once again unable to give a course of lectures, invited Smith to deputise in his stead, giving him full authority to use the lecture room and plants from the garden. The "indefatigable" William Webb smoothed the way, over-riding any objections and securing a new venue when the Professors of Mineralogy and Chemistry, Edward Daniel Clarke and James Cumming, refused to vacate the botany lecture room.[60] With all possible impediments seemingly cleared, Smith's first course of Cambridge lectures was advertised to begin on Monday 6 April.

The day before the lectures were due to start, the vice-chancellor was presented with an address, signed by 18 college tutors, effectively banning their students from "attending the Public Lectures of any Person, who is neither a Member of the University, nor a Member of the Church of England".[61] The vice-chancellor, not wishing to cause dissention within the university, requested Smith not to lecture, and the course was abandoned. Many within the university leapt to Smith's defence but there was little that could be done; a proposal to produce a remonstrance from pro-Smith tutors was not taken up for fear of giving authority to the original objection. As with all the setbacks in this long campaign, Smith initially responded with indifference, though he felt that the controversy had gained him "much ground" towards the professorship. He was bolstered in this opinion by news that four of the original signatories had since recanted. Refusing to admit defeat, Smith and his wife stayed in Cambridge for almost two weeks: "we show ourselves every where, at the Senate house, at church, & among our acquaintance".[62] Smith's supporters at Cambridge reacted with dismay at the turn of events, lamenting both the loss to the university and to Smith.

Galvanised by their messages of support, Smith produced a pamphlet on the subject, entitled *Considerations Respecting Cambridge, More Particularly Relating to its Botanical Professorship*, setting another literary quarrel in motion. The contents of the pamphlet, though personal, were not a private matter. "Had they concerned an individual only", Smith wrote, "they would never have appeared before the public; but they involve the interests of science, of education and of a great University".[63] Smith related the importance of botanical teaching, the nature of the professorship and lectureship and the details of the campaign. Respecting his non-Anglicanism, he pointedly stated that he had:

> No bigoted or sectarian feelings or prejudices, miscalled principles, which would have interfered [...] with my complete sociability. [...] I had always been in the habit of attending frequently the public worship of the church, and of taking the sacrament there, many years since; not on any particular occasion, nor with any particular object, except the principle of Christian communion.[64]

His ire was reserved for the tutors who had petitioned against him. Such an alarming "ignorance of the history, laws, and precedents of the University", he claimed, would lead future scholars to conclude that there was an error in the date of the tutors' objection, "that instead of April 4, 1818, we ought perhaps to read April 1, 1300".[65]

Many of Smith's friends reacted with enthusiasm: Brownlow North, Bishop of Winchester, was complimentary, and William Roscoe read the pamphlet with "equal impatience & pleasure. [...] Every page envinces a firm consciousness of rectitude, a candour of manner, & a love of science".

He was in no doubt of its helping the cause.[66] Those at Cambridge were less convinced: Martin Davy, Master of Gonville and Caius College, feared for the disgrace of the university and was convinced the pamphlet would "cut off all hopes of any future success".[67] A robust defence against Smith's pamphlet appeared in June, authored by James Henry Monk, the Regius Professor of Greek and one of the signatories of the tutors' objection. Entitled *A Vindication of the University of Cambridge*, Monk refuted each of Smith's defences, and claimed that of the 28 tutors in the university, three were unable to offer their opinions to the vice-chancellor, so that technically Smith only had the support of seven. He concluded "the President of the Linnaean Society came to Cambridge upon a *fool's errand*".[68]

A commentary of both works appeared in *The Quarterly Review*, leaving little ambiguity of how Smith's pretensions were viewed by the Establishment. The reviewer sneered at Smith's audacity at even having dared to think of the botany chair, and, dismissing the considerable achievements of the Linnean Society, sarcastically commented:

> The combat would have even yet been more important, had it been a regular and embodied charge of the whole Linnaean Society against the University. The former, then, would of course, have brought into the field their auxiliary forces, the Horticultural and Gooseberry societies, with the irregular troops, the tulip-fanciers and prize-auricula-men.[69]

Smith's pamphlet was a "remarkable instance of that egotism and self-importance, which an exclusive devotion to science is so apt to generate in a man by leading him to exalt, in an undue degree, the importance of his own pursuits". Most wounding of all was the reviewer's narrow-minded demolition of Smith's 'occasional conformity': "Is it possible that any man, who persuades himself that he is sincere, can sanction, by his presence and participation, the performance of a solemn rite and act of adoration, the whole tenor of which, in his heart, he disbelieves and disapproves?"[70]

Many were appalled by the mean-spirited and reactionary opinions contained in Monk's pamphlet and *The Quarterly Review* distasteful, leading polymath William Whewell to remark that he was "afraid Monk's talent will not be found to be in pamphlet writing".[71] Smith's associates naturally took their friend's side: the American physician Francis Boott "well satisfied with its malignity—as it is in perfect unison with the illiberal treatment you received at Cambridge". "I hope", Boott wisely advised, "you will not attempt to answer the calumnies they assail you with".[72]

As with the Salisbury dispute, Smith was unable to heed such cautions, and on 18 March 1819 he issued another pamphlet in response to both Monk and *The Quarterly Review* with the title *A Defence of the Church and Universities of England*. Smith offered further clarification of his claims and entered into an explanation of his private religion. This time around his friends had a greater sense of trepidation; Goodenough felt that Smith had made himself vulnerable to his adversaries. In any event, this marked the end of both the dispute and of Smith's campaign. Thomas Martyn remained as the inactive Professor of Botany until his death in 1825. His successor was John Stevens Henslow, who would go on to teach Charles Darwin botany. Smith, reflecting on the whole debacle, was certain that he would "ever consider it an honour to have been thought of & invited by so large a portion of the enlightened & learned part of the University".[73] Though Smith can be accused of conducting a confused and hesitant campaign, this unhappy episode is much more to Cambridge's shame than Smith's. In 1823, an American correspondent, Dr David Hosack, enclosed a clipping from *The Statesman* newspaper, which stated that:

> This appointment would have indeed reflected more honour on the university, than on this distinguished philosopher. But unfortunately the interests of science and the prosperity of that great seminary of education were wantonly immolated on the altar of bigotry.[74]

Smith received some consolation later in 1819, when he was invited to become Professor of Botany at both the Royal Institution and the Liverpool Royal Institution. He accepted both unpaid posts. During and after the period of the Cambridge campaign Smith greatly expanded the reach of his lectures. In addition to his semi-regular series at the Royal

Institution he also gave courses at the Liverpool Royal Institution (1818 and 1820), the Birmingham Philosophical Institution (1819 and 1822) and the Bristol Institution (1825).

Smith had been particularly aggrieved by *The Quarterly Review*'s attack on his religious principles. He addressed these criticisms in the closing pages of *A Defence of the Church and Universities of England*, focusing on the reviewer's hypocrisy in describing the sacrament as 'an act of adoration'—"can he allude to the popish adoration of the bread and wine, so particularly disclaimed in the book of Common Prayer? [...] None can misunderstand the command "*do this in remembrance of me*", any more than that other, equally plain, "*do unto others as you would that they should do unto you*".[75]

Smith relied on his religion to support him throughout his life, and it consistently informed his scientific work. He concluded the preface of *The English Flora*, his last work, with a passage delineating his belief in the God of nature:

> He who feeds the sparrows, and clothes the golden lily of the fields in a splendour beyond that of Solomon himself, invites us, his rational creatures, to confide in his promises of eternal life. [...] Let those who hope to inherit these promises, and those who love science for its own sake, cherish the same benevolent dispositions. Envy and rivalship, in one case, are no less censurable than bigotry and uncharitableness in the other. The former are as uncompatible with the love of nature as the latter with the love of God, and they altogether unfit us for the enjoyments of happiness here or hereafter.[76]

Pleasance Smith later described his principles: "That a man can be no Christian, *as to faith*, who does not judge for himself; nor *as to practice*, who does not allow others to do so without presuming to censure or hinder them".[77] Smith continued to worship at the Octagon Chapel his whole life, and in 1815, following the death of Francis, he took his brother's place as deacon. He also wrote hymns, 16 of which were published, and which continued to appear in hymnals for some 80 years after Smith's death. They often contained a natural history slant, 'When power divine in mortal form', one of the most popular, being typical:

God calms the tumult and the storm;
He rules the seraph and the worm:
No creature is by him forgot
Of those who know, or know him not.[78]

Octagon Chapel, Colegate, Norwich. Originally Presbyterian in creed, the congregation gradually adopted Unitarian beliefs. Smith worshipped and served as a deacon here.

How Immense Has Been the Improvement of Botany

With the Cambridge professorship now irrevocably settled, and just *Flora Græca* remaining amongst his on-going projects (the first half of the third volume saw publication in 1819), Smith began to think of new literary ventures. Amongst the potential works was a new illustrated publication on garden plants, a flora of Britain written in English and a *Mantissa*, or botanical supplement. Smith's old Edinburgh friend Francis Hamilton (formerly

Buchanan) favoured the latter. The *Mantissa* would allow Smith to utilise the wealth of new plant material at his disposal, and according to Hamilton would be the work "upon which any lasting reputation must depend".[79] Hamilton believed that an English translation of *Flora Britannica* was a work for "inferior hands". Despite this, Smith met with the publishers Longman & Co. to discuss the work in June 1819 where he received a warm reception; though they declined to purchase the copyright they agreed to go in shares for the first edition and to publicise it as much as possible, hinting that they would reconsider the copyright if it proved a success. They also pressed Smith to write a "Dictionary of Botany", convinced it would prove popular. A standardised form of botanical terminology had been a crusade of Smith's from the earliest days of his career, and he took the bait: "nothing w[oul]d be more easy, & I could make it serve as a relaxation, or occasional labour". Though Pleasance's father had left them comfortably solvent, they were by no means rich. Smith resolved to borrow £100 or £200 during the writing process to tide them over, confident that the two works would "repay my trouble very well".[80]

On 3 February 1820, Smith's 88-year-old mother, Frances Smith, died, "with out any previous infirmity, the delight of all, old & young".[81] Less than two months later, on 27 March, Pleasance's mother also died. She was 81 years old. Keen to escape the melancholy air, in May the Smiths set out together on a long tour of the country. Starting in London, the couple included a stop in Liverpool so Smith could give a course of lectures.[82] On 19 June, whilst they were travelling, Sir Joseph Banks, the leader of British botany for over 50 years, died at his Spring Grove home in Isleworth. Despite Smith's private opinion of Banks's saturnine behaviour, he fully acknowledged the profound influence Banks had had on his life, dating back to that fateful breakfast at Soho Square in December 1783. In response to a Royal Society request for donations for a monument to Banks to be placed in the British Museum, Smith subscribed £10 (the maximum individual donation permitted) and wrote:

> No one has a greater claim on his gratitude & regard than I have, nor can any one be more ready to acknowledge it.[83]

A full-length statue was commissioned from sculptor Francis Chantrey, and it now resides in the Natural History Museum, London. As the Linnean Society's first Honorary Member, Banks had provided immeasurable support to its first endeavours, and his home at Soho Square acted as a fulcrum for scientific exchange and debate. Despite their occasionally fraught relationship, there was a genuine feeling of mutual respect between the two botanists. In an article for *Encyclopædia Britannica*, Smith acknowledged the special impact Banks and his librarian Daniel Solander had on botany:

> Their taste, their knowledge, their liberality, have diffused a charm and a popularity over all their pursuits; and those who never heard of botany before, have learned to consider it with respect and admiration, as the object to which a man of rank, riches, and talents, devotes his life and fortune.[84]

Though he eventually favoured Jussieu's natural orders over Linnaeus's sexual system, Banks had stated his admiration of Smith's defence of Linnaeus, and of Smith's "deep skill in the mysteries of classification". Banks recognised the enormous strides botany had made in the last half century, and the significant role Smith had played:

> How immense has been the improvement of botany since I attached myself to the study, and what immense facilities are now offered to students, that had not existed till lately! Your descriptions and Sowerby's drawings, of British plants [*English Botany*], would have saved me years of labour, had they then existed.[85]

The Linnean Society commissioned its own memorial to Banks in the form of a marble bust, also by Chantrey. Banks left his librarian Robert Brown a lifetime interest in 32 Soho Square and its scientific contents, after which the collections were to pass to the British Museum. In May 1821 the Linnean Society concluded negotiations to move into the Soho Square half of the house (Brown kept the Dean Street side) on a 30-year lease at the annual rent of £140, less than what they were currently paying for their

Gerrard Street rooms. The Society was to remain at Soho Square until 1857, at which point it moved to Burlington House, Piccadilly (the Society moved into their current rooms at Burlington House in 1873).

Puppies are Chattering About Natural Orders

A year full of grief, Smith spent the remainder of 1820 buried in his work; the result, *A Grammar of Botany* was published in January 1821. The first six chapters focused on vegetable physiognomy and the theory of systematic arrangement, chapter seven set out the Linnaean artificial system, "somewhat reformed", followed by a description of the natural system of Jussieu, the first time it had been fully presented in English.[86] Smith remained as dedicated as ever to Linnaeus, stating in the preface:

> It is evident that no such mode of [natural] classification can, at present, serve the purposes of analytical investigation, to make out an unknown plant. That is the exclusive object of the Artificial System of Linnaeus, which, of all the schemes hitherto contrived, is alone, perhaps, universally applicable to the end in question.[87]

Of the scorn frequently heaped on the Linnaean system by disciples of Jussieu, Smith remarked: "a dictionary quarrels not with a grammar, nor a history with a chronological table. It is pernicious, as well as foolish, to set them at variance".[88]

Grammar of Botany was greeted with acclaim from Smith's colleagues within the Linnaean school. Samuel Goodenough, expecting merely an updated version of *Introduction to Botany*, on opening it perceived "a grammar of prime excellence".[89] Thomas Martyn also immediately identified the "hand of a Master—concise yet full—remarkable for clearness and neatness", and recognised that with the publication of *The English Flora*, alongside *Grammar* and *Introduction to Botany*, the "British Botanist will find every thing that he wants in these three works of yours".[90]

Though no one could ever replace the multifarious Banks, Smith, having now attained the statesman-like age of 61, assumed the position of Britain's leading botanist, by right of his extensive publications, his 33 years presiding over the Linnean Society: and continued possession of the Linnaean collections. In early 1821, a letter arrived from Josef August Schultes, Professor of Natural History at the University of Landshut in Bavaria, in which Smith was hailed as both "the Lord Treasurer of Botany" and "the only orthodox Botanist in Europe". Such honorifics were in large part derived from the taxonomic power of Linnaeus's herbarium, through which Smith could establish if "any pretended new species is true and legal coinage or not". Schultes also praised Smith himself, particularly as a promoter of the science. Schultes had translated Smith's *Introduction to Botany* into German in 1819, and it now served as the basis for his own lectures. He thought it superior to even Linnaeus's *Philosophia Botanica*, not least as Smith had produced a primer "to be given in the hands of the purest virgin". As soon as *Grammar of Botany* arrived in Germany, Schultes set his son to translating it.[91]

Smith had been formulating plans for *The English Flora* as early as 1803, when Dawson Turner sent him sheets of a planned pocket English flora by naturalist and medical practitioner William Turton. Smith perceived this as a "very unhandsome attempt to interfere with my interest in the Compendium as well as my Flora", and quashed Turton's plans, though it was to be another 20 years before he had the time to commence his own.[92] In 1821, with only his *Flora Græca* commitments remaining, Smith began work on *The English Flora*, which he had longed for "more than a schoolboy for his holidays".[93]

By March 1822 Smith was "steadily at work" on the new book. He anticipated that it would be "quite an original Flora—the whole subject being revised after so many years' experience, & nothing, or worse than nothing, done by most writers since I began". He intended to "fix the language, revise all generic & specific char[acter]s, enrich & correct synonyms, add remarks on nat[ura]l affinities, clear away the mischief done by compilers". It was, he admitted, a "Herculean labour", but Smith was confident in his botanical skills.[94] He declined Macleay's recommendation to peruse an alternate annotated copy of *Flora Britannica*, finding his "own materials & observations best". He jested "do not think me a growing coxcomb for this".[95] Smith dedicated at least five hours a day to writing, and not infrequently all of his daylight hours and most of his evenings.[96]

This was set against a backdrop of continued indulgence tempered with intermittent ill-health. The summer of 1816 was typical, in which he undertook a tour of the country with Thomas William Coke that saw a stay at Woburn Abbey, home of the Duke of Bedford. The lords and ladies in attendance spent their evenings enacting tableaux of famous paintings, and Lady Morley, Frances Parker, entertained the guests by giving "her old imitations of animals behind the scene".[97] Such parties became a frequent part of Smith's annual itinerary and Dawson Turner, as usual, looked on disapprovingly. Turner's only consolation was that the death of Pleasance's father had added only "a little to his income & for my own part I am glad it has not added more, for it has had the effect of inducing him more to indulge himself, which at once makes him less useful to society & injures his health".[98] Illustrating this point is Coke's daughter Eliza, who wrote of "a dreadful *glum* dinner" in 1822, with a very "*précieuse*" Lady Smith in attendance and "Sir James Smith eating himself sick with a *load* of preserved pine-apple".[99] He was also active in Norwich society, playing a supporting role in the establishment of the Norfolk and Norwich Triennial Music Festival in 1824, and a more instrumental role in the founding of the Norfolk and Norwich Museum in 1825, of which he became the first president.

Now in his sixties, he was often incapacitated with recurring headaches and bowel complaints, and from 1822 to 1824 he suffered an annual bout of cholera. He dedicated so much time to writing that he could only allow himself an hour's exercise every two or three days, though by the end of 1824 reported that his health was now "much restored. [...] I have regained flesh & colour, though I have lost most of my teeth quite sound". For years he had listened to "fools without number" who had urged him to "to live well" and exercise, but upon collapsing after a 34-mile drive into the country on medical advice, Smith now preferred to rely on his own clinical judgement: "I know rest is the only cure".[100] His friends, too, were beginning to feel the toll of sickness and infirmity. In October 1822, after a period of ill health, James Sowerby died at the age of 65. Smith deeply felt the death of his long-time collaborator, with whom, despite their occasional professional differences, he had achieved extraordinary feats in the field of botany. "I feel that I have lost a long tried and faithful friend," Smith wrote to Sowerby's family, "ever ready to serve me, & in whom I have always found the strictest honour, liberality worthy of a prince, & the most unaffected friendship & kindness. But above all, your father was a true Christian, in heart & deed, as well as in faith".[101]

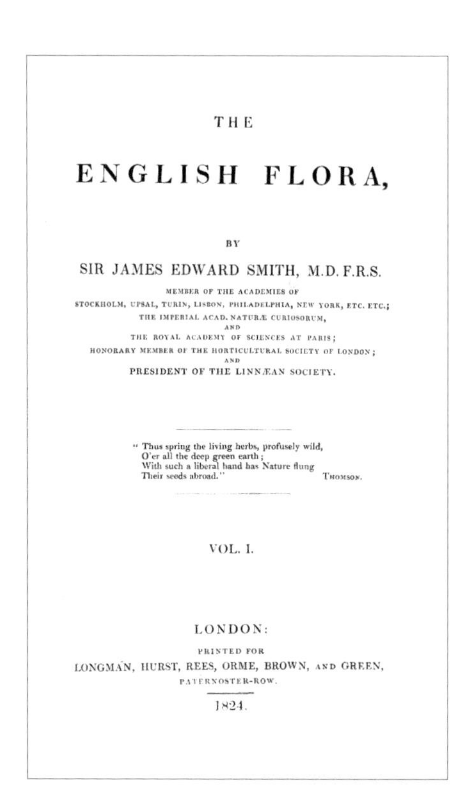
THE

ENGLISH FLORA,

BY

SIR JAMES EDWARD SMITH, M.D. F.R.S.

MEMBER OF THE ACADEMIES OF
STOCKHOLM, UPSAL, TURIN, LISBON, PHILADELPHIA, NEW YORK, ETC. ETC.;
THE IMPERIAL ACAD. NATURÆ CURIOSORUM,
AND
THE ROYAL ACADEMY OF SCIENCES AT PARIS;
HONORARY MEMBER OF THE HORTICULTURAL SOCIETY OF LONDON;
AND
PRESIDENT OF THE LINNÆAN SOCIETY.

"Thus spring the living herbs, profusely wild,
O'er all the deep green earth;
With such a liberal hand has Nature flung
Their seeds abroad." THOMSON.

VOL. I.

LONDON:
PRINTED FOR
LONGMAN, HURST, REES, ORME, BROWN, AND GREEN,
PATERNOSTER-ROW.

1824.

Title page of Smith's *The English Flora* (1824–1828).

The first two volumes of *The English Flora* were published early in 1824 to favourable reviews. Smith had more than fulfilled his brief. *The Philosophical Magazine* commended the convenience and candour of the work, highlighting the inclusion of the natural affinities of each genus alongside the Linnaean character: "not only is the individual species pointed out in the clearest way to the student by means of the artificial system, but the natural relations to other species and genera, and much of its history and physiology".[102] Yet, the ever-growing influence of the natural system, overwhelmingly favoured by the younger generation, horrified the fastidious systematist:

> Puppies are chattering about natural orders which they do not understand, & mean while they embroil all real knowledge, as [John] Lindley about Roses, [William Jackson] Hooker ab[ou]t Willows. To elucidate but one species would be really useful, but all they do is mostly for the worse, & for the sake of seeming to correct their superiors, they rather blunder than do nothing.

Of the adherents of Jussieu, Robert Brown was the only writer whom Smith found "most in the right".[103] Responding to a parcel of Indian plants sent by Nathaniel Wallich, superintendent of the Calcutta Botanic Garden, at this time, Smith apologised if he made remarks "especially about names" before asking if Wallich would be willing to take a lead in keeping the science "as classical, elegant & correct as possible [...] against illiterate gardeners, Frenchmen, &c, &c". Referring Wallich to his *Cyclopædia* articles, he avowed himself a defender of the "Linnaean fortress", though admitted that he was "thankful for, & concur in, all sound correction & improvement".[104] Smith and the remaining Linnaeans, however, were, losing the war, with their long cherished system increasingly seen as an inferior, suitable only for children, women and amateurs, according to John Lindley "unworthy of the attention of men of enlightened minds".[105] Lindley waited until after Smith's passing in 1828 before delivering the death knell to Linnaean botany, using his inaugural lecture as the University of London's first Professor of Botany to call for botany to move into a more "advanced state of science". To do so, it was necessary to abandon Linnaeus's sexual system of plant classification, which threatened to "convert one of the most curious and interesting of all sciences into a meagre and aimless system of names", and instead of taxonomy focus on plant morphology and physiology.[106] The Linnaean sexual system remained in use with popular writers as an easily understood method for identifying plants, but by the 1840s the accessible format of epistolary or dialogic botanical books had became out-dated, replaced by more technical, objective works.

Of all of Linnaeus's innovations, his system of binomial nomenclature was to prove his most enduring legacy, still used by scientists today.

Smith was so ill in the summer of 1824 that for the first time ever he was prevented from undertaking his annual trip to London. It also caused a complete interruption of his literary labours and correspondence. He had recovered by the beginning of 1825 but was now dedicating himself solely to *The English Flora*; "I cannot write books and letters too".[107] By May 1825, half of the print-run of *The English Flora*'s first two volumes had been sold, covering the publisher's expenses: the remaining 800 copies would be pure profit.[108] His resolve to finish the remainder was also boosted by a significant milestone; the completion of more than half the text of *Flora Græca*.

That year, another close friend and Linnean ally, Alexander Macleay, departed from Smith's life, though not to old age or disease – Macleay had accepted the post of Colonial Secretary in New South Wales, Australia. Though they had most frequently communicated on Society business, an exchange of 31 years could not help but engender a true friendship. In a rare emotional outpouring Smith wrote: "I have ever felt the warmest estimation for your character [...]. I have always known where to find you, & was always sure you would do the kindest & most judicious thing. Judge then if I can part with you unmoved".[109] A portrait of Macleay, by Sir Thomas Lawrence, was commissioned by the Society and funded by subscription, before his departure.

Smith remained much in demand as a lecturer, and on 2 May gave the first of 10 botanical lectures at the London Institution, which had been established in 1806. He finished the course on 2 June to a "thunder of applause" and received his 100 guinea fee.[110] Ten days later, he set out for Bristol, engaged to give another course of lectures at the Bristol Institution. Making the journey "in great heat" in a single day, he had only just got through his first lecture when his "old inflammatory complaint" revived. He struggled through the next two but was then "obliged to resign myself to bleeding, James's powder and starvation". After an enforced rest of 10 days he was able to resume and conclude the lectures, but Smith had overstretched himself. Joined by Pleasance, he stayed in a cottage near Hot

Wells until the end of September to regain his health, where he also finished third volume of *The English Flora*.[111] It was published in October.

Smith returned to London again in 1826, and though the heat was considerable, was pleased to report to Pleasance that "everybody praises my improved looks & colour, & my medical friends [...] think very slightly of my complaints". His schedule was noticeably less full than the previous year, and following his Linnean Society business, the only demands on his time were to sit for a bust commissioned by the Linnean Society from Francis Chantrey, and to look at carpet patterns: "Kaleidoscope patterns, of many small angular figures & gay colours are become very common, even in inns. I do not like them. I have seen nothing I like except one of roses & jasmine".[112]

As winter approached, a greater sense of urgency began to creep into Smith's writing. Though his health had remained good, he dreaded the onset of cold weather, "for then I can neither enjoy myself, nor the company of any friend except over my fire. I suffer already much from rheumatism". He hoped to finish *The English Flora* by the end of 1826, and even turned down an invitation to Holkham Hall from Thomas William Coke. He also remained anxious about "many family affairs, but I trust the worst is past with regard to some of them, & having done all I can, I must struggle against useless regret, or I shall not be able to make my own necessary exertions".[113]

Smith was still finishing the fourth volume of *The English Flora* in August 1827, plagued by persistent eye inflammation, the same eye that had been stricken with erysipelas 25 years before. Cold weather exacerbated it, and along with acute head pain he feared he might go blind, though his medical friends laughed at him for such a diagnosis.[114] On 12 August, Samuel Goodenough, Bishop of Carlisle, one of Smith's oldest and staunchest friends, died in his bed at Worthing, Sussex. Writing to Sir Thomas Gery Cullum shortly after the event, Smith simply wrote that he "need not say how much I lament the good Bishop". Of the original Fellows who met in 1788, only Smith and John Latham remained. Smith himself was in poor health, suffering severely from rheumatism. In November, he was laid low again by a persistent chest infection, though the printing of

The English Flora had begun. He immediately pressed on with the seventh volume of *Flora Græca*. He hoped to complete the entire work over the course of the winter. He was now regularly suffering from rheumatism, which weakened his legs and brought on indigestion, "but I totter on".[115] In truth, his health was shattered.

On Saturday, 15 March 1828, Smith and Pleasance visited a new friend, Edward Lombe, the MP for Arundel, whom they had met at a dinner the previous year. Pleasance later wrote how it was "a bright & cheerful morning, when Mr Lombe received us with cordiality, & at parting gave each of us a bunch of Violets from a basketful then arrived from Milton". As they left, Smith invited Lombe to visit their home in Surrey Street the following Monday. Pleasance later wrote, "before that time came He who invited had for many hours ceased to breathe".[116] After returning to Surrey Street, Smith suffered a seizure and never regained consciousness. He died at 6 o'clock in the morning of 17 March, at the age of 68.

EPILOGUE

The news of Smith's death reached London the following day, whilst the Linnean Society was in session. The meeting was immediately adjourned, the members separating "in mournful silence". Though many were aware of Smith's precarious health, the news still came as a surprise. William George Maton wrote "the lovers of science will join in lamenting it, throughout the civilized world, and our Society must feel it to be irreparable—they have lost their corporate parent, as well as one of their greatest ornaments".[1] Edward Smith-Stanley, Smith's successor as president of the Linnean Society, wrote to William Fitt Drake that Smith's loss "in the friendly & social circles in which he so much delighted must be long & deservedly felt; nor will the place be filled in the estimation of the public & literary world, with so much advantage to their objects; & such high credit to himself be soon or easily supplied".[2] Smith was buried in the Reeve family vault at St Margaret's Church, Lowestoft, the same church he had married in 32 years before, on 24 March 1828.

Smith's own copies of the fourth volume of *The English Flora* arrived from the publisher just days before his death. The four volumes had covered all the flowering plants and ferns, and in 1833 William Jackson Hooker added a volume covering mosses, followed by a volume from Miles Berkeley on fungi in 1836. As for his other great work, *Flora Græca*, at the time of his death Smith had prepared the first half of the seventh volume. Robert Brown took up the remaining half before volumes eight, nine and 10 passed to the editorship of John Lindley. The second half of the final volume was finally published in 1840, some 44 years after the death of John Sibthorp.

In his will, Smith left the entirety of his natural history collections, including those of Linnaeus, to his executors, William Fitt Drake and Pleasance, "to be disposed of all together [...] in one lot, by sale, to some publick or corporate body". The proceeds were to be divided equally amongst his surviving siblings and Francis's widow. It may have occasioned surprise that Smith did not leave them to the Society founded under Linnaeus's name, but Smith on his own was not a wealthy man. The vast majority of his wealth, gifted through Pleasance's family, all reverted back to his wife on his death. Bought with Smith family money, it was now time for the investment to be returned, with interest. The executors initially offered the collections to the Society for £5,000, though they eventually accepted £3,150 for them, incurring a debt that was not paid off until 1861. The Linnaean collections remain with the Society to this day.

Two years after Smith's death, one of the last surviving of his close friends, Dawson Turner, gave a tribute to Smith at the fifth annual meeting of the Norfolk and Norwich Museum:

> By his works he has erected to himself an imperishable monument; and upon every occasion, in these works, he has uniformly studied to promote the happiness of mankind and the glory of God. As possessor of the Linnaean Herbarium, his conduct was at all times eminently liberal, opening its treasures, without reserve, to men of every rank and station, and of every clime. As founder and president of the [Linnean] Society [...], his amiable and condescending affability won him the regard of every member of that body, whilst that establishment gave a character and a permanency, and an importance to the study of natural history in England, which it otherwise would not have attained.[3]

Today, James Edward Smith is chiefly remembered for two things: his purchase of the collections of Carl Linnaeus and his founding of the Linnean Society of London. As in his lifetime, in posthumous assessment the two are inextricably linked. But in both cases he is often criticised—for 'purchasing' his way into the scientific community, and for having the

Linnaeus's collections on the *Appearance*, pursued by a gunship dispatched by the King of Sweden.

temerity to sell, "for a handsome profit", and not gift the collections to the Society that he 'abandoned' following his move to Norwich. Particularly, he has been unfavourably compared to his London mentor, Sir Joseph Banks, who made a comparable private investment in science by financing from his own pocket the botanical element of the *Endeavour* voyage of 1769–1771. The extraordinary haul of specimens Banks returned with made him:

> A major public figure and statesman of science. But Smith's venture lacked the epic of discovery that could mark him out personally as a hero and scientific practitioner of the first rank. Indeed, to acquire another person's collections was typically to identify oneself as a patron or connoisseur, rather than a possessor, of knowledge.[4]

In this interpretation, the apocryphal story of the King of Sweden sending a gunship to bring back the collections is Smith's equivalent of the *Endeavour* voyage, adding colour and excitement to the otherwise more prosaic reality of a series of letters crossing the North Sea. In his glee, Smith is supposed to have had a medal struck showing on one side the English ship chased by Swedish, and on other side the inscription "the pursuit of the ship containing the Linnean collection by order of the King of Sweden"; there is no surviving record of such a medal.[5] While Banks returned a celebrity, and maintained a public profile for the rest of his life, he remains conspicuous for having published nothing from his private collection. Smith, on the other hand, lost no time in communicating the riches of Linnaeus's collections to the scientific community of Britain. Within four years of their arrival in London, Smith had published English translations of two of Linnaeus's key texts relating to his views on nature (*Reflections on the Study of Nature* [1785] and *Dissertation on the Sexes of Plants* [1786]); the surviving woodblocks from Olof Rudbeck's *Campi Elysii* (*Reliquiæ Rudbeckianæ* [1789]) and various plants from the herbarium never yet presented to the public before (*Plantarum Icones* [1789–1791]). This was in addition to his travels in Europe, his Grand Botanical Tour, spent not in dissolution but in studying the herbariums and flora of the continent, and enlisting the most eminent natural historians of the era to become founding Foreign Members of an as yet unfounded and unproven scientific society.

For the duration of Smith's career he was driven by a desire to communicate and collaborate, as witnessed in his voluminous correspondence; his extensive herbarium, built through countless gifts and exchanges; his numerous publications, written in both Latin and English, often with the assistance of men like James Sowerby and John Abbot; and his greatest achievement, the Linnean Society itself. He served his apprenticeship in Edinburgh, forming and testing his ideas in the Natural History Society, so that by the time he arrived at Soho Square in 1784 he was ready to assert his position in the botanical community, before he had heard even a whisper of the Linnaean collections. The gratitude that the Linnean Society felt for Smith, and the honour they derived from having him at its helm, is displayed in his repeated re-election to the presidential chair year after year, even after leaving London.

The Society has remained at the forefront of biological research. It was at a meeting of the Linnean Society on 1 July 1858 that a joint presentation of two papers by Charles Darwin and Alfred Russel Wallace, entitled *On the Tendency of Species to form Varieties; and on the Perpetuation of Varieties and Species by Natural Means of Selection*, first communicated to the world their theory of evolution by natural selection. The Society celebrated its bicentenary in 1988 and played a central role in the global celebrations for the tercentenary of the birth of Carl Linnaeus in 2007. As custodian of the Linnaean collections the Society has remained committed to Smith's original vision for them of broadening access, through a scheme to digitise and publish online the plant, insect, shell and fish specimens, as well as the manuscripts, correspondence and annotated library that rewrote nature.

As for Smith's publications, *The English Flora* remains his greatest triumph, a monument to his diligence as a botanist. It is credited as having "opened a new era in British botany", thanks to the exacting accuracy with which Smith had compiled his descriptions after a lifetime of study. Smith always prided himself on verifying everything with his own eyes and correcting every synonym. *The English Flora* remains an essential guide to the pre-Linnaean literature on each species, and his descriptions have saved countless subsequent authors from having to draw up their own descriptions of the British flora.[6] There is something elegiac in the fact that he died so soon after receiving the fourth volume, which completed the flowering plants and ferns, from the publishers.

One person's story remains unfinished, one of the very last witnesses to Smith's achievements. This was his wife, "dear Pleasy". She never remarried, zealously guarding her late husband's legacy for the 49 years that she survived him. She died in 1877 at the age of 103. Beginning in 1832 when she presented to the public the two-volume work *Memoir and Correspondence of the Late Sir James Edward Smith MD*, Pleasance presented a carefully edited version of her husband's story to the world. She continued to exert her control when she gave Smith's correspondence to the Linnean Society in two separate gifts of 1857 and 1872. The 3,519 letters extant in the collection are just a proportion of the total Smith received in his lifetime. Pleasance, believing that only his scientific correspondence would be of interest to future generations, systematically destroyed an unknown quantity of letters. These included the vast majority of the family correspondence, including most of her own letters, and whole series from Smith's young associates, including Robert Batty, who, from the scant surviving references appears to have remained a constant presence in Smith's life, William Younge, with whom he toured Europe, and the unfortunate Francesco Borone. Another victim of this epistolary cull is Pleasance herself, who remains a shadowy but clearly significant figure in Smith's life. Other casualties include much of the correspondence regarding Smith's altercation with Queen Charlotte and the feud with Richard Salisbury. The destruction of swathes of his correspondence has had the unfortunate result of neutering Smith's achievements and hiding many of the struggles that he faced in his efforts to pursue a career in natural history, and which I hope this biography has gone some way to rectifying.

One of the most beautiful and fitting of all of Smith's obituaries appeared anonymously in *The Philosophical Magazine*, which was reprinted in Pleasance Smith's *Memoir and Correspondence*, and in the previous modern treatment of Smith's life by Margot Walker (1988), and with which this work also concludes:

> As a naturalist, he contributed greatly to the advancement of science; and stood pre-eminent for judgement, accuracy, candour, and industry. He was disposed to pay due respect to the great authorities that had preceded him, but without suffering his deference for them to impede the exercise of his own judgement. He was equally open to real improvement, and opposed the affectation of needless innovation. He found the science of botany, when he approached it, locked up in a dead language; he set it free by transfusing it with his own. He found it a severe study, fitted only for the recluse; he left it of easy acquisition to all. In the hands of his predecessors, with the exception of his immortal master, it was dry, technical, and scholastic; in his, it was adorned with grace and elegance and might attract the poet as well as the philosopher.[7]

NOTES

Institutional Key

BL	The British Library, London
BLY	The Beinecke Library, Yale University
EUL	Edinburgh University Library Centre for Research Collections
HSP	Historical Society of Pennsylvania
KCL	King's College London
LS	The Linnean Society of London
NHM	The Natural History Museum, London
NRO	Norfolk Record Office, Norwich
OMNH	Oxford Museum of Natural History
RBGK	Royal Botanic Gardens Kew
RS	The Royal Society, London
SLO	Sherardian Library, Oxford
SRO	Suffolk Record Office, Lowestoft
TC	Trinity College, Cambridge
TNA	The National Archives, Kew

PROLOGUE

1 Berkenhout, J, (1770). *Outlines of the Natural History of Great Britain and Ireland*, London: Elmsly, vol. 2, p.i.

2 Smith, J E, 'Introductory Discourse on the Rise and Progress of Natural History', *Transactions of the Linnean Society of London*, 1791 1(1), p.55.

3 Linnaeus's sexual system was an artificial arrangement, meaning that the plants were ordered and grouped on the basis of a few selected characteristics, as opposed to a natural system, in which plants are arranged according to a larger number of varying characteristics.

4 Stearn, W T, in Blunt, W, (2001). *The Compleat Naturalist: A Life of Linnaeus*, London:

Frances Lincoln Ltd., pp.247–251.

5 The 1753 edition of *Species Plantarum* is now considered the starting point of modern botanical nomenclature, with the 10th edition of *Systema Naturæ* (1758) the equivalent for zoological nomenclature.

6 Smith, J E, (1824–1828). *The English Flora*, London: Longman, Hurst, Rees, Orme, Brown and Greene, vol. 1, preface.

7 George, S, (2007). *Botany, Sexuality and Women's Writing 1760–1830*, Manchester: Manchester University Press, p.3.

8 Allen, D E, (1994). *The Naturalist in Britain: A Social History*, Chichester: Princeton University Press, 2nd ed., pp.37–39.

9 Smith, J E, 'Biographical Memoirs of Several Norwich Botanists', *Transactions of the Linnean Society of London*, 1804 7(1), p.299.

10 LS Smith herbarium 1186.1.1

11 Smith, J E, & Sowerby, J, (1793–1814). *English Botany; or, Coloured Figures of British Plants*, London: [privately], tab. 742.

12 Smith, P (ed.), (1832). *Memoir and Correspondence of the Late Sir James Edward Smith, M.D.*, London: Longman & Co., vol. 1, p.16.

13 LS JES/COR/9/37 Josef August Schultes to Smith, 28 March 1821

CHAPTER ONE

1 The little that is known about Smith's childhood is taken largely from either *Memoir and Correspondence of the Late Sir James Edward Smith* (1832) by Pleasance Smith, Smith's widow, or from Smith's adult recollections, communicated via letters, lectures and articles.

2 Smith, P (ed.), (1832). *Op. cit.*, vol. 1, pp.4–7.

3 LS JES/COR/19/51 Smith to James Smith, 11 April 1787

4 Smith, P (ed.), (1832). *Op. cit.*, vol. 1, pp.8–10; p.18; pp.323–324.

5 (1783). *The Norwich Directory*, Norwich: printed and sold by W. Chase and Co., p.64.

6 Larwood, J, (1800). *Erratics: By a Sailor; Containing Rambles in Norfolk, and Elsewhere*, London: D. Ogilvy & Son, p.112.

7 Corfield, P J, 'From Second City to Regional Capital', in Rawcliffe, C, & Wilson, R, (eds.), (2004). *Norwich since 1550*, London: Hambledon and London, p.153.

8 Wesley, J, (1992). *The Works of John Wesley: Journal and Diaries IV (1755–1765)*, Nashville: Abingdon Press, vol. 21, p.131.

9 Smith, P (ed.), (1832). *Op. cit.*, vol. 1, pp.3–4.

10 NRO MS 4379 A catalogue of Title pages of Books read

11 Smith, P (ed.), (1832). *Op. cit.*, vol. 1, p.9.

12 Smith, J E, 'Biographical Memoirs of Several Norwich Botanists', *Transactions of the Linnean Society of London*, 1804 7(1), pp.295–296.

[13] Smith, J E, 'Botany', *Encyclopædia Britannica* (1824), vol. 1.
[14] Smith, P (ed.), (1832). *Op. cit.*, vol. 1, p.324.
[15] *Ibid.*, pp.71–72.
[16] *Ibid.*, pp.73–74.
[17] Preserved in the Linnean Society Library
[18] Smith, J E, 'Biographical Memoirs of Several Norwich Botanists', *Op. cit.*, pp.295–301.
[19] Smith, P (ed.), (1832). *Op. cit.*, vol. 1, p.324.
[20] *Ibid.*, pp.324–325.
[21] LS MS 304 Draft of a lecture on history of botany, [1808]
[22] Smith, J E, (1798). *Tracts Relating to Natural History*, London: [privately], p.vi.
[23] Smith, P (ed.), (1832). *Op. cit.*, vol. 1, p.326,
[24] LS JES/COR/19/7 Smith to James Smith, 9 December 1781
[25] Smith, P (ed.), (1832). *Op. cit.*, vol. 1, pp.14–15.
[26] LS JES/COR/8/89 Humphry Repton to Smith, 5 November 1800
[27] LS JES/COR/4/48 James Dickson to Smith, 2 October 1781
[28] LS JES/COR/21/112 Smith to James Dickson, 1 July 1781
[29] LS JES/COR/4/48 James Dickson to Smith, 2 October 1781
[30] LS JES/COR/21/112 Smith to James Dickson, 1 July 1781
[31] LS MS 304 Draft of a lecture on history of botany, [1808]
[32] LS JES/COR/19/3 James Smith to Smith, 27 October 1781
[33] LS JES/COR/21/114 Smith to James Dickson, 11 September 1781
[34] LS JES/COR/19/3 James Smith to Smith, 27 October 1781
[35] LS JES/COR/19/10 Smith to James Smith, 11 March 1782
[36] LS JES/COR/19/4 Smith to James Smith, 2 November 1781
[37] Smith would go on to enjoy a very profitable relationship with the Marquess's widow, Mary Watson-Wentworth.
[38] LS JES/COR/19/12 Smith to James Smith, 15 April 1782
[39] Wormersley, T, & Crawford, D H, (2010). *Bodysnatchers to Lifesavers: Three Centuries of Medicine in Edinburgh*, Edinburgh: Luath Press Ltd, p.30.
[40] LS JES/COR/19/6 Smith to James Smith, 30 November 1781
[41] Rosner, L, (1991). *Medical Education in the Age of Improvement: Edinburgh Students and Apprentices 1760–1826*, Edinburgh: Edinburgh University Press, pp.49–56.
[42] LS JES/COR/19/6 Smith to James Smith, 30 November 1781
[43] LS JES/COR/19/4 Smith to James Smith, 2 November 1781
[44] LS JES/COR/19/4 Smith to James Smith, 2 November 1781
[45] LS JES/COR/19/5 James Smith to Smith, 12 November 1781
[46] LS JES/COR/19/6 Smith to James Smith, 30 November 1781
[47] LS JES/COR/19/8 James Smith to Smith, 17 January 1782
[48] Rosner, L, (1991). *Op. cit.*, p.29.

[49] LS JES/COR/25/4 Humphry Repton to Smith, 23 January 1783
[50] LS JES/COR/25/4 Humphry Repton to Smith, 23 January 1783
[51] LS JES/COR/19/10 Smith to James Smith, 11 March 1782
[52] LS JES/COR/19/5 James Smith to Smith, 12 November 1781
[53] LS JES/COR/19/10 Smith to James Smith, 11 March 1782
[54] LS JES/COR/19/4 Smith to James Smith, 2 November 1781
[55] LS JES/COR/19/5 James Smith to Smith, 12 November 1781
[56] LS JES/COR/19/6 Smith to James Smith, 30 November 1781
[57] Smith, P (ed.), (1832). *Op. cit.*, vol. 1, p.39.
[58] LS JES/COR/19/9 James Smith to Smith, 25 February 1782
[59] LS JES/COR/19/5 James Smith to Smith, 12 November 1781
[60] LS JES/COR/19/5 James Smith to Smith, 12 November 1781
[61] LS JES/COR/19/6 Smith to James Smith, 30 November 1781
[62] LS JES/COR/19/8 James Smith to Smith, 17 January 1782
[63] LS JES/COR/19/10 Smith to James Smith, 11 March 1782
[64] LS JES/COR/19/12 Smith to James Smith, 15 April 1782
[65] LS JES/COR/19/5 James Smith to Smith, 12 November 1781
[66] LS JES/COR/19/14 James Smith to Smith, 2 June 1782
[67] Smith, P (ed.), (1832). *Op. cit.*, vol. 1, p.39.
[68] LS JES/COR/19/5 James Smith to Smith, 12 November 1781
[69] LS JES/COR/19/12 Smith to James Smith, 15 April 1782
[70] Smith, P (ed.), (1832). *Op. cit.*, vol. 1, pp.74–78.
[71] Allen, D, 'James Edward Smith and the Natural History Society of Edinburgh', *Journal of the Society for the Bibliography of Natural History*, 1978 8(4), p.486.
[72] EUL EUA GD17 Records of the Society for Investigating Natural History, vol. 1, 1782–1783
[73] *Laws of the Society Instituted at Edinburgh, 1782, for the Investigation of Natural History* (1803), Edinburgh: Printed by C Stewart for the Society, p.25.
[74] Smith, P (ed.), (1832). *Op. cit.*, vol. 1, p.65.
[75] LS JES/COR/19/29 Smith to James Smith, 6 March 1783
[76] Allen, D, 'James Edward Smith and the Natural History Society of Edinburgh', *Op. cit.*, pp.488–491.
[77] LS JES/COR/19/13 Smith to Frances Smith, 16 May 1782
[78] Smith, P (ed.), (1832). *Op. cit.*, vol. 1, p.77.
[79] *Ibid.*, p.77.
[80] Rosner, L, (1991). *Op. cit.*, p.56.
[81] LS JES/COR/19/15 Smith to James Smith, 10 June 1782
[82] LS JES/COR/19/18 James Smith to Smith, 3 August 1782
[83] LS JES/COR/18/3 Smith to Thomas Woodward, 12 August 1782
[84] LS JES/COR/19/25 James Smith to Smith, 7 October 1782

[85] Smith, P (ed.), (1832). *Op. cit.*, vol. 1, p.78.
[86] *Ibid.*, pp.77–79.
[87] LS JES/COR/19/13 Smith to Frances Smith, 16 May 1782
[88] LS JES/COR/19/27 Smith to James Smith, 28 November 1782
[89] LS JES/COR/19/26 James Smith to Smith, 3 November 1782
[90] LS JES/COR/19/27 Smith to James Smith, 28 November 1782
[91] LS JES/COR/19/13 Smith to Frances Smith, 16 May 1782
[92] LS JES/COR/19/19 Smith to James Smith, 6 August 1782
[93] LS JES/COR/19/22 Smith to James Smith, 29 August 1782
[94] Including *Sibbaldia procumbens* (creeping sibbaldia), *Azalea* [*Loiseleuria*] *procumbens* (alpine azalea), *Alchemilla alpina* (alpine lady's-mantle), *Polygonum viviparum* [*Persicaria vivipara*] (alpine bistort), and *Saxifraga stellaris* (hairy kidney-wort) see LS JES/COR/18/5 Smith to Thomas Woodward, 28 September 1782
[95] LS JES/COR/19/22 Smith to James Smith, 29 August 1782
[96] LS JES/COR/18/5 Smith to Thomas Woodward, 28 September 1782
[97] LS JES/COR/19/28 Smith to James Smith, 31 December 1782
[98] LS JES/COR/19/27 Smith to James Smith, 28 November 1782
[99] LS JES/COR/19/27 Smith to James Smith, 28 November 1782
[100] LS JES/COR/19/27 Smith to James Smith, 28 November 1782
[101] EUL EUA GD17 Records of the Society for Investigating Natural History, vol. 1, 1782–1783
[102] EUL EUA GD17 Records of the Society for Investigating Natural History, vol. 2, 1783–1784, ff.221–231.
[103] Smith, P (ed.), (1832). *Op. cit.*, vol. 1, p.77.
[104] LS JES/COR/19/28 Smith to James Smith, 31 December 1782
[105] Smith, P (ed.), (1832). *Op. cit.*, vol. 1, p.64.

CHAPTER TWO

[1] Lawrence, S C, (1996). *Charitable Knowledge: Hospital Pupils and Practitioners in Eighteenth-century London*, Cambridge: Cambridge University Press, p.184.
[2] Waddington, K, (2003). *Medical Education at St Bartholomew's Hospital, 1123–1995*, Woodbridge: The Boydell Press, p.27.
[3] LS JES/COR/19/29 Smith to James Smith, 6 March 1782
[4] Waddington, K, (2003). *Op. cit.*, vol. 1, p.28.
[5] LS JES/COR/SM/2 Smith to James Smith, 18 October 1783
[6] Smith, P (ed.), (1832). *Op. cit.*, vol. 1, pp.89–90.
[7] LS JES/COR/SM/2 Smith to James Smith, 18 October 1783
[8] Smith, P (ed.), (1832). *Op. cit.*, vol. 1, p.91.
[9] LS JES/COR/23/18 Thomas Charles Hope to Smith, 12 January 1784
[10] Carter, H, (1988). *Sir Joseph Banks, 1743–1820*, London: British Museum (Natural

History), p.539.

[11] Gascoigne, J, (1994). *Joseph Banks and the English Enlightenment: Useful Knowledge and Polite Culture*, Cambridge: Cambridge University Press, p.10.

[12] Carter, H, (1988). *Op. cit.*, p.173.

[13] LS JES/COR/8/56 John Pitchford to Smith, April 1782

[14] NHM BANKS MSS A Record of Weights, 1778–1814

[15] LS JES/COR/19/30 James Smith to Smith, 12 January 1784

[16] Stoever, D H, & Trapp, J, (trans.), (1794). *The Life of Sir Charles Linnaeus*, London: B & J White, p.313.

[17] LS JES/COR/19/30 James Smith to Smith, 12 January 1784

[18] Smith, P (ed.), (1832). *Op. cit.*, vol. 1, pp.92–94.

[19] LS JES/COR/19/30 James Smith to Smith, 12 January 1784

[20] Smith, P (ed.), (1832). *Op. cit.*, vol. 1, p.102.

[21] *Ibid.*, pp.102–103.

[22] LS JES/COR/18/11 Thomas Woodward to Smith, 29 April 1784

[23] LS JES/COR/24/57 John Pitchford to Smith, 2 May 1784

[24] Smith, P (ed.), (1832). *Op. cit.*, vol. 1, p.107; pp.123–125.

[25] Jackson, B D, (1923). *Linnaeus*, London: H F & G Witherby, pp.351–352.

[26] Stoever, D H, & Trapp, J, (trans.), (1794). *Op. cit.*, p.313.

[27] Smith to Johan Gustaf Acrel, 11 November 1785 (transcript at LS, original in Hagströmer Library, Karolinska Institutet, Stockholm, Sweden)

[28] Jackson, B D, (1923). *Op. cit.*, pp.350–355.

[29] LS JES/COR/18/10 Smith to Thomas Woodward, 20 April 1784

[30] LS JES/COR/26/63 William Withering to Smith, 27 May 1784

[31] LS Rules & Orders of the Society, 13 October 1783

[32] Stewart, L, 'Other Centres of Calculation, or, Where the Royal Society Didn't Count: Commerce, Coffee-Houses and Natural Philosophy in Early Modern London, *The British Journal for the History of Science*, (1999) 32(2), p.138.

[33] Sorrenson, R, 'Towards a History of the Royal Society in the Eighteenth Century', *Notes and Records of the Royal Society of London*, 1996 50(1), p.33.

[34] Miller, D P, 'The Usefulness of Natural Philosophy: The Royal Society and the Culture of Practical Utility in the Later Eighteenth Century', *The British Journal for the History of Science*, (1999) 32(2), p.200.

[35] Smith, P (ed.), (1832). *Op. cit.*, vol. 1, p.120.

[36] LS JES/COR/23/22 Thomas Charles Hope to Smith, 25 October 1784

[37] NHM BANKS COLL DRY f 62 Claes Grill to Jonas Dryander, 26 October 1784

[38] Stoever, D H, & Trapp, J, (trans.), (1794). *Op. cit.*, p.314.

[39] LS JES/SM/1 James Smith to Robert Reeve, 8 November 1784

[40] LS JES/COR/23/52 John Latham to Robert Batty, 15 November 1784

[41] LS JES/COR/5/37 John Sibthorp to Smith, 1 January 1785

[42] LS JES/COR/11/3 Samuel Goodenough to Smith, 31 January 1785
[43] Smith, P (ed.), (1832). *Op. cit.*, vol. 1, p.119.
[44] LS JES/COR/5/44 L'Héritier to Smith, 14 March 1785 [translated from French]
[45] LS JES/COR/5/37 John Sibthorp to Smith, 1 January 1785
[46] LS JES/COR/18/16 Smith to Thomas Woodward, 27 January 1785
[47] LS JES/COR/24/59 John Pitchford to Smith, 26 November 1784
[48] LS JES/COR/18/17 Thomas Woodward to Smith, 1 February 1785
[49] Linnaeus, C, & Smith, J E (ed.), (1811). *Lachesis Lapponica*, London: White and Cochrance, p.ix.
[50] LS JES/COR/18/16 Smith to Thomas Woodward, 27 January 1785
[51] LS JES/COR/18/15 Thomas Woodward to Smith, 18 January 1785
[52] LS JES/COR/6/120 John Lightfoot to Smith, 5 May 1785
[53] RS EC/1785/05 Smith, Sir James Edward nomination paper
[54] Smith, P (ed.), (1832). *Op. cit.*, vol. 1, pp.135–139.
[55] Smith to Johan Gustaf Acrel, 16 May (transcript at LS, original in Hagströmer Library, Karolinska Institutet, Stockholm, Sweden)
[56] LS JES/COR/18/19 Thomas Woodward to Smith, 23 April 1785
[57] LS JES/COR/18/20 Smith to Thomas Woodward, 19 May 1785
[58] LS JES/COR/18/21 Thomas Woodward to Smith, 9 June 1785
[59] Smith to Johan Gustaf Acrel, 16 May (transcript at LS, original in Hagströmer Library, Karolinska Institutet, Stockholm, Sweden)
[60] Smith, P (ed.), (1832). *Op. cit.*, vol. 1, p.137.
[61] Linnaeus, C, & Smith, J E (trans.) (1785). *Reflections on the Study of Nature*, London: George Nicol, p.vii–viii.
[62] Smith, P (ed.), (1832). *Op. cit.*, vol. 1, p.107.
[63] Humphry Sibthorp, Professor of Botany at Oxford from 1747 to 1784 gave just one course during his 37 years in the chair; whilst his successor, his son John Sibthorp, spent a large part of his tenure (1784–1796) travelling and collecting in Europe. At Cambridge, John Martyn, professor from 1733 to 1762, stopped lecturing in 1735, and was succeeded by his son, Thomas Martyn, professor from 1762 to 1825. Thomas Martyn ceased his lectures in 1796.
[64] Porter, R, 'The New Taste for Nature in the Eighteenth Century', *The Linnean*, 1988 4(1), pp.16–19.
[65] Smith to Johan Gustaf Acrel, 8 October 1788 (transcript at LS, original in Hagströmer Library, Karolinska Institutet, Stockholm, Sweden)
[66] LS JES/COR/23/25 Thomas Charles Hope to Smith, 26 October 1785
[67] Smith, P (ed.), (1832). *Op. cit.*, vol. 1, pp.144–147.
[68] LS JES/COR/18/25 Smith to Thomas Woodward, 30 March 1786
[69] Linnaeus, C, & Smith, J E (trans.), (1786). *Dissertation on the Sexes of Plants*, London: George Nicol, p.vii.

[70] Smith, P (ed.), (1832). *Op. cit.*, vol. 1, p.146.
[71] Linnaeus, C, & Smith, J E (trans.), (1786). *Op. cit.*, pp.xiii–xiv.
[72] Smith, J E, (1793). *A Sketch of a Tour on the Continent, in the years 1786 and 1787*, London: [privately], vol. 1, p.2.

CHAPTER THREE

[1] LS MS 670 Smith tour journal, 18 June 1786
[2] Smith, J E, (1793). *Op. cit.*, vol. 1, p.5.
[3] LS JES/COR/19/32 Smith to Frances Smith, 15 July 1786
[4] LS JES/COR/1/46 Sir Joseph Banks to Jean-Nicolas-Sébastien Allamand, 16 June 1786 [in Smith's hand]
[5] LS MS 670 Smith tour journal, 23 June 1786
[6] LS JES/COR/18/28 Thomas Woodward to Smith, 13 August 1786
[7] Smith, J E, (1793). *Op. cit.*, vol. 1, p.45.
[8] LS MS 670 Smith tour journal, 8 July 1786; 10 July 1786
[9] LS JES/COR/18/27 Smith to Thomas Woodward, 14 July 1786
[10] Smith, J E, & Oosterdijk, N G, (1786). *Disputatio Physiologica Inauguralis. Quædam de Generatione Complectens*, Lugduni Batavorum: Apud Fratres Murray, preface; p.5.
[11] LS JES/COR/19/33 Smith to Mrs Howorth, 15 July 1786
[12] LS JES/COR/19/35 Smith to James Smith, 21 August 1786
[13] LS JES/COR/19/33 Smith to Mrs Howorth, 15 July 1786
[14] LS MS 670 Smith tour journal, 20 July 1786
[15] Black, J, (2003). *France and the Grand Tour*, Basingstoke: Palgrave Macmillan, p.159.
[16] Smith, J E, (1793). *Op. cit.*, vol. 1, p.47.
[17] LS JES/COR/19/39 Smith to Mrs Pitchford, 6 October 1786
[18] Smith, J E, (1793). *Op. cit.*, vol. 1, p.64.
[19] *Ibid.*, p.66.
[20] LS JES/COR/19/35 Smith to James Smith, 21 August 1786
[21] Smith, J E, (1793). *Op. cit.*, vol. 1, p.69.
[22] LS MS 670 Smith tour journal, 6 August 1786
[23] LS JES/COR/19/35 Smith to James Smith, 21 August 1786
[24] Smith, J E, (1793). *Op. cit.*, vol. 1, p.70.
[25] *Ibid.*, p.206.
[26] *Ibid.*, p.71.
[27] LS JES/COR/19/35 Smith to James Smith, 21 August 1786
[28] LS MS 670 Smith tour journal, 7 August 1786
[29] LS JES/COR/19/35 Smith to James Smith, 21 August 1786
[30] Smith, J E, (1793). *Op. cit.*, vol. 1, p.74.

[31] LS MS 670 Smith tour journal, 8 August 1786; 19 August 1786
[32] LS MS 670 Smith tour journal, 20 August 1786
[33] LS MS 670 Smith tour journal, 10 September 1786
[34] LS JES/COR/19/39 Smith to Mrs Patterson, 6 October 1786
[35] LS JES/COR/18/29 Thomas Woodward to Smith, 16 March 1787
[36] NHM BANKS COLL DRY f64 Smith to Jonas Dryander, 28 August 1786
[37] Romani, R, (2002). *National Character and Public Spirit in Britain and France, 1750–1914*, Cambridge: Cambridge University Press, p.13.
[38] LS JES/COR/19/35 Smith to James Smith, 21 August 1786
[39] LS JES/COR/19/39 Smith to Mrs Pitchford, 6 October 1786
[40] LS JES/COR/19/36 Smith to James Smith, 13 September 1786
[41] NHM DTC 5 f52 James Edward Smith to Sir Joseph Banks, 13 September 1786
[42] LS JES/COR/19/37 James Smith to Smith, September 1786
[43] LS JES/COR/19/61 Smith to James Smith, 3 August 1787
[44] LS JES/COR/19/38 Smith to Mrs Howorth, 24th September 1786
[45] LS MS 670 Smith tour journal, 18 and 19 September 1786
[46] LS JES/COR/19/38 Smith to Mrs Howorth, 24 September 1786
[47] Smith, J E, (1793). *Op. cit.,* vol. 1, p.135.
[48] LS JES/COR/19/40 James Smith to Smith, 26 October 1786
[49] LS MS 670 Smith tour journal, 31 October 1786
[50] LS MS 670 Smith tour journal, 1 November 1786; 5 November 1786
[51] Smith, J E, (1793). *Op. cit.,* vol. 1, pp.140–141.
[52] LS JES/COR/19/41 Smith to James Smith, 18 November 1786
[53] Smith, J E, (1793). *Op. cit.,* vol. 1, p.146.
[54] LS JES/COR/19/41 Smith to James Smith, 18 November 1786
[55] Smith, J E, (1793). *Op. cit.,* vol. 1, pp.160–164.
[56] LS JES/COR/19/42 Smith to James Smith, 5 December 1786
[57] Smith, J E, (1793). *Op. cit.,* vol. 1, p.170.
[58] LS JES/COR/19/42 Smith to James Smith, 5 December 1786
[59] LS MS 670 Smith tour journal, 4 December 1786
[60] Smith, J E, (1793). *Op. cit.,* vol. 1, pp.181–184.
[61] LS JES/COR/19/53 Smith to Frances Smith, 7 May 1787
[62] LS JES/COR/18/29 Thomas Woodward to Smith, 16 March 1787
[63] LS JES/COR/19/44 Smith to James Smith, 30 December 1786; Smith, J E, (1793). *Op. cit.,* vol. 1, pp.187–188; pp.194–196.
[64] LS MS 670 Smith tour journal, 16 December 1786
[65] LS JES/COR/19/44 Smith to James Smith, 30th December 1786
[66] Smith, J E, (1793). *Op. cit.,* vol. 1, p.204.
[67] *Ibid.*, pp.204–210.
[68] LS MS 670 Smith tour journal, 24 December 1786

[69] LS MS 670 Smith tour journal, 24 December; 25 December 1786
[70] Smith, J E, (1793). *Op. cit.,* vol. 1, p.221.
[71] LS MS 670 Smith tour journal, 26 December, 27 December and 28 December 1786
[72] LS JES/COR/19/44 Smith to James Smith, 30 December 1786
[73] LS JES/COR/19/46 Smith to Frances Smith, 22 January 1787
[74] LS MS 670 Smith tour journal, 1 January 1787
[75] Smith, J E, (1793). *Op. cit.,* vol. 1, p.258.
[76] LS JES/COR/19/44 Smith to James Smith, 30 December 1786
[77] LS MS 670 Smith tour journal, 8 January 1787
[78] Smith, J E, (1793). *Op. cit.,* vol. 1, pp.240–241.
[79] *Ibid.,* pp.261–263.
[80] Hunt, L, 'Letters from Abroad, No. 3', in Pickering, L (ed.) (1966), *Lord Byron, Leigh Hunt and the "Liberal"*, pp.145–146.
[81] Smith, J E, (1793). *Op. cit.,* vol. 1, p.273.
[82] LS MS 670 Smith tour journal, 24 January 1787
[83] LS JES/COR/19/47 Smith to James Smith, 12 February 1787
[84] Smith, J E, (1793). *Op. cit.,* vol. 1, pp.317–318.
[85] LS JES/COR/19/47 Smith to James Smith, 12 February 1787
[86] Smith, J E, (1793). *Op. cit.,* vol. 1, pp.338–339.
[87] LS JES/COR/19/48 Smith to James Smith, 5 March 1787
[88] LS MS 670 Smith tour journal, 8 February and 13 February 1787
[89] Smith, J E, (1793). *Op. cit.,* vol. 2, pp.37–38; pp.47–52.
[90] LS MS 670 Smith tour journal, 18 February 1787
[91] LS MS 670 Smith tour journal, 20 February 1787
[92] LS JES/COR/19/48 Smith to James Smith, 5 March 1787
[93] LS MS 670 Smith tour journal, 21 February 1787
[94] Smith, J E, (1793). *Op. cit.,* vol. 2, p.66; pp.74–75.
[95] LS JES/COR/19/48 Smith to James Smith, 5 March 1787
[96] LS JES/COR/19/49 Smith to James Smith, 26 March 1787
[97] Smith, J E, (1793). *Op. cit.,* vol. 2, p.113.
[98] *Ibid.,* pp.121–122.
[99] LS MS 670 Smith tour journal, 13th March 1787
[100] Smith, J E, (1793). *Op. cit.,* vol. 2, pp.120–121.
[101] LS JES/COR/1/49 Sir Joseph Banks to Sir William Hamilton, 24th September 1786 [copy in Smith's hand]
[102] LS MS 670 Smith tour journal, 17 March 1787
[103] Smith, J E, (1793). *Op. cit.,* vol. 2, pp.129–130.
[104] Smith, J E, (1791–1792). *Spicilegium Botanicum,* London: [privately], tab.18
[105] Smith, J E, (1793). *Op. cit.,* vol. 2, pp.133–137.
[106] LS JES/COR/19/51 Smith to James Smith, 11 April 1787

107 LS JES/COR/19/53 Smith to Frances Smith, 7 May 1787
108 LS MS 670 Smith tour journal, 17 May 1787
109 Smith, J E, (1793). *Op. cit.,* vol. 2, pp.422–423.
110 LS JES/COR/19/56 Smith to James Smith, 8 June 1787
111 LS MS 670 Smith tour journal, 21 May 1787
112 LS JES/COR/19/58 Smith to James Smith, 2 July 1787
113 LS JES/COR/19/59 Smith to Mrs Howorth, 7 July 1787
114 LS JES/COR/19/58 Smith to James Smith, 2 July 1787
115 LS JES/COR/19/47 Smith to James Smith, 12 February 1787
116 LS JES/COR/10/108 William Younge to Smith, 17 July 1787
117 LS JES/COR/19/37 Smith to James Smith, September 1786
118 LS JES/COR/11/8 Samuel Goodenough to Smith, 11 March 1787
119 LS MS 670 Smith tour journal, 12 August 1787
120 Smith, J E, (1793). *Op. cit.,* vol. 3, p.127; p.137.
121 LS JES/COR/19/62 Smith to James Smith, 27 August 1787
122 LS JES/COR/10/108 William Younge to Smith, 17 July 1787
123 LS JES/COR/19/62 Smith to James Smith, 27 August 1787
124 LS MS 670 Smith tour journal, 28 August 1787
125 Smith, J E, (1793). *Op. cit.,* vol. 1, p.278.
126 Smith, J E, (1793). *Op. cit.,* vol. 3, p.183.
127 LS MS 670 Smith tour journal, 1 October 1787
128 JES/COR/11/9 Samuel Goodenough to Smith, 13 August 1787
129 Smith, J E, (1793). *Op. cit.,* vol. 3, p.233.

CHAPTER FOUR

1 Smith, J E, (1793). *Op. cit.,* vol. 3, p.232.
2 BL Add Mss 28545 f96 Smith to Aylmer Bourke Lambert, 19 March 1788
3 LS JES/COR/18/34 Smith to Thomas Woodward, 10 July 1788; JES/MS238/3 Smith to Richard Pulteney, 21 December 1789
4 'The Pantheon', *Survey of London: vol.umes 31 and 32: St James Westminster, Part 2* (1963), pp. 268–283.
5 Smith, P (ed.), (1832). *Op. cit.,* vol. 1, p.145.
6 *Ibid.,* pp.342–344.
7 *Ibid.,* pp.342–344.
8 NHM DTC5 f149 Smith to Sir Joseph Banks, 2 April 1787
9 LS JES/COR/1/50 Sir Joseph Banks to Smith, 11 May 1787
10 LS JES/COR/11/8 Samuel Goodenough to Smith, 11 March 1787
11 LS JES/COR/11/9 Samuel Goodenough to Smith, 13th August 1787
12 LS JES/ADD/54 Thomas Marsham to Smith, 21 September 1786
13 LS JES/COR/11/5 Samuel Goodenough to Smith, 3 July 1786

[14] LS JES/COR/11/5 Samuel Goodenough to Smith, 3 July 1786

[15] Foote, Y, 'Marsham, Thomas (1747/8–1819)', *Oxford Dictionary of National Biography*, Oxford University Press, 2004 [http://www.oxforddnb.com/view/article/18161, accessed 25 April 2014]

[16] Smith to Acrel, 8 September 1788 (transcript at LS, original in Hagströmer Library, Karolinska Institutet, Stockholm, Sweden)

[17] LS JES/ADD/53 Thomas Marsham to Smith, 1st September 1786

[18] OMNH WJ/A/1/1 Smith to William Jones, 8 September 1786

[19] LS JES/COR/11/6 Samuel Goodenough to Smith, 25 September 1786

[20] LS JES/ADD/53 Thomas Marsham to Smith, 1st September 1786

[21] LS JES/COR/5/104 William Jones to Smith, 20 September 1786

[22] OMNH WJ/A/1/2 Smith to William Jones, 19 February 1787

[23] LS MS 670 Smith tour journal, 26 August 1787

[24] LS JES/COR/11/7 Samuel Goodenough to Smith, 3 November 1786

[25] LS Minute Book 1788–1802 Set of Rules for the "Linnaean Society"

[26] LS JES/COR/24/6 Thomas Marsham to Smith, 28 January 1788

[27] LS JES/COR/24/7 Thomas Marsham to Smith, [February 1788]

[28] Curtis, W H, (1941). *William Curtis 1746–1799*, Winchester: Warren and Son Ltd., pp.81–82.

[29] BL Add Mss 28545 f96 Smith to Aylmer Bourke Lambert, 19 March 1788

[30] LS Minute Book 1788–1802 Set of Rules for the "Linnaean Society"

[31] LS JES/COR/24/6 Thomas Marsham to Smith, 28 January 1788

[32] LS JES/COR/11/8 Samuel Goodenough to Smith, 11 March 1787

[33] LS JES/COR/24/6 Thomas Marsham to Smith, 28 January 1788

[34] LS JES/COR/24/63 John Pitchford to Smith, 6 February 1788

[35] The name of the Linnean Society was fluid for some time after its establishment. The opening pages of both the Fellows and General Meetings minute books list the 'Linnaean Society', though when mentioned in the minutes themselves 'Linnean' is also used. The confusion arose from whether the Society's name should embrace Linné, his ennobled name, or Linnaeus, the Latinised form. Eventually 'Linnean Society' was settled upon. It has long since been accepted that 'Linnean' refers to the Society, whilst 'Linnaean' relates to Linnaeus himself, his collections or his work.

[36] Curtis, W H, (1941). *Op. cit.*, p.82.

[37] LS JES/COR/24/79 Richard Pulteney to Smith, 19 April 1789

[38] LS JES/MS238/3 Smith to Richard Pulteney, 21 December 1789

[39] Smith, J E, 'Introductory Discourse on the Rise and Progress of Natural History', *Op. cit.*, pp.51–52.

[40] *Ibid.*, p.52.

[41] *Ibid.*, pp.52–55.

[42] Smith, J E, 'Some Observations on the Irritability of Vegetables', *Philosophical Transactions of the Royal Society of London*, 1788 78, p.161.

[43] *Ibid.*, p.164

[44] *General Evening Post* (London, England), June 7, 1788–June 10, 1788; Issue 8513.

[45] LS JES/ADD/107 Petrus Camper to James Edward Smith, 22 June 1788, and Smith's reply, 21 July 1788 [copy]

[46] LS JES/ADD/107 Petrus Camper to James Edward Smith, 22 June 1788, and reply, 21 July 1788 [copy]

[47] LS JES/COR/1/108 Pierre Broussonet to Smith, 10 March 1788

[48] LS JES/COR/1/109 Pierre Broussonet to Smith, 27 April 1788

[49] LS JES/COR/18/36 Smith to Thomas Woodward, 17 September 1788

[50] LS JES/COR/24/65 John Pitchford to Smith, 21 May 1788

[51] LS JES/COR/18/34 Smith to Thomas Woodward, 10 July 1788; Smith to Johan Acrel, 8 September 1788 (transcript at LS, original in Hagströmer Library, Karolinska Institutet, Stockholm, Sweden)

[52] LS JES/COR/18/36 Smith to Thomas Woodward, 17 September 1788

[53] LS JES/COR/19/65 James Smith to Smith, 20 September 1788

[54] Smith to Johan Acrel, 8 September 1788 (transcript at LS, original in Hagströmer Library, Karolinska Institutet, Stockholm, Sweden)

[55] LS JES/COR/24/67 John Pitchford to Smith, 2 July 1788

[56] LS JES/COR/10/42 Walter Vaughan to Smith, 11 March 1789

CHAPTER FIVE

[1] LS JES/COR/18/20 Smith to Thomas Woodward, 19 May 1785

[2] *The Monthly Review*, London 81: 111 August 1789

[3] LS JES/COR/1/20 Johan Gustaf Acrel to Smith, 24 September 1792 [translated from Latin]

[4] *World* (1787) (London, England), Saturday, April 25, 1789; Issue 723.

[5] LS JES/COR/14/5 Smith to Edmund Davall, 24 April 1789

[6] 'Curtis, William' in Rees, A, (ed.), (1802–1819). *The Cyclopædia or, Universal dictionary of Arts, Sciences, and Literature*, London: Longman, Hurst, Rees, Orme & Brown.

[7] Hooker, W J, (1827). *Curtis's Botanical Magazine: Or, Flower–garden displayed*, London: Samuel Curtis, vol. 1, p.xxii.

[8] LS JES/COR/14/5 Smith to Edmund Davall, 24 April 1789

[9] Smith to Johan Gustaf Acrel, 30 July 1789 (transcript at LS, original in Hagströmer Library, Karolinska Institutet, Stockholm, Sweden)

[10] Translated as "Figured plans hitherto not published or unknown mostly from Linnaeus's herbarium"

[11] Smith, J E, (1789–1791). *Plantarum Icones Hactenus Ineditæ, Plerumque ad Plantas in*

Herbario Linnaeano Conservatas Delineatæ, London: Impensis Benj. White et Filii, fasc. 3, preface [translated from Latin].

[12] Smith, J E, (1789–1791). *Op. cit.*, fasc. 2, preface [translated from Latin].

[13] Smith, J E, (1789–1791). *Op. cit.*, fasc. 1, preface [translated from Latin].

[14] *The Monthly Review*, London 81: 112 August 1789

[15] *The Critical Review; Or, Annals of Literature*, London 67: 513 June 1789

[16] LS JES/COR/1/18 Johan Gustav Acrel to Smith, 6 November 1789 [translated from Latin]

[17] Smith, J E, 'Tentamen Botanicum de Filicum Generibus Dorsiferarum', *Mémoires de l'Académie Royale des Sciences de Turin*, 1793 5, pp.401–422; translation available in Smith's *Tracts Relating to Natural History* (1798)

[18] LS JES/COR/4/1 Jean Dana to Smith, 19 August 1789 [translated from French]

[19] LS JES/COR/7/61 Gabriel de la Boulaye to Smith, 29 November 1789 [translated from French]

[20] LS JES/COR/14/8 Smith to Edmund Davall, 2 July 1789

[21] Aiton, W, (1789). *Hortus Kewensis; or, a Catalogue of the Plants Cultivated in the Royal Botanic Garden at Kew*, London: Printed for George Nicol, vol. 3, p.496.

[22] LS JES/COR/14/47 Smith to Edmund Davall, 21 February 1792

[23] 'Smithia', in Rees, A, (ed.), (1802–1819). *Op. cit.*

[24] LS JES/COR/14/73 Edmund Davall to Smith, 27 January 1795

[25] LS JES/COR/14/73 Edmund Davall to Smith, 27 January 1795

[26] LS JES/COR/10/99 Jacob Wyttenbach to Smith, 16 April 1788 [translated from French]; JES/COR/9/41 Jean Senebier to Smith, 3 March 1788 [translated from French]

[27] LS JES/COR/14/73 Edmund Davall to Smith, 27 January 1795

[28] LS JES/COR/14/6 Edmund Davall to Smith, 5 May 1789

[29] LS JES/COR/14/8 Smith to Edmund Davall, 2 July 1789

[30] LS JES/COR/14/2 Edmund Davall to Smith, 1 February 1789

[31] LS JES/COR/14/7 Edmund Davall to Smith, 22 May 1789

[32] LS JES/COR/14/73 Edmund Davall to Smith, 27 January 1795

[33] LS JES/COR/14/12 Edmund Davall to Smith, 24 November 1789

[34] LS JES/COR/14/13 Edmund Davall to Smith, 25 January 1790

[35] LS JES/COR/15/77 Mary Watson-Wentworth to Smith, 8 December 1788

[36] LS JES/COR/15/78 Mary Watson-Wentworth to Smith, 10 December 1788

[37] LS JES/COR/14/11 Smith to Edmund Davall, 17 November 1789

[38] LS JES/COR/15/86 Mary Watson-Wentworth to Smith, 9 November 1789

[39] LS JES/COR/14/10 Edmund Davall to Smith, 27 October 1789

[40] LS JES/COR/14/10 Edmund Davall to Smith, 27 October 1789

[41] LS JES/COR/14/11 Smith to Edmund Davall, 17 November 1789

[42] LS JES/COR/14/12 Edmund Davall to Smith, 24 November 1789

[43] LS JES/COR/14/14 Edmund Davall to Smith, 27 February 1790
[44] LS JES/COR/14/11 Smith to Edmund Davall, 17 November 1789
[45] LS JES/COR/14/73 Edmund Davall to Smith, 27 January 1795
[46] LS JES/COR/14/13 Edmund Davall to Smith, 29 January 1790
[47] LS JES/COR/14/15 Smith to Edmund Davall, 9 March 1790
[48] LS JES/COR/14/11 Smith to Edmund Davall, 17 November 1789
[49] LS JES/COR/14/11 Smith to Edmund Davall, 17 November 1789
[50] Smith, J E, (1804–1808). *Exotic Botany*, London: J Sowerby, vol. 2, t.80.
[51] LS JES/COR/15/86 Mary Watson-Wentworth to Smith, 9 November 1789
[52] LS JES/COR/25/11 William Roxburgh to Smith, 17 October 1791
[53] *World* (1787) (London, England), Friday, December 25, 1789; Issue 927.
[54] LS JES/COR/14/15 Smith to Edmund Davall, 9 March 1790
[55] Smith, P (ed.), (1832). *Op. cit.*, vol. 1, p.519.
[56] LS JES/COR/15/88 Mary Watson-Wentworth to Smith, 25 February 1790
[57] LS JES/COR/14/15 Smith to Edmund Davall, 9 March 1790
[58] LS JES/COR/2/12 Jane Barrington to Smith, 3 May 1790
[59] LS JES/COR/20/64 Jane Barrington to Smith, 14 November 1799
[60] Shteir, A B, (1996). *Cultivating Women, Cultivating Science*, London: John Hopkins University Press, p.4.
[61] Martyn, T, (1787). *Letters on the Elements of Botany, Addressed to a Lady*, London: B. White, 2nd ed., preface.
[62] *The English Review*, London 6: 401 December 1785
[63] LS JES/COR/2/13 Jane Barrington to Smith, 4 July 1790
[64] Withering, W, (1776). *A Botanical Arrangement of all the Vegetables Naturally Growing in Great Britain*, Birmingham: Cadel, p.xlvi.
[65] A Botanical Society at Lichfield, (1783). *A System of Vegetables*, Lichfield; London: John Jackson, p.1.
[66] LS JES/COR/1/51 Sir Joseph Banks to Smith, 15 August 1787

CHAPTER SIX

[1] LS JES/COR/14/15 Smith to Edmund Davall, 9 March 1790
[2] LS JES/COR/14/17 Smith to Edmund Davall, 30 March 1790
[3] LS JES/COR/18/39 Thomas Woodward to Smith, 15 January 1790
[4] LS JES/COR/14/22 Smith to Edmund Davall, 11 July 1790
[5] LS JES/COR/1/116 Pierre Broussonet to Smith, 21 June 1789 [translated from French]
[6] Lamarck, J B, (1789). *Encyclopédie Méthodique: Botanique*, Paris: Panckoucke, vol.. 3, pt. 1, p.vii [translated from French].
[7] LS JES/MS238/6 Smith to Richard Pulteney, 22 March 1790
[8] Smith, J E, (1789–1791). *Op. cit.*, fasc. 2, preface [translated from Latin].

[9] LS JES/COR/5/97 Nikolaus von Jacquin to Smith, 4 July 1790 [translated from French]

[10] LS JES/COR/4/57 René Louiche Desfontaines to Smith, 20 July 1790 [translated from French]

[11] Stafleu, F A, (1971). *Linnaeus and the Linnaeans: The Spreading of their Ideas in Systematic Botany*, Utrecht: A. Oosthoek's Uitgeversmaatschappij N.V. for the International Association for Plant Taxonomy, p.303.

[12] LS JES/COR/1/121 Pierre Broussonet to Smith, 25 May 1790 [translated from French]

[13] LS JES/COR/5/20 Antoine Laurent de Jussieu to Smith, 20 March 1789 [translated from French]

[14] Smith, J E, (1793). *Op. cit.*, vol 1, pp.122–123.

[15] Stevens, P F, (1994). *The Development of Biological Systematics: Antoine-Laurent de Jussieu, Nature, and the Natural System*, New York, Chichester: Columbia University Press, p.2.

[16] LS JES/COR/4/71 Jonas Dryander to Smith, 16 September 1789

[17] NHM BANKS COLL DRY f68 Smith to Jonas Dryander, 21 September 1789

[18] LS JES/COR/1/121 Pierre Broussonet to Smith, 25 May 1790 [translated from French]

[19] Smith, J E, (1793). *Op. cit.*, vol. 1, p.122.

[20] LS JES/COR/1/117 Pierre Broussonet to Smith, 29 July 1789 [translated from French]

[21] LS JES/MS238/4 Smith to Richard Pulteney, 2 February 1790

[22] LS JES/COR/4/57 René Louiche Desfontaines to Smith, 20 July 1790 [translated from French]

[23] LS JES/COR/5/62 Charles L'Héritier de Brutelle to Smith, 25 December 1790 [translated from French]

[24] LS JES/COR/7/62 Gabriel de la Boulaye to Smith, 20 September 1790 [translated from French]

[25] LS JES/COR/4/57 René Louiche Desfontaines to Smith, 20 July 1790 [translated from French]

[26] Stafleu, F A, (1971). *Op. cit.*, p.291.

[27] LS JES/COR/14/8 Smith to Edmund Davall, 2 July 1789

[28] Smith, J E, (1789–1791). *Op. cit.*, fasc. 2, preface.

[29] LS JES/COR/15/81 Mary Watson-Wentworth to Smith, 2 July 1789

[30] LS JES/COR/14/8 Smith to Edmund Davall, 2 July 1789

[31] LS JES/COR/14/22 Smith to Edmund Davall, 11 July 1790

[32] LS JES/COR/14/25 Smith to Edmund Davall, 28 September 1790

[33] LS JES/COR/14/11 Smith to Edmund Davall, 17 November 1789

[34] Smith, J E, (1790–1793). *Icones Pictæ Plantarum Rariorum Descriptionibus et Observa-*

tionibus, London: [privately], fasc. 1, preface.

[35] *The Monthly Review* ser.2. 4: 302 March 1791

[36] LS JES/COR/15/95 Mary Watson-Wentworth to Smith, 8 November 1790

[37] LS JES/COR/14/29 Edmund Davall to Smith, 11 February 1791

[38] LS JES/COR/18/56 Thomas Woodward to Smith, 31 March 1792

[39] LS JES/COR/14/35 Smith to Edmund Davall, 27 May 1791

[40] Desmond, R, (2003). *Great Natural History Books and their Creators*, London: British Library, p.103.

[41] Smith, J E, & Sowerby, J, (1790–1814). *Op. cit.*, vol. 1, preface.

[42] *The Analytical Review*, London 9: 294 April 1790

[43] Desmond, R, (1987). *A Celebration of Flowers: Two Hundred Years of Curtis's Botanical Magazine*, London: Royal Botanic Gardens with Collingridge, p.37.

[44] LS JES/COR/18/43 Smith to Thomas Woodward, 29 November 1790

[45] Text for plates 16, 17 and 18 by George Shaw

[46] LS JES/COR/18/43 Smith to Thomas Woodward, 29 November 1790

[47] Smith, J E, & Sowerby, J, (1790–1814). *Op. cit.*, vol. 4, preface.

[48] *Ibid.*, vol. 1, preface.

[49] *Ibid.*, vol. 1, tab.1.

[50] Ultimately derived from Welsh naturalist Edward Lhuyd

[51] Smith, J E, & Sowerby, J, (1790–1814). *Op. cit.*, tab.35.

[52] LS JES/COR/24/73 John Pitchford to Smith, 3 December 1790

[53] *The Analytical Review*, London 9: 294 April 1790

[54] LS JES/COR/14/27 Smith to Edmund Davall, 15 December 1790

[55] LS JES/COR/18/44 Thomas Woodward to Smith, 25 December 1790

[56] LS JES/COR/18/46 Thomas Woodward to Smith, 20 March 1791

[57] LS JES/COR/14/29 Edmund Davall to Smith, 11 February 1791

[58] *The Gentleman's Magazine*, London 73: 494 June 1793

[59] LS JES/COR/14/44 Smith to Edmund Davall, 30 December 1791

[60] Smith, J E, & Sowerby, J, (1790–1814). *Op. cit.*, vol. 7, preface.

[61] LS JES/COR/14/44 Smith to Edmund Davall, 30 December 1791

[62] Curtis, W H, (1941). *Op. cit.*, pp.107–112.

[63] Smith, J E (1790–1793). *Op. cit.*, fasc. 1, preface.

[64] Smith, J E, (1791–1792). *Spicilegium Botanicum*, London: [privately], fasc. 1, preface.

[65] Sowerby went on to publish *Coloured Figures of English Fungi and Mushrooms* (1796–1803; 1809–1815), in which he fully utilised his own considerable taxonomic skills.

[66] LS JES/COR/18/50 Smith to Thomas Woodward, 2 July 1791

[67] Smith, J E, & Sowerby, J, (1790–1814). *Op. cit.*, vol. 4, preface.

CHAPTER SEVEN

1. LS JES/COR/2/35 Carlo Bellardi to Smith, 20 October 1790 [translated from Italian]
2. LS JES/COR/18/50 Smith to Thomas Woodward, 2 July 1791
3. LS JES/COR/10/28 Carl Peter Thunberg to Smith, 19 October 1790 [translated from Latin]
4. *The Monthly Review* ser.2. 7: 166 February 1792
5. LS JES/COR/18/55 Smith to Thomas Woodward, 20 March 1792
6. LS JES/COR/18/56 Thomas Woodward to Smith, 31 March 1792
7. LS JES/COR/13/3 Sir Thomas Gery Cullum to Smith, 22 August 1791
8. *The Monthly Review* ser.2. 7: 166 February 1792
9. LS Minute Book of the Linnaean Society of London 1788–1802
10. LS Minute Book of the Society for the Promotion of Natural History
11. *The Analytical Review* 12: 278 March 1792
12. *The Monthly Review* ser.2. 8: 562 August 1792
13. LS JES/COR/18/53 Smith to Thomas Woodward, 17 February 1792
14. Linnaeus, C, & Smith, J E (ed.), (1792). *Flora Lapponica*, London: White and Son, 2nd ed., pp.i–v.
15. LS JES/COR/18/50 Smith to Thomas Woodward, 2 July 1791
16. 'The Pantheon', *Survey of London: vol.umes 31 and 32: St James Westminster, Part 2(1963)*, pp. 268–283.
17. LS JES/COR/14/47 Smith to Edmund Davall, 21 February 1792
18. LS JES/COR/18/53 Smith to Thomas Woodward, 17 February 1792
19. (1790). *Free English territory in Africa* [An account of the district purchased for the settlement at Sierra Leone], London.
20. LS JES/SM/3 Smith to James Smith, 19 April 1792
21. LS JES/COR/18/54 Thomas Woodward to Smith, 19 February 1792
22. LS JES/COR/14/48 Smith to Edmund Davall, 17 March 1792
23. LS JES/COR/14/47 Smith to Edmund Davall, 21 February 1792
24. LS JES/COR/1/24 Adam Afzelius to Smith, 2 July 1792
25. Goodenough was intimate with George III. In 1789, during the King's first bout of madness, he reliably informed Smith that "the string upon which he goes off is Politicks, particularly the German" (LS JES/COR/11/11)
26. LS JES/COR/14/47 Smith to Edmund Davall, 21 February 1792; LS JES/COR/18/53 Smith to Thomas Woodward, 17 February 1792
27. LS JES/COR/18/54 Thomas Woodward to Smith, 19 February 1792
28. LS JES/COR/18/56 Thomas Woodward to Smith, 31 March 1792
29. NHM Sowerby collection 20.59 f399 Smith to James Sowerby, [November 1793]
30. LS JES/COR/18/55 Smith to Thomas Woodward, 20 March 1792
31. LS JES/COR/21/108 Philadelphia Dawson to Smith, 20 March 1792

[32] LS JES/SM/3 Smith to James Smith, 19 April 1792
[33] LS JES/COR/18/59 Smith to Thomas Woodward, 22 June 1792
[34] NHM BANKS COLL DRY f69 28 June 1792
[35] LS JES/COR/4/6 Erasmus Darwin to Smith, 12 September 1792
[36] LS JES/COR/14/53 Smith to Edmund Davall, 26 October 1792
[37] LS JES/SM/4 Smith to James Smith, 5 August 1792
[38] LS JES/COR/18/61 Smith to Thomas Woodward, 31 October 1792
[39] Linnaeus, C, & Smith, J E (ed.), (1792). *Op. cit.*, p.235.
[40] LS JES/COR/14/53 Smith to Edmund Davall, 26 October 1792
[41] LS JES/COR/18/26 Thomas Woodward to Smith, 18 November 1792
[42] LS JES/COR/14/53 Smith to Edmund Davall, 26 October 1792
[43] LS JES/COR/14/54 Smith to Edmund Davall, 9 November 1792
[44] LS JES/COR/18/66 Thomas Woodward to Smith, 11 January 1793
[45] LS JES/COR/18/67 Smith to Thomas Woodward, 4 February 1793
[46] LS JES/COR/18/64 Thomas Woodward to Smith, 6 December 1792
[47] LS JES/COR/24/103 Richard Pulteney to Smith, 15 November 1793
[48] LS JES/COR/14/54 Smith to Edmund Davall, 9 November 1792
[49] LS JES/COR/18/67 Smith to Thomas Woodward, 4 February 1793
[50] LS JES/COR/14/55 Edmund Davall to Smith, 11 January 1793
[51] LS JES/COR/18/65 Smith to Thomas Woodward, 9 January 1793
[52] LS JES/COR/14/59 Smith to Edmund Davall, 12 May 1793
[53] LS JES/COR/18/67 Smith to Thomas Woodward, 4 February 1793
[54] Smith, J E, 'Tentamen Botanicum de Filicum Generibus Dorsiferarum', *Mémoires de l'Académie Royale des Sciences de Turin*, (1793) 5, pp.401–422.
[55] LS JES/SM/5 Smith to James Smith, 27 June 1793
[56] LS JES/COR/10/29 Carl Peter Thunberg to Smith, 28 December 1791 [translated from Latin]
[57] LS JES/COR/10/75 Johan Carl Wilcke to Smith, 15 December 1792 [translated from Latin]
[58] LS JES/COR/9/72 Dietrich Stoever to Smith, 8 October 1791 [translated from Latin]
[59] Stoever, D H, (1792). *Leben des Ritters Carl von Linné*, Hamburg: Hoffmann.
[60] LS JES/COR/14/72 Smith to Edmund Davall, 26 September 1794
[61] Nelson, E C, 'John White A.M., M.D., F.L.S. (c.1756–1832), Surgeon– General of New South Wales: A New Biography of the Messenger of the Echidna and Waratah', *Archives of Natural History*, (1998) 25 (2), pp.175–176.
[62] LS JES/COR/18/51 Smith to Thomas Woodward, 19 December 1791. 379 specimens sent by White are extant in Smith's herbarium.
[63] LS JES/COR/14/50 Smith to Edmund Davall, 27 June 1792
[64] Smith, J E, (1793–1795). *A Specimen of the Botany of New Holland*, London:

J Sowerby, preface.

[65] LS JES/COR/14/62 Smith to Edmund Davall, 24 September 1793

[66] Smith, J E, (1793–1795). *Op. cit.*, London: J Sowerby, pp.4–5.

[67] LS JES/COR/7/87 Henry Muhlenberg to Smith, 1 December 1792

[68] LS JES/COR/3/105 José Francisco Corrêa de Serra to Smith, 18 November 1813

[69] LS JES/ADD/77 Henry Muhlenberg to Smith, 12 June 1794

[70] HSP 7068 Smith to Henry Muhlenberg, 9 March 1793

[71] LS JES/COR/7/92 Henry Muhlenberg to Smith, 28 June 1798

[72] Muhlenberg, H, 'Supplementum Indicis florae Lancasteriensis' in *Transactions of the American Philosophical Society: Held at Philadelphia for Promoting Useful Knowledge*, vol. 4 (Philadelphia, 1799; reprint, New York: Kraus Reprint, 1966), p.242.

[73] HSP 7068 Smith to Henry Muhlenberg, 9 March 1793

[74] LS JES/COR/14/56 Smith to Edmund Davall, 26 February 1793; LS JES/COR/14/60 Smith to Edmund Davall, 2 July 1793

[75] LS JES/COR/18/70 Thomas Woodward to Smith, 29 March 1793

[76] LS JES/COR/14/59 Smith to Edmund Davall, 12 May 1793

[77] *The Gentleman's Magazine* 73: 102 February 1793

[78] *The Gentleman's Magazine* 73: 333 April 1793

[79] LS JES/COR/14/62 Smith to Edmund Davall, 24 September 1793

[80] LS JES/COR/14/44 Smith to Edmund Davall, 30 December 1791

[81] LS JES/SM/3 Smith to James Smith, 19 April 1792

[82] LS JES/COR/15/116 Mary Watson-Wentworth to Smith, 7 September 1793

[83] LS JES/COR/18/76 Thomas Woodward to Smith, 21 September 1793

[84] LS JES/COR/14/62 Smith to Edmund Davall, 24 September 1793

[85] LS JES/COR/18/78 Thomas Woodward to Smith, 31 December 1793

[86] LS JES/COR/14/44 Smith to Edmund Davall, 30 December 1791

[87] LS JES/COR/14/17 Smith to Edmund Davall, 30 March 1790

[88] LS JES/COR/10/110 William Younge to Smith, 10 October 1792

[89] LS JES/COR/1869 Smith to Thomas Woodward, 26 March 1793

[90] LS JES/COR/14/56 Smith to Edmund Davall, 26 February 1793

[91] LS JES/COR/14/18 Smith to Edmund Davall, 25 April 1790

[92] LS JES/COR/14/38 Edmund Davall to Smith, 22 July 1791

[93] Jewson, C B, (1975). *The Jacobin City: A Portrait of Norwich 1788–1802*, London: Blackie & Sons, p.80; p.39.

[94] LS JES/COR/14/53 Smith to Edmund Davall, 26 October 1792

[95] LS JES/COR/14/59 Smith to Edmund Davall, 12 May 1793

[96] Burke, E, (1791). *A Letter From Mr Burke to a Member of the National Assembly, Paris*, London, 2nd ed., pp.33–34.

[97] Smith, J E, (1793). *Op. cit.*, vol. 1, p.112.

[98] LS JES/COR/10/110 William Younge to Smith, 10 October 1792

[99] LS JES/COR/14/56 Smith to Edmund Davall, 26 February 1793

[100] Smith, J E, (1793). *Op. cit.*, vol. 1, p.xxix.

[101] *The Critical Review; Or, Annals of Literature* 11: 155 May 1794

[102] *The British Critic, and Quarterly Theological Review* 3: 245 March 1794

[103] LS JES/COR/14/70 Smith to Edmund Davall, 6 June 1794

[104] LS JES/COR/14/67 Smith to Edmund Davall, 14 March 1794

[105] Smith describes a Temple of Modern Philosophy in the grounds of René Louis de Girardin's, Marquess of Vauvray estate, dedicated to various philosophers and thinkers, including Rousseau, Newton, Descartes and Priestley: "Poor Dr Priestley! he who erected this pillar would scarcely, though a catholic, have assisted to destroy thy habitation, and ruin thy hive of literary treasures, intended for the use of all mankind! nor would he have exulted at the mistaken zeal of those who did" (Smith, J E (1793). A sketch of the tour on the Continent, in the years 1786 and 1787, London: [privately], vol. 1, p.101)

[106] LS JES/COR/18/80 Smith to Thomas Woodward, 9 February 1794

[107] Smith, J E, (1793). *Op. cit.*, vol. 1, p.115.

[108] *The British Critic, and Quarterly Theological Review* 3: 245 March 1794

[109] LS JES/COR/11/20 Samuel Goodenough to Smith, 18 March 1794

[110] LS JES/COR/14/74 Smith to Edmund Davall, 16 March 1795

[111] LS JES/COR/14/70 Smith to Edmund Davall, 6 June 1794

[112] LS JES/COR/11/21 Samuel Goodenough to Smith, 31 March 1794

[113] LS JES/MS410/1 Smith to Thomas Woodward, 4 November 1794

[114] LS JES/COR/14/74 Smith to Edmund Davall, 16 March 1795

[115] LS JES/COR/20/66 Shute Barrington to Smith, 31 March 1794

CHAPTER EIGHT

[1] LS JES/COR/14/70 Smith to Edmund Davall, 6 June 1794

[2] LS JES/CO/14/67 Smith to Edmund Davall, 14 March 1794

[3] KCL G/PP2/23 JE Smith Lectures on Botany MS f49. [Smith also used this opportunity to highlight the neglect shown to great scientists, asking why they remained unsung by the state in comparison to "the warrior or statesman who has statues and monuments erected over his clay, in remembrance of these sanguinary exploits which disgrace human nature"]

[4] Smith, J E, (1795). *Syllabus of a Course of Lectures on Botany*, London: [privately], p.iii–iv.

[5] *Morning Post and Fashionable* World (London, England), Thursday, March 19, 1795; Issue 7217.

[6] LS JES/COR/14/72 Smith to Edmund Davall, 26 September 1794

[7] LS JES/COR/14/70 Smith to Edmund Davall, 6 June 1794

[8] LS JES/COR/18/87 Thomas Woodward to Smith, 27 September 1794

[9] LS JES/COR/14/67 Smith to Edmund Davall, 14 March 1794
[10] LS JES/COR/5/38 John Sibthorp to Smith, 9 August 1794
[11] LS JES/COR/18/92 Smith to Thomas Woodward, 11 January 1795
[12] LS JES/COR/5/39 John Sibthorp to Smith, 1 November 1794
[13] LS JES/COR/14/74 Smith to Edmund Davall, 16 March 1795
[14] Smith, J E, (1798). *Tracts Relating to Natural History*, London: [privately], p.302.
[15] LS JES/COR/8/9 Barnaba Oriani and Luigi Borone to Smith, 28 March 1795 [translated from Italian]
[16] LS JES/COR/18/94 Smith to Thomas Woodward, 14 March 1795
[17] LS JES/COR/11/23 Samuel Goodenough to Smith, 15 March 1795
[18] LS JES/COR/18/94 Smith to Thomas Woodward, proved 14 March 1795
[19] TNA PROB 11/1261/24 Will of James Smith, Merchant of Norwich, Norfolk, 4 May 1795
[20] LS JES/COR/11/25 Samuel Goodenough to Smith, 3 May 1795
[21] Moore-Colyer, R J (ed.), (1992). *A Land of Pure Delight: Selections from the letters of Thomas Johnes of Hafod, Cardiganshire (1748–1816)*, Gomer, pp.12–13.
[22] LS JES/COR/18/100 Smith to Thomas Woodward, 28 August 1795
[23] LS JES/COR/16/27 Thomas Johnes to Smith, 22 March 1795
[24] LS JES/COR/18/100 Smith to Thomas Woodward, 28 August 1795
[25] LS JES/COR/16/10 Mariamne Johnes to Smith, 12 April 1796
[26] LS JES/COR/11/25 Samuel Goodenough to Smith, 3 May 1795
[27] LS JES/COR/18/97 Thomas Woodward to Smith, 28 April 1795
[32] LS JES/ADD/57 Thomas Marsham to Smith, 5 February 1796
[28] LS JES/COR/14/77 Smith to Edmund Davall, 28 October 1795
[29] LS JES/COR/14/79 Edmund Davall to Smith, 29 December 1795
[30] LS JES/COR/14/73 Edmund Davall to Smith, 27 January 1795
[31] LS JES/COR/14/67 Smith to Edmund Davall, 14 March 1794
[32] LS JES/COR/14/79 Edmund Davall to Smith, 29 December 1795
[33] LS JES/COR/14/80 Smith to Edmund Davall, 17 April 1796
[34] LS JES/COR/14/81 Edmund Davall to Smith, 18 September 1796
[35] King, T, (1796). *Linnean Cabinet of Minerals: A Catalogue of the Genuine and Entire Collection of the Late Celebrated Swedish Naturalist, Sir Charles Linne*, London: [s.n.]. [Annotated copy in the Linnean Society Library]
[36] LS JES/COR/20/32 William Babington to Smith, 15 March 1796
[37] LS JES/ADD/57 Thomas Marsham to Smith, 5 February 1796
[38] Day, M C, & Fitton, M G, 'Re-curation of the Linnaean Hymenoptera (Insecta), With a Reassessment of the Taxonomic Importance of the Collection', *Biological Journal of the Linnean Society of London*, (1978) 10, pp.182–186.
[39] LS JES/MS238/17 Smith to Richard Pulteney, 1 May 1797
[40] Haworth, A, 'Review of the Rise and Progress of the Science of Entomology in

Great Britain', *Transactions of the Entomological Society of London*, 1807 1, p.51.

[41] Smith, J E, & Abbot, J, (1797). *The Natural History of the Rarer Lepidopterous Insects of Georgia*, London: J. Edwards, dedication.

[42] LS JES/COR/5/111 William Jones to Smith, 9 September 1797

[43] TC O.13.1 f27 Thomas Woodward to Dawson Turner, 30 May 1796

[44] LS JES/COR/14/82 Smith to Edmund Davall, 2 November 1798

[45] LS JES/COR/11/29 Samuel Goodenough to Smith, 25 August 1796

[46] LS JES/COR/11/30 Samuel Goodenough to Smith, 16 September 1796

[47] LS JES/ADD/58 Thomas Marsham to Smith, 22 September 1796

[48] LS JES/ADD/59 Thomas Marsham to Smith, 28 September 1796

[49] LS JES/COR/11/32 Samuel Goodenough to Smith, 13 November 1796

[50] NHM MSS BANKS COLL DRY f76 Smith to Jonas Dryander, 3 January 1797

[51] LS JES/COR/14/83 Smith to Edmund Davall, 17 January 1798

[52] BLY Osborn d148 vol. 2 f1 Lady East to Pleasance Smith, 11 April 1799

[53] BLY Osborn d148 vol. 2 f3 Lady East to Pleasance Smith, 23 November 1799

[54] LS JES/COR/14/86 Smith to Edmund Davall, 15 March 1798

[55] LS JES/COR/19/72 Smith to Pleasance Smith, 26 April 1798

[56] NHM Sowerby collection 19.55 f55 Smith to James Sowerby, 16 July 1799

[57] NHM Sowerby collection 19.55 f45 Smith to James Sowerby, 10 January 1799

[58] NHM Sowerby collection 19.55 f46 Smith to James Sowerby, 14 January 1799

[59] NHM Sowerby collection 19.55 f76 Smith to James Sowerby, 25 June 1800

[60] RBGK Samuel Goodenough Correspondence f8 Smith to Samuel Goodenough, 12 April 1797

[61] LS JES/MS238/17 Smith to Richard Pulteney, 1 May 1797

[62] Thornton, R J, [1797]. *Advertisement to the New Illustration of the Sexual System of Linnaeus*, [London: the author].

[63] LS JES/AM/31 Alexander Macleay to Smith, 31 December 1802

[64] LS JES/COR/24/8 Thomas Martyn to Smith, 20 September 1797

[65] NHM MSS BANKS COLL DRY f78 Smith to Jonas Dryander, 16 August 1797

[66] LS JES/COR/24/8 Thomas Martyn to Smith, 20 September 1797

[67] LS JES/ADD/63 Thomas Marsham to Smith, 20 July 1797

[68] TC Turner O.13.1 f131 Smith to Dawson Turner, 12 June 1800

[69] Thornton, R J, (1799–1807). *A New Illustration of the Sexual System of Linnaeus*, London: [privately].

[70] LS JES/COR/14/83 Smith to Edmund Davall, 17 January 1798

[71] LS JES/COR/16/39 Thomas Johnes to Smith, 5 June 1797

[72] LS JES/COR/16/40 Smith to Pleasance Smith, 25 October 1797

[73] LS JES/COR/15/125 Mary Watson–Wentworth to Smith, 25 November 1797

[74] LS JES/COR/19/73 Smith to Pleasance Smith, 2 May 1798

[75] LS JES/COR/16/52 Thomas Johnes to Smith, 13 December 1798; LS

JES/COR/16/55 Thomas Johnes to Smith, 23 June 1799; LS JES/COR/16/57 Thomas Johnes to Smith, 6 September 1799

76 LS JES/COR/16/17 Mariamne Johnes to Smith, 13 January 1804

77 LS JES/COR/3/68 Bracy Clark to Smith, 4 December 1797

78 LS JES/COR/14/83 Smith to Edmund Davall, 17 January 1798

79 LS JES/COR/14/85 Edmund Davall to Smith, 13 February 1798

80 LS JES/COR/14/84 Henriette Davall to Smith, 13 February 1798 [translated from French]

81 LS JES/COR/14/86 Smith to Edmund Davall, 15 March 1798

82 LS JES/COR/3/70 Bracy Clark to Smith, 22 March 1798

83 LS JES/COR/3/71 Bracy Clark to Smith, 10 July 1798

84 LS JES/COR/18/88 Henriette Davall to Smith, 16 July 1798

85 LS JES/COR/3/72 Bracy Clark to Smith, 27 September 1798

86 LS JES/COR/14/89 Henriette Davall to Smith, 8 October 1798

87 LS JES/COR/17/5 Smith to William Roscoe, 25 August 1803

88 Leigh, Sotheby & Son Auctioneers (1803). *A Catalogue of the Library of Natural History formed by Edmund Davall [to] be sold by auction*, London: [the auctioneers] [annotated copy in Linnean Society Library]

89 TC O.13.2 f188 Smith to Dawson Turner, 16 July 1803; LS JES/COR/19/74 Smith to Pleasance Smith, 1 July 1803

90 Konig, C, & Sims, J, (eds.), (1805). *Annals of Botany*, London: [privately], vol. 1, p.576.

CHAPTER NINE

1 LS JES/ADD/66 Thomas Marsham to Smith, 10 December 1798

2 LS JES/AM/3 Alexander Macleay to Smith, 25 February 1800

3 LS FM Minute book, 24 May 1800

4 LS JES/AM/4 Smith to Jonas Dryander, 10 June 1800

5 The final amount came to £460 5s 6d, with Fellows contributing £422.

6 LS JES/AM/5 Alexander Macleay to Smith, 19 July 1800

7 LS JES/AM/22 Alexander Macleay to Smith, 22 March 1802

8 LS JES/AM/31 Alexander Macleay to Smith, 31 December 1802

9 LS JES/AM/20 Smith to Alexander Macleay, 12 December 1801

10 'Sibthorp, John' in Rees, A, (ed.), (1802–1819). *Op. cit.*

11 LS JES/COR/1/56 Sir Joseph Banks to Smith, 15 February 1796

12 LS JES/COR/18/116 Thomas Woodward to Smith, 28 March 1799

13 LS JES/COR/5/29 Davies Giddy to Smith, 18 June 1799

14 LS JES/COR/22/95 John Hawkins to Smith, 17 May 1799

15 LS JES/COR/5/33 John Hawkins to Smith, 25 June 1799

16 LS JES/COR/5/34 John Hawkins to Smith, 13 February 1800

[17] NHM MSS BANKS COLL DRY f85 Smith to Jonas Dryander, 1 March 1800
[18] NHM MSS BANKS COLL DRY f86 Smith to Jonas Dryander, 5 January 1801
[19] LS JES/COR/4/72 Jonas Dryander to Smith, [3 March 1800]
[20] NHM MSS BANKS COLL DRY f87 Smith to Jonas Dryander, 28 February 1801
[21] LS JES/COR/5/34 John Hawkins to Smith, 13 February 1800
[22] NHM Sowerby collection 19.55 f84 Smith to James Sowerby, 20 October 1800
[23] NHM Sowerby collection 19.56 f171 Smith to James Sowerby, 27 December 1804
[24] NHM Sowerby collection 19.55 f93 Smith to James Sowerby, 2 May 1801
[25] SLO MSS Sherard 248 f19 John Hawkins to Smith, 3 November 1801
[26] LS JES/JS/8 Smith to James Sowerby, 29 August 1802
[27] NHM MSS BANKS COLL DRY f89 Smith to Jonas Dryander, 2 May 1801
[28] Smith, P, (1832). *Op. cit.*, vol. 1, p.459.
[29] TC O.13.3 f124 Smith to Dawson Turner, 22 February 1805
[30] LS JES/AM/9 Smith to Alexander Macleay, 23 February 1801
[31] NHM Sowerby collection 19.56 f175 Smith to James Sowerby, 6 January 1805
[32] NHM Sowerby collection 19.56 f197 Smith to James Sowerby, 19 December 1805
[33] Smith, J E, 'Observations on the British Species of Bromus, with Introductory Remarks on the Composition of a Flora Britannica', *Transactions of the Linnean Society of London*, 1798 4(1), pp.276–281.
[34] Smith, J E, (1800–1804). *Flora Britannica*, London: J White & Son, vol. 1, preface. [translated from Latin]
[35] LS JES/COR/1/67 Sir Joseph Banks to Smith, 3 March 1800
[36] LS JES/COR/15/13 Sir Thomas Frankland to Smith, 29 April 1800
[37] Smith, J E, (1800). *Compendium Floræ Britannicæ*, London: J White & Son, preface.
[38] *The Monthly Review* ser.2. 34: 52 January 1801
[39] LS JES/COR/10/26 Jussieu, Lamarck et al to Smith, 3 December 1800 (translated from French)
[40] LS JES/COR/11/40 Samuel Goodenough to Smith, 24 October 1800
[41] Stamens and pistils are in separate flowers, but both growing on the same plant, such as Corylus sp. (hazelnut)
[42] Stamens and pistils not only in separate flowers, but those flowers situated on two separate plants, such as Salix sp. (willow)
[43] Stamens and pistils separate in some flowers, united in others, either on the same plant, or on two or three different ones.
[44] *The Monthly Magazine* 2: 207 April 1801
[45] Smith, J E, 'Remarks on some British Species of Salix', *Transactions of the Linnean Society of London*, 1802 6(1), pp.111–112.
[46] TC O.13.1 f197 Smith to Dawson Turner, 13 October 1801
[47] TC O.13.1 f170 Smith to Dawson Turner, 22 February 1801
[48] TC O.13.1 f155 Smith to Dawson Turner, 14 November 1800

[49] TC O.13.1 f198 Samuel Goodenough to Dawson Turner, 18 October 1801

[50] LS Winch MS f93 Dawson Turner to Nathaniel Winch, 28 May 1802

[51] Liverpool Botanic Garden, (1802). *An Address, Delivered Before the Proprietors of the Garden May 3, 1802*, p.42.

[52] NHM DTC 13 f121 James Currie to Sir Joseph Banks, 23 May 1802

[53] Liverpool Botanic Garden, (1802). *Op. cit.*, p.42.

[54] TC O.13.2 f32 Smith to Dawson Turner, 21 May 1802

[55] Dr James's Fever Powder, a medicine first patented in 1746 by Dr Robert James, was a favourite remedy of Smith's. A cure-all, alongside fevers, it was also said to be effective in curing gout, scurvy and distemper in cattle. The primary ingredients were arsenic and calcium phosphate.

[56] NHM Sowerby collection 19.56 f115 Smith to James Sowerby 24 June 1802

[57] BLY Osborn D148 vol. 2 f5 Lady East to Pleasance Smith, 24 June 1802

[58] BL Add Mss 28545 f100 William Fitt Drake to Aylmer Bourke Lambert, 15 June 1802

[59] TC O.13.2 f53 Smith to Dawson Turner, 26 July 1802

[60] BLY Osborn D148 vol. 2 f24 Andrew Caldwell to Pleasance Smith, 5 October 1802

[61] BL Add Mss 28545 f104 Smith to Aylmer Bourke Lambert, 15 September 1802

[62] TC O.13.2 f115 Smith to Dawson Turner, 8 January 1803

[63] RBGK WJH/2/1 f 7 William Jackson Hooker to Dawson Turner, 10 January 1806

[64] TC O.13.2 f173 Smith to Dawson Turner, 20 May 1803

[65] LS JES/COR/15/135 Mary Watson-Wentworth to Smith, 30 May 1803

[66] TC O.13.2 f188 Smith to Dawson Turner 16 July 1803

[67] LS JES/COR/19/75 Smith to Pleasance Smith, 8 Jul 1803

[68] LS JES/COR/17/38 Smith to William Roscoe, 16 October 1806

[69] Roscoe, H, (1833). *The Life of William Roscoe*, London: T. Cadell, vol. 1, p.162.

[70] LS JES/COR/3/13 Andrew Caldwell to Smith, 11 June 1796

[71] LS JES/COR/19/74 Smith to Pleasance Smith, 1 July 1803

[72] TC O.13.2 f188 Smith to Dawson Turner 16 July 1803

[73] LS JES/COR/19/75 Smith to Pleasance Smith, 8 Jul 1803

[74] TC O.13.2 f188 Smith to Dawson Turner 16 July 1803

[75] LS JES/COR/17/6 William Roscoe to Smith, 28 August 1803

[76] LS JES/COR/17/7 Smith to William Roscoe, 23 September 1803

[77] Sanderson, F E, 'The Liverpool Abolitionists', in Anstey, R, and Hair, P E H (eds.), (1976). *Liverpool, the African Slave Trade, and Abolition*, Historic Society of Lancashire and Cheshire Occasional Series Vol. 2, p.221.

[78] NHM Sowerby collection 19.57 f210 Smith to James Sowerby, 13 November [1806]

[79] LS JES/COR/17/40 Smith to William Roscoe, 11 November 1806

[80] LS JES/COR/17/44 Smith to William Roscoe, 16 January 1807

[81] LS JES/COR/17/43 William Roscoe to Smith, 13 January 1807

[82] Sanderson, F E, 'The Liverpool Abolitionists', *Op. cit.*, p.224.

[83] LS JES/COR/17/46 Smith to William Roscoe, 26 February 1807

[84] LS JES/COR/17/49 William Roscoe to Smith, 6 May 1807

[85] LS JES/COR/4/40 Humphry Davy to Smith, 20 January 1804

[86] LS JES/COR/4/41 Humphry Davy to Smith, 25 March 1805

[87] SRO Diary of Pleasance Smith's visit to London, 1804

[88] LS JES/COR/19/79 Pleasance Smith to Smith, 1 June 1806

[89] LS JES/COR/17/7 Smith to William Roscoe, 23 September 1803

[90] *The Monthly Review* 47: 362 August 1805

[91] Ramsay, E B, 'Biographical Notice of the late Sir J. E. Smith, President of the Linnaean Society', *The Edinburgh Journal of Science*, vol. 1 1829, p.9.

[92] *The Philosophical Magazine* 3: 391 May 1828

[93] Smith, J E, (1804–1808). *Exotic Botany*, London: [privately], vol. 1, preface.

[94] NHM Sowerby collection 19.56 f154 Smith to James Sowerby, 1 July 1804

[95] NHM Sowerby collection 19.56 f164 Smith to James Sowerby, 23 November 1804

[96] NHM Sowerby collection 19.56 f161 Smith to James Sowerby, 8 November 1804

[97] NHM Sowerby collection 19.56 f179 Smith to James Sowerby, 17 February 1805

[98] LS JES/COR/17/22 William Roscoe to Smith, 5 April 1805

[99] NHM Sowerby collection 19.56 f185 Smith to James Sowerby, 10 September 1805

CHAPTER TEN

[1] LS JES/COR/17/21 Smith to William Roscoe, 18 January 1805

[2] Smith, J E, 'Characters of a new Genus of Plants named Salisburia', *Transactions of the Linnean Society of London*, 1797 3(1), pp.330–332.

[3] Salisbury, R A, 'Species of Erica', *Transactions of the Linnean Society of London*, 1802 6(1), pp.316–388.

[4] LS JES/COR/11/36 Samuel Goodenough to Smith, 21 February 1797

[5] NHM DTC 10(2) f268 Richard Salisbury to Sir Joseph Banks, 6 April 1798

[6] NHM DTC 10(2) f270 Sir Joseph Banks to Richard Salisbury, 10 April 1798

[7] NHM DTC 16 f192 Smith to Sir Joseph Banks, 10 January 1806

[8] RBGK JBK 1 7 f324 Smith to Sir Joseph Banks, 16 January 1806

[9] NHM DTC 16 f192 Smith to Sir Joseph Banks, 10 January 1806

[10] Salisbury, R A, (1805–1808). *Paradisus Londinensis*, London: [privately], vol. 1, preface.

[11] NHM DTC 16 f192 Smith to Sir Joseph Banks, 10 January 1806

[12] BL AddMss 28454 f116 Smith to Aylmer Bourke Lambert, 26 July 1805

[13] Smith, J E, (1804–1808). *Op. cit.*, vol. 1, p.86.

[14] LS JES/COR/17/24 Smith to William Roscoe, 12 October 1805

[15] Salisbury, R A, (1805–1808). *Op. cit.* tab.14.

16 LS JES/COR/17/24 Smith to William Roscoe, 12 October 1805
17 TC O.13.4 f7 Smith to Dawson Turner, 11 January 1806
18 RBGK JBK 1 7 f320 Richard Salisbury to Smith, 26 October 1805 [copy]
19 RBGK JBK 1 7 f321 Smith to Richard Salisbury, 30 October 1805 [copy]
20 TC O.13.3 f217 Smith to Dawson Turner, 1 November 1805
21 RBGK JBK 1 7 f322 Richard Salisbury to Smith, 9 January 1806
22 RBGK Dawson Turner papers vol. 1 f66 Dawson Turner to William Borrer, 19 January 1806
23 NHM DTC 16 f220 Sir Joseph Banks to Smith, 15 January 1806
24 LS JES/COR/1/77 Sir Joseph Banks to Smith, 20 January 1806
25 LS JES/COR/11/53 Smith to Samuel Goodenough, 2 September 1806
26 Salisbury, R A, (1806). *The Generic Characters in the English Botany, collated with those of Linné*, London: [privately], p.iv.
27 LS JES/COR/11/51 Samuel Goodenough to Smith, 4 April 1806
28 TC O.13.4 f52 Smith to Dawson Turner, 11 April 1806
29 LS JES/COR/17/31 Smith to William Roscoe, 2 April 1806
30 LS JES/JS/12 Smith to James Sowerby, 8 March 1806
31 TC O.13.4 f52 Smith to Dawson Turner, 11 April 1806
32 RBGK Dawson Turner papers vol. 1 f72 Dawson Turner to William Borrer, 31 March 1806
33 TC O.13.4 Smith to Dawson Turner, March 1806
34 LS JES/COR/17/31 Smith to William Roscoe, 2 April 1806
35 LS JES/COR/11/53 Smith to Samuel Goodenough, 2 September 1806
36 LS JES/COR/11/53 Smith to Samuel Goodenough, 2 September 1806
37 LS JES/JS/12 Smith to James Sowerby, 8 March 1806
38 LS JES/COR/17/44 Smith to William Roscoe, 16 January 1807
39 NHM Sowerby collection 19.57 f215 Smith to James Sowerby, 4 February 1807
40 NHM Sowerby collection 19.57 f214 Smith to James Sowerby, 1 January 1807
41 Smith, J E, (1807). *An Introduction to Physiological and Systematical Botany*, London: Longman, Hurst, Rees, & Orme, p.vii.
42 *The Annual Review* 3: 755 [May] 1805.
43 LS JES/COR/11/56 Samuel Goodenough to Smith, 19 January 1807
44 *The Annual Review* 3: 755 [May] 1805.
45 LS JES/COR/19/79 Pleasance Smith to Smith, 1 June 1806
46 LS JES/COR/17/54 Smith to William Roscoe, 4 July 1807
47 LS JES/COR/11/56 Samuel Goodenough to Smith, 19 January 1807
48 'Clitoria' in Rees, A, (ed.), (1802–1819). *Op. cit.*
49 Smith, J E, (1807). *Op. cit.*, preface.
50 BL AddMss 28545 f126 Smith to Aylmer Bourke Lambert, 26 January 1808
51 Smith, J E, (1807). *Op. cit.*, p.378.

[52] *Ibid.*,p.366.

[53] TC O.13.6 f53 Patrick Neill to Dawson Turner, 25 April 1808

[54] *The Annual Review* 6: 749 180.

[55] LS JES/COR/17/58 Smith to William Roscoe, 25 February 1808

[56] LS JES/COR/17/51 Smith to William Roscoe, 14 May 1807

[57] Salisbury, R A, (1805–1808). *Op. cit.*, vol. 2, tab. 92.

[58] *Ibid.*, tab. 92.

[59] *The Monthly Magazine* 25: 90 February 1808

[60] BL AddMss 28545 f128 Smith to Aylmer Bourke Lambert, 20 February 1808

[61] *The Monthly Magazine* 25: 191 April 1808

[62] RBGK Dawson Turner papers vol. 1 f176 Dawson Turner to William Borrer, 26 February 1808

[63] TC O.13.6 f64 James Brodie to Dawson Turner, 1 June 1808

[64] Walker, M, (1988). *Sir James Edward Smth M.D., F.R.S., P.L.S. 1759–1828 First President of the Linnean Society of London*, London: The Linnean Society of London, p.42.

[65] Salisbury, R A, (1808). *A Letter to the Editor of the Monthly Magazine*, London: [privately], pp.5–6.

[66] Salisbury, R A, (1805–1808). *Op. cit.*, vol. 2, tab. 90.

[67] Salisbury, R A, (1805–1808). *Op. cit.*, vol. 2, tab. 98.

[68] TC O.13.6 f25 Smith to Dawson Turner, 9 March 1808

[69] LS JES/COR/6/63 Aylmer Bourke Lambert to Smith, 31 March 1808

[70] TC O.13.6 f39 Smith to Dawson Turner, 2 April 1808

[71] LS JES/COR/11/66 Smith to Samuel Goodenough, 7 April 1808

[72] RBGK Dawson Turner papers vol. 1 f184 Dawson Turner to William Borrer, 17 April 1808

[73] TC O.13.6 f45 Smith to Dawson Turner, 8 April 1808

[74] Salisbury, R A, (1805–1808). *Op. cit.*, vol. 2, tab.117.

[75] LS JES/AM/49 Smith to Alexander Macleay, 29 September 1808

[76] LS JES/AM/50 Smith to Alexander Macleay, 20 November 1808

[77] Smith, J E, (1809). *An Introduction to Physiological and Systematical Botany*, London: Longman, Hurst, Rees, and Orme, 2nd ed., p.263; Smith, J E, & Sowerby, J, (1790–1814). *Op. cit.*, tab.1966.

[78] Smith, J E, 'Characters of a new Liliaceous Genus called Brodiaea', *Transactions of the Linnean Society of London*, 1810 9(1), pp.1–5.

[79] LS JES/COR/19/82 Smith to Pleasance Smith, 24 May 1808

[80] BL AddMss 32439 f303 Smith to Robert Brown, 14 January 1810

[81] BL AddMss 32439 f307 Robert Brown to Smith, February 1810

[82] Mabberley, D, (1985). *Jupiter Botanicus: Robert Brown of the British Museum*, London: British Museum (Natural History), pp.150–151; p.156.

[83] *The Gardener's Magazine* 11: 380 July 1835
[84] TC O.13.6 f45 Smith to Dawson Turner, 8 April 1808
[85] TC O.13.6 f127 Lewis Weston Dillwyn to Dawson Turner, 27 November 1808
[86] LS JES/COR/17/61 Smith to William Roscoe, 14 August 1808
[87] LS JES/ADD/8 James Brodie to Smith, 28 January 1809
[88] TC O.13.7 f1 James Brodie to Dawson Turner, 5 January 1809
[89] RBGK William Borrer papers vol. 2 f253 Dawson Turner to William Borrer, November 1809
[90] Martins, S W, (2010). *Coke of Norfolk 1754–1842: A Biography*, Woodbridge: The Boydell Press, p.156.
[91] RBGK William Borrer papers vol. 2 f311 Dawson Turner to William Borrer, 2 November 1810
[92] RBGK William Borrer papers vol. 2 f348 Dawson Turner to William Borrer, 11 July 1811
[93] LS JES/COR/19/88 Smith to Pleasance Smith, 9 May 1811
[94] LS JES/AM/58 Smith to Alexander Macleay, 27 October 1810
[95] LS JES/COR/11/90 Samuel Goodenough to Smith, 9 November 1810
[96] TC O.13.8 f108 Charles Koenig to Dawson Turner, 25 November 1810
[97] BL AddMss 28454 f132 Smith to Aylmer Bourke Lambert, 16 March 1808
[98] *The Monthly Magazine* 25: 128 March 1808
[99] BL AddMss 28454 f132 Smith to Aylmer Bourke Lambert, 16 March 1808
[100] *The Eclectic Review* 8: 592 July 1812
[101] RBGK William Borrer papers vol. 2 f285 Dawson Turner to William Borrer, 18 June 1810
[102] Linnaeus, C, & Smith, J E (ed.), (1811). *Op. cit.*, preface.
[103] RBGK William Borrer papers vol. 2 f351, Dawson Turner to William Borrer, August 1811
[104] LS JES/JS/18 Smith to James Sowerby, 3 February 1814
[105] Sowerby, J, (1814). *General Indexes to the Thirty-six Volumes of English Botany*, London: [privately], pp.v–vi.

CHAPTER ELEVEN

[1] LS JES/COR/13/22 Thomas Martyn to Sir Thomas Gery Cullum, 2 June 1813
[2] Gorham, G C, & Martyn, T (1830). *Memoirs of John Martyn… and of Thomas Martyn…*, London: Hatchard & Son, p.244.
[3] LS JES/COR/7/7 Thomas Martyn to Smith, 27 May 1813
[4] LS JES/COR/7/8 Thomas Martyn to Smith, 11 June 1813
[5] LS JES/COR/13/23 Smith to Sir Thomas Gery Cullum, 26 June 1813
[6] LS JES/COR/13/23 Smith to Sir Thomas Gery Cullum, 26 June 1813
[7] LS JES/COR/19/87 Smith to Pleasance Smith, 29 April 1811

[8] 'Extracts from the Minutes of the Council of the Linnean Society of London', *Transactions of the Linnean Society of London*, 1815 11(1), pp.vii–ix.

[9] LS JES/AM/82 Smith to Alexander Macleay, 13 July 1813

[10] LS JES/COR/17/87 Smith to William Roscoe, 2 August 1813

[11] LS JES/COR/7/11 Thomas Martyn to Smith, 26 August 1813

[12] Smith, J E, (1818). *Considerations Respecting Cambridge, More Particularly Relating to its Botanical Professorship*, London: [privately], p.14.

[13] LS JES/AM/84 Smith to Alexander Macleay, 28 February 1814

[14] LS JES/COR/13/26 Sir Thomas Gery Cullum to Smith, 18 February 1814

[15] LS JES/AM/84 Smith to Alexander Macleay, 28 February 1814

[16] LS JES/COR/17/92 Smith to William Roscoe, 5 July 1814

[17] LS JES/COR/17/92 Smith to William Roscoe, 5 July 1814

[18] LS JES/AM/85 Smith to Alexander Macleay, 29 July 1814

[19] LS JES/COR/19/92 Smith to Pleasance Smith, 4 August 1814

[20] LS JES/COR/6/82 Aylmer Bourke Lambert to Smith, 6 August 1814

[21] LS JES/COR/12/9 Samuel Goodenough to Smith, 26 August 1814

[22] NHM Sowerby collection 20.58 f315 Smith to James Sowerby, 19 August 1814; f317 Smith to Sowerby, 25 October 1814

[23] LS JES/COR/19/92 Smith to Pleasance Smith, 4 August 1814

[24] LS JES/COR/13/31 Smith to Sir Thomas Gery Cullum, 8 November 1814

[25] LS JES/COR/7/33 William Lort Mansel to Smith, 4 December 1814

[26] LS JES/COR/13/34 Smith to Sir Thomas Gery Cullum, 20 December 1814

[27] LS JES/COR/12/16 Samuel Goodenough to Smith, 12 December 1815

[28] TNA PROB11/1572/242 Will of Robert Reeve, Gentleman of Lowestoft, Suffolk, 26 August 1815

[29] LS JES/COR/19/97 Smith to Pleasance Smith, 13 September 1815

[30] LS JES/AM/93 Smith to Alexander Macleay, 12 October 1815

[31] LS JES/COR/19/97 Smith to Pleasance Smith, 14 September 1815; NHM Sowerby 20–58 f320a Smith to James Sowerby, 15 November 1815

[32] LS JES/COR/19/97 Smith to Pleasance Smith, 14 September 1815

[33] LS JES/COR/19/99 Smith to Pleasance Smith, 19 September 1815

[34] LS JES/COR/19/100 Smith to Pleasance Smith, 25 September 1815

[35] LS JES/COR/19/102 Smith to Pleasance Smith, 13 October 1815

[36] LS JES/COR/19/93 Smith to Pleasance Smith, 11 June 1815

[37] RBGK Dawson Turner papers Vol. 2 f466 Dawson Turner to William Borrer, 15 January 1815

[38] LS JES/COR/12/12 Samuel Goodenough to Smith, 17 January 1815

[39] TC O.13.17 f7 Smith to Dawson Turner, 15 January 1819

[40] LS JES/COR/6/84 Aylmer Bourke Lambert to Smith, 31 January 1815

[41] LS JES/COR/5/101 Joseph Franz von Jacquin to Smith, 21 January 1815; LS

JES/COR/9/101 Olof Swartz to Smith, 19 November 1817

[42] RBGK Dawson Turner papers vol. 2 f493 Dawson Turner to William Borrer, 19 December 1815

[43] TNA C 211/15/L139 Sarah Maria Lloyd, widow of Heigham House Asylum, Heigham, Norwich, Norfolk: commission and inquisition of lunacy, 14 January 1843

[44] LS JES/COR/12/11 Samuel Goodenough to Smith, 24 November 1814

[45] LS JES/AM/91 Smith to Alexander Macleay, 5 September 1815

[46] LS JES/COR/12/17 Samuel Goodenough to Smith, 29 January 1816

[47] LS MS 237 f92 Thomas Marsham to Alexander Macleay, 2 March 1815

[48] LS JES/COR/12/17 Samuel Goodenough to Smith, 29 January 1816; LS JES/COR/12/18 Samuel Goodenough to Smith, 12 February 1816

[49] LS JES/COR/12/106 Samuel Goodenough to Smith, 12 May 1826

[50] LS JES/AM/100 Smith to Alexander Macleay, 26 January 1816

[51] LS MS 237 f109c Thomas Marsham to Alexander Macleay, 21 May 1816

[52] LS MS 237 f110 Thomas Marsham to Alexander Macleay, 20 January 1817

[53] LS JES/COR/12/38 Samuel Goodenough to Smith, 8 December 1817

[54] LS JES/AM/138 Alexander Macleay to Smith, 31 January 1818

[55] LS JES/COR/12/99 Samuel Goodenough to Smith, 17 February 1825

[56] LS JES/AM/100 Smith to Alexander Macleay, 26 January 1816

[57] LS JES/AM/102 Smith to Alexander Macleay, 4 February 1816

[58] LS JES/COR/7/40 Martin Davy to Smith, 11 February 1816

[59] LS JES/COR/7/41 George Peacock to Smith, 13 October 1817

[60] LS JES/COR/13/60 Smith to Sir Thomas Gery Cullum, 24 March 1818

[61] Smith, J E, (1818). *Op. cit.*, p.57.

[62] LS JES/SM/6 Smith to Frances Smith, 10 April 1818

[63] Smith, J E, (1818). *Op. cit.*, preface.

[64] *Ibid.*, pp.8–10.

[65] *Ibid.*, p.58.

[66] LS JES/COR/17/115 William Roscoe to Smith, 21 May 1818

[67] LS JES/COR/7/44 Martin Davy to Smith, 3 May 1818

[68] Monk, J H, (1818). *A Vindication of the University of Cambridge*, London: John Murray, 2nd ed., p.88

[69] *The Quarterly Review* 19: April 1819 p.434.

[70] *Ibid.*, p.434.

[71] TC Trinity/Add Ms. a/215/1 William Whewell to Julius Hare, 26 July 1818

[72] LS JES/COR/20/118 Francis Boott to Smith, 30 August 1818

[73] LS JES/COR/13/93 Smith to Sir Thomas Gery Cullum, 8 September 1825

[74] *The Statesman*, New York, 4 June 1823 [in LS JES/ADD/40 David Hosack to Smith, 6 June 1823]

[75] Smith, J E, (1819). *A Defence of the Church and Universities of England*, London: Longman, Hurst, Rees, Orme & Brown, p.100.

[76] Smith, J E, (1824). *The English Flora*, London: Longman, Rees, Brown and Orme, p.xxxii.

[77] Smith, P (ed.), (1832). *Memoir and Correspondence of the Late Sir James Edward Smith*, M.D., London: Longman & Co., vol. 2, p.377.

[78] *Christ in Song: For All Religious Services Nearly One Thousand Best Gospel Hymns, New and Old with Responsive Scripture Readings (Rev. and Enl.)* (1908), p.455

[79] LS JES/COR/2/139 Francis Hamilton to Smith, 7 November 1818

[80] LS JES/COR/19/109 Smith to Pleasance Smith, 10 June 1819

[81] LS JES/ADD/117 Smith to Nathaniel Wallich, 6 March 1820

[82] LS JES/COR/13/65 Smith to Sir Thomas Gery Cullum, 25 August 1820

[83] LS JES/COR/1/97 Circular from the Royal Society to Smith, 19 July 1820

[84] Smith, P (ed.), (1832). *Op. cit.*, vol.2, pp.455–456.

[85] LS JES/COR/20/51 Sir Joseph Banks to Smith, 25 December 1817

[86] Smith, J E, (1821). *Grammar of Botany*, London: Longman, Hurst, Rees, Orme, and Brown, p.40; p.x.

[87] *Ibid.*, p.xiii.

[88] *Ibid.*, pp.xiii–xiv.

[89] LS JES/COR/12/67 Samuel Goodenough to Smith, 19 January 1821

[90] LS JES/ADD/72 Thomas Martyn to Smith, 9 March 1821

[91] LS JES/COR/9/38 Josef August Schultes to Smith, 15 July 1821

[92] TC O.13.2 f136 Smith to Dawson Turner, 14 February 1803

[93] LS JES/MS321/4 Smith to Nathaniel Winch, 23 November 1821

[94] LS JES/COR/12/73 Smith to Samuel Goodenough, 3 March 1822

[95] LS JES/AM/163 Smith to Alexander Macleay, 1 February 1823

[96] LS JES/AM/161 Smith to Alexander Macleay, 8 January 1823

[97] LS JES/COR/19/107 Smith to Pleasance Smith, 27 July 1816

[98] RBGK Dawson Turner to William Borrer Vol. 2 f503 Dawson Turner to William Borrer, 19 February 1817

[99] In Wake, J (2010). *Sisters of Fortune: Marianne, Bess, Louisa and Emily Caton 1788–1874*, London: Chatto & Windus, p.186 [Eliza Coke to J Spencer-Stanhope, 30 Oct 1822 Spencer-Stanhope 2:39]

[100] LS JES/AM/174 Smith to Alexander Macleay, 20 December 1824

[101] NHM Sowerby collection 20.59 f351 Smith to James de Carle Sowerby, 31 October 1822

[102] *The Philosophical Magazine* 63: 219 March 1824

[103] LS JES/AM/174 Smith to Alexander Macleay, 20 December 1824

[104] LS JES/ADD/117 Smith to Nathaniel Wallich, 6 March 1820

[105] Lindley, J, (1829). *An Introductory Lecture delivered in the University of London, on*

Thursday, April 30, 1829, London: Printed for John Taylor, p.10.

106 Lindley, J, (1848). *The Ladies' Botany of Professor Lindley*, London: James Ridgway & Sons, 4th ed., p.3.

107 LS JES/COR/26/80 Smith to James Yates, 8 January 1825

108 LS JES/COR/19/129 Smith to Pleasance Smith, 10 May 1825

109 LS JES/AM/179 Smith to Alexander Macleay, 13 March 1825

110 LS JES/COR/19/131 Smith to Pleasance Smith, 4 June 1825

111 LS JES/COR/17/137 Smith to William Roscoe, 6 August 1825

112 LS JES/COR/19/135 Smith to Pleasance Smith, 3 July 1826

113 LS JES/COR/17/141 Smith to William Roscoe, 7 October 1826

114 LS JES/COR/13/106 Smith to Sir Thomas Gery Cullum, 4 September 1827

115 JES/COR/17/149 Smith to William Roscoe, 29 December 1827

116 BLY Osborn d148 vol. 3 f8 Edward Lombe to Pleasance Smith

EPILOGUE

1 BLY Osborn d148 vol. 3 f5 William George Maton to William Fitt Drake, 22 March 1828

2 BLY Osborn d148 vol. 3 f2 Edward Smith-Stanley to Pleasance Smith, 19 March 1828

3 Loudon, J C (ed.), (1830). *The Magazine of Natural History*, London: Longman, Rees, Orme, Brown & Greene, p.158.

4 White, P, 'James Edward Smith and the Purchase of Knowledge', *Endeavour*, 1999 23(3), pp.126–128.

5 Jackson, B D, (1923). *Linnaeus*, London: H F & G Witherby, p.355

6 Allen, D, (2010). *Books and Naturalists*, London: HarperCollins UK, p.137.

7 *The Philosophical Magazine* 17: 391 April 1828

BIBLIOGRAPHY

(1783). *The Norwich Directory*, Norwich: printed and sold by W. Chase and Co.

(1803). *Laws of the Society Instituted at Edinburgh, 1782, for the Investigation of Natural History*, Edinburgh: Printed by C Stewart for the Society.

'Extracts from the Minutes of the Council of the Linnean Society of London', *Transactions of the Linnean Society of London*, 1816 11(1), pp.vii–x.

'Great Marlborough Street Area', *Survey of London: volumes 31 and 32: St James Westminster*, Part 2 (1963), pp. 250–267.

'The Pantheon', *Survey of London: volumes 31 and 32: St James Westminster*, Part 2 (1963), pp. 268–283.

A Botanical Society at Lichfield, (1783). *A System of Vegetables*, Lichfield London: John Jackson.

Aiton, W, (1789). *Hortus Kewensis; or, a Catalogue of the Plants Cultivated in the Royal Botanic Garden at Kew*, London: Printed for George Nicol, 3 vols.

Allen, D E, (1994). *The Naturalist in Britain: A Social History*, Chichester: Princeton University Press, 2nd ed.

Allen, D E, (2010). *Books and Naturalists*, London: Collins.

Allen, D E, 'James Edward Smith and the Natural History Society of Edinburgh', *Journal of the Society for the Bibliography of Natural History*, 1978 8(4), pp.483–493.

Anstey, R, & Hair, P H (eds.), (1976). *Liverpool, the African Slave Trade, and Abolition*, Historic Society of Lancashire and Cheshire Occasional Series Volume 2.

Barringer, C, (1984). *Norwich in the Nineteenth Century*, Norwich: Gliddon.

Berkenhout, J, (1770). *Outlines of the Natural History of Great Britain and Ireland*, London: Elmsly, 3 vols.

Black, J, (2003). *France and the Grand Tour*, Basingstoke: Palgrave Macmillan.

Black, J, (2003). *Italy and the Grand Tour*, London: Yale University Press.

Blunt, W, (2002). *The Compleat Naturalist: A Life of Linnaeus*, London: Frances Lincoln Ltd.

Bouch, C, (1948). *Prelates and People of the Lake Counties: A History of the Diocese of Carlisle, 1133–1933*, Kendal: Titus Wilson.

Bowden, J K, (1989). *John Lightfoot: His Work and Travels*, Kew: Bentham–Moxon Trust, Royal Botanic Gardens.

Braidwood, S, (1994). *Black Poor and White Philanthropists: London's Blacks and the Foundation of the Sierra Leone Settlement 1786–1791*, Liverpool: Liverpool University Press.

Brock, W H, & Meadows, A J, (1998). *The Lamp of Learning: Two Centuries of Publishing at Taylor & Francis*, London: Taylor & Francis.

Browne, J, 'Botany for Gentlemen: Erasmus Darwin and "The Loves of the Plants"', *Isis*, 1989 80(4), pp.592–621.

Bush, C, 'Erasmus Darwin, Robert John Thornton and Linnaeus' Sexual System', *Eighteenth–Century Studies*, 1974 7(3), pp.295–320.

Calhoun, J V, 'A Glimpse Into A "Flora Et Entomologia": The Natural History Of The Rarer Lepidopterous Insects Of Georgia By J. E. Smith And J. Abbot (1797)', *Journal of the Lepidopterists' Society*, 2006 60(1), pp.1–37.

Carter, H, (1988). *Sir Joseph Banks, 1743–1820*, London: British Museum (Natural History).

Cherry, D A, (2012). *Alexander Macleay: From Scotland to Sydney*, Kulnura: Paradise Publishers.

Belden, F E (ed.), (1908). *Christ in Song: For All Religious Services*, Washington DC: Review & Herald Publishing Association.

Christenhusz, M M, & Chase, M W, 'Trends and Concepts in Fern Classification', *Annals of Botany*, 2014 113(4), pp.571–594.

Curtis, W H, (1941). *William Curtis 1746–1799*, Winchester: Warren & Son Ltd.

Darwin, E (1794–1796). *Zoonomia; or, the Laws of Organic Life*, London: [privately], 2 vols.

Day, M C, & Fitton, M G, 'Re–curation of the Linnaean Hymenoptera (Insecta), With a Reassessment of the Taxonomic Importance of the Collection', *Biological Journal of the Linnean Society of London*, 1978 10(2), pp.181–198.

De Beer, G R, 'Edmund Davall, F.L.S.: An Unwritten Chapter in the History of Swiss Botany', *Proceedings of the Linnean Society of London*, 1947 159(1), pp.42–65.

Desmond, R, (1987). *A Celebration of Flowers: Two Hundred Years of Curtis's Botanical Magazine*, London: Royal Botanic Gardens & Collingridge.

Desmond, R, (1994). *Dictionary of British and Irish Botanists and Horticulturists*, London: Taylor & Francis Ltd.

Desmond, R, (2003). *Great Natural History Books and Their Creators*, London: British Library.

Desmond, R, (2007). *The History of the Royal Botanic Gardens Kew*, London: Royal Botanic Gardens.

Duffy, E, (1979). *Rousseau in England: The Context for Shelley's Critique of the Enlightenment*, Los Angeles: University of California Press.

Earland, A, (1911). *John Opie and His Circle*, London: Hutchinson & Co.

Edmondson, J, & Smith, C, 'The Linnean Society's Smith Herbarium: A Resource for Eighteenth-Century Garden History Research', *Garden History*, 1999 27(2), pp.244–252.

Edmondson, J, (2005). *A Growing Concern: William Roscoe and Liverpool's First Botanical Garden*, Liverpool: University of Liverpool.

Elliott, P A, (2010). *Enlightenment, Modernity and Science: Geographies of Scientific Culture and Improvement in Georgian England*, London: I. B. Tauris.

Farrell, S M, 'Wentworth, Mary Watson–, marchioness of Rockingham', *Oxford Dictionary of National Biography*, Oxford: Oxford University Press, 2004.

Fawcett, T, 'An Eighteenth-Century Book Club at Norwich', *The Library*, 1968 s5 23(1), pp.47–50.

Foote, Y, 'Marsham, Thomas', *Oxford Dictionary of National Biography*, Oxford: Oxford University Press, 2004.

Foreman, A, (1999). *Georgiana: Duchess of Devonshire*, London: HarperCollins.

Frodin, D, (2002). *Guide to Standard Floras of the World*, 2nd ed., Cambridge: Cambridge University Press.

Furst, L R, (1992). *Through the Lens of the Reader: Explorations of European Narrative*, Albany: State University of New York Press.

Gage, A T, & Stearn, W T, (2001). *A Bicentenary History of the Linnean Society of London*, London: Academic Press.

Gascoigne, J, (1994). *Joseph Banks and the English Enlightenment: Useful Knowledge and Polite Culture*, Cambridge: Cambridge University Press.

Geldart, A, 'Sir James Edward Smith and Some of His Friends', *Transactions of the Norfolk and Norwich Natural History Society*, 1914 11(5), pp.642–692.

George, S, (2007). *Botany, Sexuality and Women's Writing 1760–1830*, Manchester: Manchester University Press.

Goethe, J W von, & Morrison, A W & Nisbet, C (trans.), (1885). [Goethe's] *Travels in Italy: Together with his Second Residence in Rome and Fragments on Italy*, London: Bell.

Goethe, J W von, & Constantine, D (trans.), (2012). *The Sorrows of Young Werther*, Oxford: Oxford University Press.

Gorham, G C, & Martyn, T, (1830). *Memoirs of John Martyn… and of Thomas Martyn…*, London: Hatchard and Son.

Guiney, R, 'On the Whereabouts of the 'Oxford copy' of Rudbeck's Campi Elysii', *Proceedings of the Linnean Society of London*, 1949 161(1), pp.50–56.

Hadlow, J, (2014). *The Strangest Family: The Private Lives of George III, Queen Charlotte and the Hanoverians*, London: William Collins.

Haworth, A, 'Review of the Rise and Progress of the Science of Entomology in Great Britain', *Transactions of the Entomological Society of London*, 1807 1, pp.1–69.

Hedley, O, (1975). *Queen Charlotte*, London: John Murray.

Heilbron, J L, (2003). *The Oxford Companion to the History of Modern Science*, Oxford: Oxford University Press.

Henderson, P, (2015). *James Sowerby: The Enlightenment's Natural Historian*, London: Royal Botanic Gardens.

Heringman, N (ed.), (2003). *Romantic Science: The Literary Forms of Natural History*, Albany: State University of New York Press.

Hewson, H, (1999). *Australia: 300 Years of Botanical Illustration*, Collingwood: CSIRO Publishing.

Hibbert, C, (1969). *The Grand Tour*, New York: Putnam.

Hibbert, C, (1982). *The French Revolution*, London: Penguin Books.

Holmes, R, (2009). *The Age of Wonder*, London: HarperPress.

Humphrey, H, (1961). *Makers of North American Botany*, New York: Ronald Press Co.

Inglis-Jones, E, (1950). *Peacocks in Paradise*, London: Faber & Faber.

Jackson, B D, (1923). *Linnaeus*, London: H F & G Witherby.

Jackson, B D, 'History of the Linnean Collections, prepared for the Centenary Anniversary of the Linnean Society by the Senior Secretary', *Proceedings of the Linnean Society of London*, 1890 100(1), pp.18–34.

Jarvis, C, (2007). *Order Out of Chaos*, London: Linnean Society of London with the Natural History Museum.

Jewson, C B, (1975). *The Jacobin City: A Portrait of Norwich 1788–1802*, London: Blackie & Son.

Kaufman, M H, (2003). *Medical Teaching in Edinburgh During the 18th and 19th Centuries*, Edinburgh: Royal College of Surgeons of Edinburgh.

Kelley, T M (2012). *Clandestine Marriage: Botany and Romantic Culture*, Baltimore, Maryland: The John Hopkins University Press.

King, T, (1796). *Linnean Cabinet of Minerals: A Catalogue of the Genuine and Entire Collection of the Late Celebrated Swedish Naturalist, Sir Charles Linne*, London: [s.n.].

Knight, J, (1809). *On the Cultivation of the Plants Belonging to the Natural Order of Proteeae*, London: [privately].

Konig, C, & Sims, J, (eds.), (1804–1806). *Annals of Botany*, London: [privately], 2 vols.

Lack, H W, & Mabberley, D J, (1999). *The Flora Graeca Story: Sibthorp, Bauer, and Hawkins in the Levant*, Oxford: Oxford University Press.

Lamarck, J B, (1789). *Encyclopédie Méthodique: Botanique*, Paris: Panckoucke, vol. 3.

Largen, M J, & Rogers-Price, V, 'John Abbot, an Early Naturalist & Artist in North America: His Contribution to Ornithology, with Particular Reference to a Collection of Bird Skins in the Merseyside Country Museums, Liverpool', *Archives of Natural History*, 1985 12(2), pp.231–252.

Larson, J L, 'Goethe and Linnaeus', *Journal of the History of Ideas*, 1967 28(4), pp.590–596.

Lawrence, S C, (1996). *Charitable Knowledge: Hospital Pupils and Practitioners in Eighteenth-Century London*, Cambridge: Cambridge University Press.

Leigh, Sotheby & Son Auctioneers, (1803). *A Catalogue of the Library of Natural History Formed by Edmund Davall*, London: [the auctioneers].

Lindley, J, (1829). *An Introductory Lecture delivered in the University of London, on Thursday, April 30, 1829*, London: Printed for John Taylor.

Lindley, J, (1848). *The Ladies' Botany of Professor Lindley*, 4th ed., London: James Ridgway & Sons.

Linnaeus, C, & Smith, J E (ed.), (1792). *Flora Lapponica*, 2nd ed., London: White & Son.

Linnaeus, C, & Smith, J E (ed.), (1811). *Lachesis Lapponica, or a Tour in Lapland*, London: White, Cochrane & Co.

Linnaeus, C, & Smith, J E (trans.), (1785). *Reflections on the Study of Nature*, London: George Nicol.

Linnaeus, C, & Smith, J E (trans.), (1786). *Dissertation on the Sexes of Plants*, London: George Nicol.

Liverpool Botanic Garden, (1802). *An Address, Delivered Before the Proprietors of the... Garden... May 3, 1802.*

Lyall, R, 'Observations respecting the Irritability of the Barberry, Berberis communis', *Journal of Natural Philosophy, Chemistry and the Arts*, 1811 28, pp.314–316.

Lyons, H G, (ed.), (1940). *The Record of the Royal Society for the Promotion of Natural Knowledge*, London: Royal Society.

Mabberley, D, (1985). *Jupiter Botanicus: Robert Brown of the British Museum*, London: British Museum (Natural History).

Mabberley, D, 'Dr Smith's "Anemia", or, the Prevention of Later Homonyms', *Taxon*, 1983 32(1), pp.79–87.

Macmichael, W, (1968). *The Gold-Headed Cane*, London: Royal College of Physicians.

Marshall, P J, 'Hastings, Warren', *Oxford Dictionary of National Biography*, Oxford: Oxford University Press, 2004.

Martyn, T, (1787). *Letters on the Elements of Botany, Addressed to a Lady*, 2nd ed, London: B. White.

Martyn, T, (1793). *The Language of Botany*, London: B & J White.

Matchett, G, (1822). *The Norfolk and Norwich Rembrancer and Vade-Mecum*, Norwich: Matchett & Stevenson.

Monk, J H, (1818). *A Vindication of the University of Cambridge*, 2nd ed., London: John Murray.

Moore, A W, (1985). *Norfolk & the Grand Tour: Eighteenth-Century Travellers Abroad and Their Souvenirs*, Norwich: Norfolk Museums Service.

Moore-Colyer, R J (ed.), (1992). *A Land of Pure Delight: Selections from the letters of Thomas Johnes of Hafod, Cardiganshire (1748–1816)*, Llandysul: Gomer.

Moore-Colyer, R J, 'The Hafod estate under Thomas Johnes and the fourth Duke of Newcastle', *Welsh History Review*, 1976–7 8, pp.257–284.

Moore-Colyer, R J, 'Thomas Johnes of Hafod: Translator and Bibliophile', *Welsh History*

Review, 1990-91 15, pp.399–416.

Muhlenberg, H, (1813). *Catalogus Plantarum Americae Septentrionalis, Huc Usque Cognitarum*, Lancaster, Pennsylvania: [privately].

Loudon, J C (ed.), (1830). *The Magazine of Natural History*, London: Longman, Rees, Orme, Brown and Greene.

Nelson, E C, (2011). *Hardy Heathers: From the Northern Hemisphere*, Kew: Royal Botanic Gardens.

Nelson, E C, 'John White A.M., M.D., F.L.S. (c.1756–1832), Surgeon-General of New South Wales: A New Biography of the Messenger of the Echidna and Waratah', *Archives of Natural History*, 1998 25(2), pp.149–211.

Nelson, E C, 'John White's Journal of a voyage to new South Wales', *Archives of Natural History*, 1998 25(1), pp.109–130.

Noltie, H J, (2011). *John Hope (1725–1786) Alan G Morton's Memoir of a Scottish Botanist*, Edinburgh: Royal Botanic Garden Edinburgh.

O'Brian, P, (1987). *Joseph Banks: A Life*, London: Collins Harvill.

Oliver, F W (ed.), (1913). *Makers of British Botany*, Cambridge: Cambridge University Press.

Paris, C A, & Barrington, D S, 'William Jackson Hooker and the Generic Classification of Ferns', *Annals of the Missouri Botanical Garden*, 1990 77(2), pp. 228–238.

Porter, R, 'The New Taste for Nature in the Eighteenth Century', *The Linnean*, 1988 4(1), pp.14–31.

Ramsay, E B, 'Biographical Notice of the late Sir J. E. Smith, President of the Linnaean Society', *The Edinburgh Journal of Science*, 1829 1, pp.1–16.

Rawcliffe, C, & Wilson, R, (eds.), (2004). *Norwich since 1550*, London: Hambledon & London.

Rees, A, (ed.), (1802–1819). *The Cyclopaedia, or, Universal Dictionary of Arts, Sciences, and Literature*, London: Longman, Hurst, Rees, Orme & Brown.

Roberts, J, (ed.) (2004). *George III & Queen Charlotte: Patronage, Collecting and Court Taste*, London: Royal Collection Enterprises Ltd.

Rogers, J J, (1878). *Opie and His Works: Being a Catalogue of 760 Pictures by John Opie R.A.*, London: Paul & Dominic Colnaghi & Co.

Romani, R, (2002). *National Character and Public Spirit in Britain and France, 1750–1914*, Cambridge: Cambridge University Press.

Roscoe, H, (1833). *The Life of William Roscoe*, London: T. Cadell, 2 vols.

Rosenfeld, S A, (2011). *Common Sense: A Political History*, Cambridge, Massachusetts: Harvard University Press.

Rosner, L, (1991). *Medical Education in the Age of Improvement: Edinburgh Students and Apprentices 1760–1826*, Edinburgh: Edinburgh University Press.

Salisbury, R A, (1796). *Prodromus Stirpium in Horto ad Chapel Allerton Vigentium*, London: [privately].

Salisbury, R A, (1805–1808). *The Paradisus Londinensis*, London: [privately].

Salisbury, R A, (1806). *The Generic Characters in the English Botany, Collated with Those of Linné*, London: [privately].

Salisbury, R A, (1808). *A Letter to the Editor of the Monthly Magazine*, London: [privately].

Savage, S, 'Studies in Linnaean Synonymy. 2. Sir James Edward Smith and the Linnaean Herbarium', *Proceedings of the Linnean Society of London*, 1937 149(1), pp.6–11.

Skuncke, M, (2014). *Carl Peter Thunberg, Botanist and Physician*, Uppsala: Swedish Collegium for Advanced Study.

Shapin, S, (2011). *Leviathan and the Air-Pump: Hobbes, Boyle, and the Experimental Life*, Princeton, N.J.: Princeton University Press.

Shtier, A B, (1996). *Cultivating Women, Cultivating Science: Flora's Daughter and Botany in England 1760–1860*, London: John Hopkins Press.

Sibthorp, J, & Smith, J E (ed.), (1806–1840). *Flora Graeca: Sive Plantarum Rariorum Historia…*, London: [privately].

Simmons, A M, & Wiseman, B R, 'James Edward Smith: Taxonomic Author of the Fall Armyworm', *Florida Entomologist*, 1993 76(2), pp.271–276.

Simpson, M, (2007). *Rousseau: A Guide for the Perplexed*, London: Continuum.

Smith Jr., C E, 'Henry Muhlenberg: Botanical Pioneer', *Proceedings of the American Philosophical Society*, 1962 106(5), pp. 443–460.

Smith, J E (1790–1793). *Icones Pictae Plantarum Rariorum Descriptionibus et Observationibus*, London: [the author].

Smith, J E & Oosterdijk, N G, (1786). *Disputatio Physiologica Inauguralis. Quaedam de Generatione Complectens*, Lugduni Batavorum: Apud Fratres Murray.

Smith, J E, & Abbot, J, (1797). *The Natural History of the Rarer Lepidoterous Insects of Georgia*, London: J. Edwards.

Smith, J E, & Smith, J, (1810). *A Tour to Hafod, in Cardiganshire: the Seat of Thomas Johnes, Esq.*, London: White & Co.

Smith, J E, & Sowerby, J, (1790–1814). *English Botany; or, Coloured Figures of British Plants*, London: [privately], 36 vols.

Smith, J E, & Sowerby, J, (1804–1808). *Exotic Botany*, London: [privately], 2 vols.

Smith, J E, (1789–1791). *Plantarum Icones Hactenus Ineditae, Plerumque ad Plantas in Herbario Linnaeano Conservatas Delineatae*, London: Benjamin White & Son.

Smith, J E, (1791–1792). *Spicilegium Botanicum*, London: [privately].

Smith, J E, (1793). *A Sketch of a Tour on the Continent, in the years 1786 and 1787*, London: [privately], 3 vols.

Smith, J E, (1793). *A Specimen of the Botany of New Holland*, London: J Sowerby.

Smith, J E, (1795). *Syllabus of a Course of Lectures on Botany*, London: [privately].

Smith, J E, (1798). *Tracts Relating to Natural History*, London: [privately]

Smith, J E, (1800). *Compendium Florae Britannicae*, London: J White & Son.

Smith, J E, (1800–1804). *Flora Britannica*, London: [privately], 3 vols.

Smith, J E, (1807). *A Sketch of a Tour on the Continent, in the years 1786 and 1787*, 2nd ed., London: Longman, 3 vols.

Smith, J E, (1807). *An Introduction to Physiological and Systematical Botany*, London: Longman, Hurst, Rees, & Orme.

Smith, J E, (1809). *An Introduction to Physiological and Systematical Botany*, 2nd ed., London: Longman, Hurst, Rees, & Orme.

Smith, J E, (1818). *Considerations Respecting Cambridge, More Particularly Relating to its Botanical Professorship*, London: [privately].

Smith, J E, (1819). *A Defence of the Church and Universities of England*, London: Longman, Hurst, Rees, Orme & Brown.

Smith, J E, (1821). *Grammar of Botany*, London: Longman, Hurst, Rees, Orme & Brown.

Smith, J E, (1824–1828). *The English Flora*, London: Longman, Rees, Brown & Orme, 4 vols.

Smith, J E, 'Biographical Memoirs of Several Norwich Botanists', *Transactions of the Linnean Society of London*, 1804 7(1), pp.295–301.

Smith, J E, 'Characters of a new Genus of Plants named Salisburia', *Transactions of the Linnean Society of London*, 1797 3(1), pp.330–332.

Smith, J E, 'Introductory Discourse on the Rise and Progress of Natural History', *Transactions of the Linnean Society of London*, 1791 1(1), pp.1–51.

Smith, J E, 'Observations on the British Species of Bromus, with Introductory Remarks on the Composition of a Flora Britannica', *Transactions of the Linnean Society of London*, 1798 4(1), pp.276–302.

Smith, J E, 'Remarks on some British Species of Salix', *Transactions of the Linnean Society of London*, 1802 6(1), pp.110–124.

Smith, J E, 'Some Observations on the Irritability of Vegetables', *Philosophical Transactions of the Royal Society of London*, 1788 78, pp.158–165.

Smith, P (ed.), (1832). *Memoir and Correspondence of the Late Sir James Edward Smith, M.D.*, London: Longman & Co, 2 vols.

Stafleu, F A, (1971). *Linnaeus and the Linnaeans*, Utrecht: International Association for Plant Taxonomy.

Stafleu, F A, 'Dates of Botanical Publications 1788–1792', *Taxon*, 1963 12(2), pp.43–87.

Stafleu, F A, 'Lamarck: The Birth of Biology', *Taxon*, 1971 20(4), pp.397–442.

Stearn, W, (1992). *Botanical Latin: History, Grammar, Syntax, Terminology and Vocabulary*, 4th ed., Newton Abbot: David & Charles.

Stevens, P F, (1994). *The Development of Biological Systematics: Antoine-Laurent de Jussieu, Nature, and the Natural System*, New York: Columbia University Press.

Stievermann, J, & Scheiding, O, (eds.), (2013). *A Peculiar Mixture: German-Language Cultures and Identities in Eighteenth-Century North America*, University Park, Pa.: Pennsylvania State University Press.

Stoever, D H, & Trapp, J, (trans.), (1794). *The Life of Sir Charles Linnaeus*, London: B & J White.

Taylor, R, & Taylor, E, (1848). *History of the Octagon Chapel, Norwich*, London: Charles Green.

Thomson, S C, 'The Great Windmill Street School', *Bulletin of the History of Medicine*, 1942 22, pp.377–391.

Thornton, R J, (1799–1807). *A New Illustration of the Sexual System of Linnaeus*, London: [privately].

Thornton, R J, [1797]. *Advertisement to the New Illustration of the Sexual System of Linnaeus*, [London: the author].

Tyron, R M, 'A Sketch of the History of Fern Classification', *Annals of the Missouri Botanical Garden*, 1952 39(4), pp.255–262.

Vane-Wright, R I, 'William Jones (1745–1818), Chelsea and the Need for a Digital Online Icones', *Antenna*, 2010 34(1), pp.16–21.

Waddington, K, (2003). *Medical Education at St Bartholomew's Hospital, 1123–1995*, Woodbridge: The Boydell Press.

Wake, J, (2010). *Sisters of Fortune: Marianne, Bess, Louisa and Emily Caton 1788–1874*, London: Chatto & Windus.

Walker, M (1988). *Sir James Edward Smith M.D., F.R.S., P.L.S. 1759–1828 First President of the Linnean Society of London*, London: The Linnean Society of London.

Wallace, P W, 'Henry Ernest Muhlenberg', *Proceedings of the American Philosophical Society*, 1948 92(2), pp.107–110.

Walters, S M, (1981). *The Shaping of Cambridge Botany*, Cambridge: Cambridge University Press.

Walters, SM, & Stow, E A, (2001). *Darwin's Mentor: John Stevens Henslow, 1796–1861*, Cambridge: Cambridge University Press.

Wesley, J, (1992). *The Works of John Wesley: Journal and Diaries IV (1755–1765)*, Nashville: Abingdon Press.

White, P, 'James Edward Smith and the Purchase of Knowledge', *Endeavour*, 1999 23(3), pp.126–129.

Williams, R L, (2001). *Botanophilia in Eighteeth-Century France: The Spirit of Enlightenment*, London: Kluwer Academic.

Withering, W, (1776). *A Botanical Arrangement of all the Vegetables Naturally Growing in Great Britain*, Birmingham: Cadel, 2 vols.

Wokler, R, (2012). *Rousseau, the Age of Enlightenment, and Their Legacies*, Princeton, New Jersey: Princeton University Press.

Wormersley, T, & Crawford, D H, (2010). *Bodysnatchers to Lifesavers: Three Centuries of Medicine in Edinburgh*, Edinburgh: Luath Press Ltd.

ACKNOWLEDGEMENTS

The writing of this book was possible only with the help and encouragement of many friends.

I thank in particular Gren Lucas, Treasurer of the Linnean Society, for placing his faith in me and for his patience and support throughout the project. Leonie Berwick gave constant reassurance to a first-time writer and whipped more than one baggy monster of a chapter into shape. Helen Cowdy produced the beautiful line drawings and maps that considerably enhance this volume.

I thank also my Linnean Society colleagues, who have helped me in so many different ways, particularly Lynda Brooks, Isabelle Charmantier, Elaine Charwat, Andrea Deneau, Gina Douglas, David Pescod and Ross Ziegelmeier.

Janet Browne, Michael Button, John Edmondson, Paul Henderson, David Mabberley and Charles Nelson provided invaluable feedback and commentary on my manuscript.

I would also like to thank James Moody for several enlightening exchanges regarding Smith; Nigel Palmer and Mike Heath for being so generous with their time and skills in translating all of Smith's Latin and French correspondence held by the Linnean Society, as well as Smith's MD thesis and various prefaces; and Viv Hendra of the Lander Gallery, Truro, who helped me locate Pleasance Smith's portrait after months of searching.

I also thank the archivists and librarians of the following institutions: Beinecke Library, Yale University; British Library; King's College London; Lowestoft Record Office; National Archives; National Archives of Scotland; Natural History Museum; Norfolk Record Office; Royal Academy of Arts; Royal Archives; Royal Botanic Garden Edinburgh; Royal Botanic Gardens Kew; Royal Society; Trinity College, Cambridge; University of Edinburgh Centre for Research Collections; and Wellcome Library.

This work was generously supported by the Council and Officers of the Linnean Society of London.

PICTURE CREDITS

All images © The Linnean Society of London except: Frances Smith (née Kinderley) and James Smith oil portraits © Ashmolean Museum, University of Oxford; Norwich Marketplace © Norfolk Museums Service (Norwich Castle Museum & Art Gallery); 'The Pantheon, the morning after the fire 1792' from 'The Burning of The Pantheon' by JMW Turner © Tate, London 2016; 'Women's fashion at the time of the French Revolution' © Tallandier/Bridgeman Images.

INDEX

1807 Abolition of the Slave Trade Bill, 246–247
1813 Doctrine of the Trinity Act, 195

Abbot, John, 214, 310
Abolitionism, 178, 245–247, 248
Académie des Sciences (Paris), 155
Académie des Sciences, Lettres et Arts (Marseilles), 90
Acharius, Erik, 240
Acrel, Johan Gustaf, 58, 59, 60–61, 62–63, 68, 70–71, 129, 132, 136, 186
Adanson, Michel, 74–75, 84, 155, 157, 159, 264
Addington, Henry (1st Viscount Sidmouth, Home Secretary), 280
Aeschynomene (jointvetches), 138
Afzelius, Adam, 174, 177–178
Agave americana (centuryplant, maguey, or American aloe), 100–101
Agrostis (bent or bentgrass), 216
Aiton, William, 137, 148, 161
Algae. *See* Cryptogamia
Allamand, Jean-Nicolas-Sébastien, 78
Allerton Hall (Roscoe's villa), 245, 282, 283
Alœ perfoliata (aloe), 101
Alströmer, Baron Clas, 61
The Analytical Review, 165, 167, 169
American Philosophical Society, 191
American Revolution, 195, 197, 201
American War of Independence, 59, 269
Amœnitates Academicæ (Linnaeus 1749), 61, 125
Ancram, Earl of, 42
Andromeda salicifolia, 154
The Annual Review, 262
Anson, Thomas (Viscount), 282–283

Antirrhinum reticulata. See *Linaria reticulata*
Appearance (ship), 63, 64, 66, 309
Aralia capitata. See *Oreopanax capitatus*
Aretino, Pietro, 253
Asperula odorata. See *Galium odoratum*
Athens, 205, 231
Augusta, Princess, 182
Auriferous pyrites, 212
Australia, 56, 137, 186–187, 188, 259, 302
Australian flora, 7, 56, 137, 187, 188, 206, 249, 265, 267
Avignon, 88, 90

Babington, William, 212–213
Baillie, Matthew, 54
Banks, Dorothea, 57
Banks, Sir Joseph, 44, 55–57, 58–60, 61, 65, 69, 70, 74, 77, 85, 101, 109, 112–113, 114, 118, 119, 124–125, 127, 128, 131, 132, 135, 137, 144–145, 148, 158, 161, 173, 174, 183–184, 186–187, 201, 214, 222, 229, 230, 233, 238, 241, 249, 252, 257, 265, 270, 278, 295–296, 297, 309, 310
  —'s herbarium, 69, 71, 234
Banks, Sarah Sophia, 57, 213
Banks's Florilegium (1980–1990), 56
Banksia (banksia), 187
Barrington, Mrs Jane 146, 148, 162
Barrington, Right Reverend Shute (Bishop of Salisbury), 146–147, 201
Basel, 106, 107
The Bastille (Paris), 157
Battarrea (formerly *Lycoperdon*) (puffball), 170
  — *phalloides* (scaley-stalked puffball, sandy stiltball, or desert stalked puffball), 170
Batty, Robert, 40, 41, 42, 44, 45, 53, 54, 68, 139, 141, 177, 193, 206, 312
Bauer, Ferdinand, 127, 204
Bedford, (6th) Duke of. *See* Russell, John
Begonia, 174
  — (Dryander), 174
Bellardi, Dr Carlo, 105, 137
Bengal, 144, 263
  — botanic garden, 148
Bentinck, Margaret Cavendish (Duchess of Portland), 69, 70, 162
Berberis (barberry), 255

— *communis* (see *Berberis vulgaris*)
— *vulgaris* (formerly *Berberis communis*) (European barberry), 123, 124
Berchem, Berthout van, 141–142
Berkeley, Miles, 307
Berkenhout, John, 3, 6, 27, 28
Berne, 106, 138, 139
Bessborough, Countess of (Henrietta 'Harriet' Ponsonby, Lady Duncannon), 184–185
Beveridge, Mrs, 33, 45, 46, 48
Billardiera (apple-berry), 188
— *scadens* (climbing apple-berry), 188
binomial system, 5–6, 154, 166, 175, 302
Birmingham, 198, 293
— riots of 1791, 198
Birmingham Philosophical Institution, 293
Black, Joseph, 32, 34, 37, 41
Blandford, Dorset, 120
Bolton, James, 42
Bonnet, Charles, 78–79, 106
Bonnie Prince Charlie. *See* Stuart, Charles Edward
Boott, Francis, 292
Borone, Francesco, 106, 151, 164, 178, 204–206, 231, 312
Borone, Luigi (father of Francesco Borone), 206
Borrer, William, 285
The Botanic Garden (E. Darwin 1789–1791), 181
— Part 2, *The Loves of the Plants* (1791), 181
Botanical Arrangement of All the Vegetables Naturally Growing in Britain, The (Withering 1787–1792), 64, 148, 167, 237
Botanical Magazine (Curtis 1787–ongoing), 117, 133, 164, 166, 168–169, 248, 260
The Botanical Repository, 260
Botany Bay, New South Wales, 186–187
Boulogne-sur-Mer, 107
Bradley, Richard, 276
Bristol, 21, 22, 27, 30, 129, 302
Bristol Institution, 293, 302
Bristol, Bishop of. *See* Mansel, William
The British Critic, 198, 199–200
British Museum, The, 72, 112, 237, 295, 296
—'s herbarium, 237
Brodiæa (Salisbury's *Hookera*) (cluster-lilies), 265, 266, 267

Brodie, James, 264, 265, 266, 269
Bromus (brome grasses, cheat grasses or chess grasses), 237
Broussonet, Dr Pierre Marie August, 44, 57, 68, 81, 82, 85, 88, 89, 90, 126–127, 154–155, 157
Brown, Robert, 259, 265, 267, 270, 284, 296, 301, 307
Brunswick, Duke of, 197
'Brunswick Manifesto', 197
Brussels, 116
Bryant, Charles, 27, 29
Bryant, Revd Henry, 27, 28, 29
Buchanan (later Hamilton), Francis, 41, 42, 118, 260, 294–295
Burke, Edmund, 196, 199
Burlington House, Piccadilly, 297
Burnett, James (Lord Monboddo), 37
Burney, Fanny, 184, 196
Byblis liniflora, 265

Calceolaria (slipperworts), 152
— *nana*, 152
— *ovata*, 152
— *plantaginea*, 152
Calcutta Botanic Garden, 301
Caldwell, Andrew, 243, 245
Calomeria amaranthoides (*Humea elegans*), 249
Calyx, 148
Cambridge, University of, 6, 32, 33, 61, 72, 273, 275–276, 278, 280, 281, 284, 288–292, 294
— Botanic Garden, 276
— Dr Walker's Lecturer, 275, 276, 277, 289
— Library, 264
— Professorship, 294
— Regius Professorship, 275, 276, 277, 291
Camper, Petrus, 119, 125–126
Campi Elysii (Rudbeck 1701–1702), 131–132, 310
Capel-Coningsby, George (5th Earl of Essex), 265
Carlisle, Bishop of. *See* Goodenough, Revd Samuel
Carlisle, Cumberland, 44
Cassiobury, 265
Catesbæa spinosa , 160
Catesby, Mark, 160, 176, 189

Catherine the Great, 3, 61
Catholic Church, the 23, 80
Catholicism 80, 98
Cavanilles, Antonio, 137, 152
Cavendish, Georgiana. *See* Devonshire, Duchess of
Cels, Jacques, 83
Cenis, Mont (Savoy), 105–106
Chantrey, Francis (sculptor), 296, 303
Chapel Allerton (near Leeds), 128, 137, 242, 251
'Characters of a new Liliaceous Genus called Brodiaea' (Smith 1810), 266
Charlotte, Queen, 6, 148, 162, 164, 179–180, 182–185, 191, 196, 198, 200–201, 208, 210, 312
Charnacé, Comte de, 89
Chelsea Physic Garden, 5, 31, 65, 72, 161
Chlora perfoliata (yellow-wort), 27
Church of England, 23, 32, 195, 276, 277, 279, 289
Cichorium intybus (chicory), 21
Cimex personatus. See *Reduvius personatus*
Citrus x sinensis (oranges), 91
Clark, Bracy, 224, 225, 226
Clarke, Edward Daniel, 276, 289
Classes, 4, 5, 125, 224. *See also* Orders
Clitoria (clitoria), 261
Coke, Eliza, 299
Coke, Thomas William (later 1st Earl of Leicester), 269–270, 278, 282, 283, 299, 303
Collinson, Peter, 253
Coloured Figures of Rare Plants. See *Icones Pictæ Plantarum Rariorum* (1790–1793)
Common Sense (Paine 1776), 201
Company of Surgeons (formerly the United Company of Barber-Surgeons), 53
Compendium Floræ Britannicæ (Smith 1800), 201, 239, 284
Conferva, 220
— *byssoides*, 220
— *villosa*, 220
Confessions (Rousseau 1770, publ. 1782), 88
Considerations Respecting Cambridge, More Particularly Relating to its Botanical Professorship (Smith 1818), 290
Cook, Captain James, 56
Cordeliers (Franciscan order), 90
Cornwall, 162,

Corybas aconitiflorus, 265
Cotignac, 91
Cottens, Henriette-Louise-Stéphanie Crinzos de. *See* Davall, Henriette
Coutinho, Rodrigo de Sousa, 105
Craven, William, 276–277, 279
Cremorne, Viscountess (Philadelphia-Hannah Dawson), 162, 179
The Critical Review, 6, 136, 198
Crowe, James, 27, 29, 31, 240
Cryptogamia, 49, 190, 192, 205, 239–240, 241, 243, 248
  algae, 157, 239
  ferns, 5, 49, 137, 185, 192, 205, 225, 239, 307, 311
  fungi, 28, 31, 157, 170, 239, 240, 307
  lichens, 5, 41, 57, 89, 100, 143, 147, 192, 239, 240, 248
  liverworts, 49, 239, 248
  mosses, 5, 28, 49, 69, 192, 205, 225, 226, 238, 239, 243, 265, 307
Cullen, William, 32, 48
Cullum, Sir Thomas Gery, 164, 275, 280, 303
Cumming, James, 289
Curtis, William, 31, 117, 118, 133, 134, 164, 166, 167–169, 173, 192, 248, 251, 259, 264
Cuvier, Georges, 156
Cyamus nelumbo. See *Nelumbo nucifera*
Cyclopædia, (*Abraham Rees's*) (Wood, Smith 1802–1819), 261, 268, 272, 281, 284, 301
Cypripedium calceolus (lady's slipper orchid), 167
Dabœcia cantabrica. See *Erica dabœcia*
Dahl, Anders, 61, 63–64
Daphne collina, 102
Dartmouth, (3rd) Earl of. *See* Lewisham, Viscount
Darwin, Erasmus, 28, 73, 79, 148, 181, 229, 261
Davall (née Crinzos de Cottens), Henriette-Louise-Stéphanie (wife to Edmund Davall), 142–143, 211, 224–226
Davall, Edmund, 138–144, 146, 151, 159, 162, 167, 168, 178, 182, 183, 184–185, 191, 194, 195, 196, 198, 200, 203, 209, 210–212, 219, 224–226, 243, 245
  — 's herbarium, 139, 142, 211, 225, 226
Davallia (deersfoot fern, hare's foot fern, shinobu fern, rabbit foot fern, ball fern), 225, 226
Davie, John (Cambridge University Vice-Chancellor 1813–1814), 276
Davy, Martin, 278, 291
Dawson, Philadelphia-Hannah. *See* Cremorne, Viscountess

De Generatione (Smith 1786), 78, 181
De Materia Medica (Dioscorides), 127
A Defence of the Church and Universities of England (Smith 1819), 292–293
Deluc, Jean-André, 106
Denman, Thomas, 129
Derby, (13th) Earl of. *See* Stanley, Edward Smith
Derbyshire, 29, 95, 129
Desfontaines, René Louiche, 83, 126, 154, 158–159, 239
Devonshire, Duchess of (Georgiana Cavendish), 184
Diandria (Linnaean class), 5
Diapensia lapponica, 142
Dickson, James, 31, 32, 118, 240
"Dictionary of Botany", 295
Dillenia, 174
— (Thunberg), 174
Dillwyn, Lewis Weston, 268, 269
Dioecia (Linnaean class), 239, 240
Dioscorides, 127
Dissertation on the Sexes of Plants (Linnaeus 1759), 221
Dissertation on the Sexes of Plants (Linnaeus, translated by Smith 1786), 74, 82, 84, 105, 310
Drake, William Fitt, 242, 243, 244, 245, 247, 253–254, 307, 308
Dryander, Jonas Carlsson, 58, 60, 61, 67, 69, 84, 118, 127, 129, 132, 137, 140, 144, 156, 157, 174, 181, 216, 218, 221, 222, 233, 234, 252, 255, 262, 263, 270
Durazzo, Marquess Ippolito, 85, 94, 95

East India Company, 145
East, Lady Hannah, 219, 242
The Eclectic Review, 271
Edict of Nantes, the (1598), 88
revocation of — (1685), 88
Edinburgh, 32, 33, 37, 38, 39, 42, 43, 44, 45, 47, 49, 50, 55, 64, 66, 67, 73, 77, 78, 88, 117, 118, 124, 128, 129, 173, 177, 181, 194, 251, 260, 294
—, University of, 6, 32, 33, 34, 35, 36, 37, 39, 40, 53, 73, 81, 203, 251, 310
The Edinburgh Journal of Science, 248
Edinburgh Review, 262
Edwards, James (publisher), 214
Ehrharta, 153
— *capensis* (veldtgrass), 153
— *erecta* (Lamarck) (see *Ehrharta panicea*)

— *panicea*, 152, 153
Elements of Botany (Rose 1775), 28
Elizabeth, Princess, 182, 183
Émile, ou de l'éducation (Rousseau 1762), 86
Encyclopædia Britannica, 296
Encyclopédie Méthodique Botanique (3 vols) (Lamarck), 152, 153, 155
—, vol 2 (1786), 152
—, vol 3 (1789), 152
HMS *Endeavour* (ship), 56, 309, 310
Engelhart, John Henry, 33, 38, 39, 45–46, 58–59, 62
English Botany; or, Coloured Figures of British Plants (Sowerby 1790–1814), 164–166, 168–170, 175, 181, 192, 201, 203, 216, 220, 232, 234, 237, 241, 254, 255, 258, 260, 266, 272, 273, 284, 296
The English Flora (Smith 1824), 293, 297, 298, 300, 302–304, 307, 311
Entomologia Britannica (Marsham 1802), 114
Entomology, 127, 208, 213, 215
Epigenesis, 79
Erica (formerly *Dabœcia*) (heath), 100, 167, 252
— *arborea* (Tree Heath), 100
— *botuliformis* ('sausage-shaped heath') (Salisbury) (see *Erica tetralix*)
— *dabœcia* (formerly *Dabœcia cantabrica*), 167
— *tetralix* (cross-leaved heath), 252
— *vagans* (Cornish heath), 167
Ermenonville, 86–87, 198
Erysipelas, 242, 252, 303
"An Essay on Collecting and Preserving Specimens of Plants" (Smith 1782), 41
Essex, (5th) Earl of. *See* Capel-Coningsby, George
Euphorbia punicea (Jamaican poinsettia), 160–161
Evolution, 37, 83, 311
Exotic Botany (Smith, Sowerby 1804–1805), 248, 249, 254–255, 260

Famille des Plantes (Adanson 1763), 74
'Fanaticism: A Vision', *The Monthly Magazine* (Smith 1808), 270
Fasciculus Plantarum Cryptogamicarum Britanniæ (Dickson 1785–1801), 240
Ferns. *See* Cryptogamia
Festuca ovina (Sheep's fescue or sheep fescue), 30
First Fleet, 186
Flavocetraria cucullata (formerly *Lichen cucullatus*), 143
Flora Anglica (Hudson 1762), 6
Flora Austriaca (Host 1761–1831), 272

Flora Britannica (Smith 1800–1804), 173, 180, 181, 201, 216, 220, 237–240, 241, 243, 247, 248, 260, 262, 268, 269, 284, 295, 298
— vols. 1 & 2 (1800), 238–239
— vol. 3 (1804), 240, 248, 268
— vol. 4 260
Flora Danica (Oeder 1761–1883), 273
Flora Dietetica (Bryant 1783), 29
Flora Gallo-provincialis (Gérard 1761), 91
Flora Græca (Sibthorp, Smith 1806–1840), 128, 204, 211, 231–232, 233, 234, 236, 237, 241, 253, 257, 259, 260, 272, 284, 294, 298, 302, 304, 307
Flora Græcia (misspelling), 234
Flora Lapponica (Linnaeus 1737), 175
Flora Lapponica (Linnaeus, ed. Smith 1792), 175, 176, 177, 182, 272
Flora Londinensis (Curtis 1777–1798), 117, 133, 134, 164, 166, 169
Flora Rossica (Pallas 1784–1815), 272
Flora Scotica (Lightfoot 1777), 29, 49, 70
Florence, 96–97
Fontana, Gregorio, 174
Fordyce, Dr George, 70, 113, 116
Forsyth, William, 65, 115, 174
Francillon, John (John Abbot's literary agent), 214
Frankland, Sir Thomas, 239
Frederick, Prince William (Duke of Gloucester), 244, 278
Freetown, 177, 178
French Revolution, The, 21, 82, 86, 127, 157, 195, 196, 273
Frere, William, 278
Frogmore House, Windsor, 179, 180, 181, 182, 184, 193, 195, 200, 201, 230
Fuchsia (fuchsia), 209
Fuci (seaweeds), 204, 240
Fucus brodiæa, 266
Fundamenta Botanica (Linnaeus 1736), 84
Fungi. *See* Cryptogamia

Galium, 27, 48
— *odoratum* (woodruff), 48
— *saxatile* (heath bedstraw), 27
Garden, Alexander, 70
Gardener's Dictionary (Miller 1759), 6,
The Gardener's Kalendar (Miller 1757), 138
The Gardener's Magazine, 268

Genera Plantarum (Jussieu 1789), 75, 84, 156–157
Genera Plantarum (1732), 173
'Genera Plantarum' (Salisbury) (fragment published 1866), 268
A General View of the Writings of Linnaeus (Pulteney 1781), 120
The Generic Characters in the English Botany, collated with those of Linné (Salisbury 1806), 257
Geneva, 80, 106, 115, 138
Genoa, 85, 88, 91, 92, 94, 95–96, 105
Gentleman's Walk, Norwich, 19, 20, 22, 23
George III, King, 6, 56, 83, 119, 145, 179, 183, 199, 277
George, Prince (Regent) (later King George IV), 4, 272, 277, 280
Geranium (geranium), 255
— *columbinum* (longstalk cranesbill), 27
— *lucidum* (shining cranesbill), 192
— *sanguineum* (bloody geranium), 30
Gérard, Louis, 91–92
Gerrard Street, London, 259, 297
Gilbert, Davies (formerly Davies Giddy), 233
Ginkgo biloba (briefly *Salisburia adiantifolia*) (maidenhair tree), 251, 268
Girardin, René Louis de (Marquess of Vauvray), 87
Glasgow, University of, 32
Gloucester and Edinburgh, Duke of. *See* William Frederick, Prince
Gloucester, Duke of. *See* Henry, Prince William
Gnaphalium stœchas. See *Helichrysum stœchas*
Goethe, Johann Wolfgang von, 101–102
Goodenia (goodenia), 188
Goodenough, Revd Samuel (Bishop of Carlisle), 66, 68, 78, 208, 209, 107, 113–114, 115–116, 117, 118, 127, 129, 169, 179, 200, 207, 208, 209, 217, 218, 229, 239, 241, 252, 258, 259, 261, 269, 281, 282, 284, 286–287, 288, 292, 297, 303
Göttingen, 61, 68
— university, 190
Gouan, Antoine, 89
A Grammar of Botany (Smith 1821), 297–298
Grand Tour, The, 85–86, 88, 96
Gray, Dr Edward Whitaker, 113
Great Marlborough Street (12), 109, 118, 120, 124, 125, 132, 145, 163, 176, 177, 203, 204, 209, 216
Great St Bernard, 143
Great Windmill Street, 53, 54, 66
Greville, Charles Francis, 101

Gustav III, King of Sweden, 58, 64, 96, 310
Guy's Hospital, 203, 204, 212, 217, 221
Gymnostomum davallianum. See *Microbryum davallianum*

Haford, Cardiganshire, 208–209, 212, 216, 223, 224, 271, 282, 283
Haller, Albrecht von, 78, 226, 237
Hamilton, Lady. *See* Hart, Emma
Hamilton, Sir William, 85, 101
Hammersmith, 209–210, 212, 216, 218
Hammersmith (Vineyard) nursery (James Lee), 161, 186, 209
Hardwicke, (3rd) Earl of. *See* Yorke, Philip
Hardwicke, Captain Thomas, 249
Harriman, Revd John, 147
Hart, Emma (née Amy Lyon) (Lady Hamilton), 101, 102
Harwich, 75, 77
Hastingia, 144, 145
— *coccinea* (Chinese hat plant, cup-and-saucer-plant or mandarin's hat), 145
"— *sanguinea*", 144
Hastings, Warren (1st Governor-General of Bengal), 144–145
Hawkins, John, 205, 231, 232, 233, 235
Haworth, Adrian, 215
Hedera capitata, 161
Hedwig, Johann, 190
Heigham Hall Asylum (Norwich), 285
Helichrysum stœchas (formerly *Gnaphalium stœchas*), 89
Hellevoetsluis, 77
Helvella acaulis. See *Stereum hirsutum*
Henry, Prince William (Duke of Gloucester), 97
Henslow, John Stevens, 292
Herbarium, 6, 29, 41, 46, 47, 58, 61, 62, 83, 90, 134, 237, 310. *See also* Bank's; Davall; Lightfoot; Linnaean Herbarium; Sibthorp; Tournefort
—, James Edward Smith's, 6, 27, 29–30, 47, 106, 188, 191, 210, 226, 244, 310
L'Héritier de Brutelle, Charles Louis, 68, 83, 126, 134, 152, 155, 158, 173
Herschell, Dr William, 284
Hibbert, George, 267
Hillingdon House (near Uxbridge, Middlesex), 140, 145, 160
HMS *Investigator*, 259
Hoffmann, Georg Franz, 190
Holkham Hall, Norfolk, 19, 269, 303
Hooke, Robert, 125

Hooker, William Jackson, 243, 254, 265, 271, 284, 301, 307
'Hookera' (Salisbury), 265, 266, 267. See also *Brodiæa*
'– pulchella' (see also *Brodiæa*), 265
Hookeria, 266
Hope, Dr John, 6, 34, 35, 41, 43, 44, 46, 47, 57, 67, 73, 74, 92
Hope, Thomas Charles, 55, 66, 67, 73, 118
Horticultural Society of London, 267
Hortus Kewensis (Aiton 1789), 137, 141, 184, 255
Hortus Malabaricus (van Rheede 1678–1703), 140
Hosack, David, 292
Hotwells, Bristol, 27
Hudson, William, 6, 29, 31, 118, 167, 237, 259
Humbertia madagascariensis. See *Thouina spectabilis*
Hume, Lady Amelia, 146, 162, 169, 185, 249
Hume, Sir Abraham, 185
Humea elegans, 249. See also *Calomeria amaranthoides*
Hunter, John, 54, 66, 70
Hunter, William, 53, 54
Hyla arborea (tree frog), 89

I Modi (The Ways) (Aretino 1527), 253
Icones Pictæ Plantarum Rariorum (Smith, Sowerby 1790–1793) (or Coloured Figures of Rare Plants), 140, 144, 159, 162, 163, 164, 166, 170, 173, 179, 180, 249, 251, 279
Imperial Society of St Petersburg, 73
Index Floræ Lancastriensis (Muhlenberg 1797), 191
Institut National des Sciences et des Arts (Paris), 127
International Code of Nomenclature (ICN), 157
Introduction to Botany (Lee 1760), 6, 28
An Introduction to Physiological and Systematical Botany (Smith 1807), 260, 261, 262, 264, 265, 266, 285, 297, 298
"Introductory Discourse on the Rise and Progress of Natural History", *Transactions of the Linnean Society of London* (Smith 1791), 121, 146

Jacobinism, 195, 196
Jacquin, Joseph Franz von, 145, 285
Jacquin, Nikolaus von, 154
Jardin des Plantes (formerly the *Jardin du Roi*), 158
Jenkinson, Robert (Prime Minister, 2nd Earl of Liverpool), 277
Jervis, Sir John (later Earl of St Vincent), 62

Johnes, Jane, 208
Johnes, Mariamne, 208–209, 215, 219, 223–224
Johnes, Thomas, 208, 223, 224, 271, 282
Jones, William, 115, 118, 216
Journal of a Voyage to New South Wales (White 1790), 187
Julie, ou la nouvelle Héloïse (Rousseau 1761), 88
Jussieu, Antoine Laurent de, 75, 84, 152, 155–157, 159, 239, 251, 254, 267, 270, 296, 297, 301

Kendal, Westmorland, 44
Kennedy, Mr (nurseryman of Hammersmith), 186, 209
Kew, Botanic Gardens at, 6, 31, 55, 56, 122, 137, 144, 148, 161, 214
Kindersley, Nathaniel Edward, 19, 26, 141, 145, 204
King Edward VI Grammar School, Norwich, 25
Kirby Lonsdale, Westmorland, 40, 42, 44, 50
Kirby, William, 288
Knight, Joseph, 267
Knight, Richard Payne, 208
Koenig, John Gerard, 137

Labillardière, Jacques Julien Houton de, 188
Lachesis Lapponica, or a Tour in Lapland (Linnaeus, trans. by Smith 1811), 271
Lamarck, the Chevalier de (Jean-Baptiste de Monet), 83, 84, 152–155, 239, 251, 264
Lambert, Aylmer Bourke, 117, 118, 216, 243, 249, 254, 262, 265, 270, 281, 284, 287
Lambeth Marsh botanic garden, 117, 133
Lancashire, 29
Lancaster, Pennsylvania, 188, 189
Landshut, University of (Bavaria), 298
Latham, John, 68, 117, 127, 303
Lawrence, Sir Thomas (artist), 302
Leathes, George, 277
Lee, James (nurseryman of Hammersmith), 6, 28, 161, 186, 209
Legge, George. *See* Lewisham, Viscount
Leiden, 73, 77, 78, 79, 129, 212
—, University of, 73, 77, 78, 112
Leith Walk botanic garden, 43
Lerici, 96
Letters on the Elements of Botany, addressed to a Lady (Martyn 1785), 147–148. See also *Lettres Élémentaires sur la Botanique* (Rousseau 1782)

A Letter to the National Assembly (Burke 1791), 196
Lettres Élémentaires sur la Botanique (Rousseau 1782), 147
Lettres sur les Anglois et les François (de Muralt 1725), 84
Levasseur, Marie-Thérèse, 87
Lewisham, Viscount (George Legge, later 3rd Earl of Dartmouth), 165
Lichen, 57, 100, 143
– *cucullatus* (see *Flavocetraria cucullata*)
– *deustus* (Smith's *Lichen miniatus*), 57
– *miniatus* (see *Lichen deustus*)
– *paschalis*, 100
Lichenographiæ Svecicæ Prodromus (Acharius 1798), 240
Lichens. *See* Cryptogamia
Lichfield, 181
– Botanical Society, 181
Life of Linnaeus (Stoever 1794), 63
Life of Lorenzo de' Medici (Roscoe 1796), 245
Lightfoot, Revd John, 29, 49, 70, 118, 119, 134, 164, 167, 237
–'s herbarium, 179, 180, 181, 183
Ligusticum cornubiensis. See *Physospermum cornubiense*
Linaria reticulata (formerly *Antirrhinum reticulata*), 161
Lindley, John (1st Professor of Botany at The University of London), 301, 307
Linnaean cabinet of minerals, 60, 212, 213
Linnaean collections, 66–69, 72, 73, 124, 129, 131, 144, 151, 167, 184, 186, 191, 204, 209, 211, 212, 213, 216, 222, 298, 308, 310, 311
Linnaean Herbarium, 58, 63, 69, 70, 72, 74, 134, 139, 142, 156, 189, 191, 203, 298, 308
Linnaeus the Younger, Carl, 58, 61, 65, 68, 69, 134, 135, 136, 174, 187
Linnaeus, Carl, 3, 4–7, 27, 28–29, 39, 56, 58, 60, 61, 62, 63, 69, 70, 71–72, 73, 74, 75, 77, 79, 82, 83, 84, 89, 95, 102, 104, 112, 113, 120, 121, 122, 125, 126, 131, 134, 135, 140, 142, 145, 148, 153, 154, 156, 157, 158, 159, 167, 173, 175, 176, 181, 182, 185, 186, 189, 192, 211, 213, 215, 221, 230, 237, 238, 241, 256, 258, 261, 262, 272, 296, 297, 298, 301–302, 308, 310, 311
Linnean Society of London, 3, 7, 66, 69, 115, 118–127, 138, 144, 145, 146, 147, 166, 169, 174, 175, 181, 182, 184, 186, 191, 209–210, 216, 217, 218, 221, 222, 229, 241, 242, 251, 252, 254, 255, 258, 259, 265, 266, 267, 272, 278, 286, 291, 296, 298, 303, 307, 308, 310–311
– Anniversary Meeting, 221, 229, 230, 252, 287
– Associates, 117, 119, 121, 127, 129, 137
–'s constitution, 229
– Council, 230, 266, 278, 287, 288

Fellows of –, 115, 117, 118, 119, 121, 126, 127, 138, 165, 174, 181, 187, 213, 218, 221, 229, 230, 252, 265, 267, 276, 283, 303
– Fellows' Meetings, 118–119, 173, 174, 216, 218, 221
– Foreign Members, 119, 126, 127, 137, 141, 155, 230, 310
– General Meetings, 118, 119, 121, 128–129, 173, 216, 221, 229
– Honorary Members/Fellows, 118, 119, 125, 221, 296
– Library, 213, 264, 270
–'s Royal charter, 229–230, 278
– Secretary, 118, 198, 229, 235, 267, 287, 288
Transactions of –, 118, 121, 123, 127, 159, 173, 175, 213, 218, 229, 237, 266, 267, 280
– Treasurer, 118, 119, 218, 229, 286, 287
Liverpool, 241, 242, 244–246, 247, 249, 283, 295
– Botanic Garden (Mount Pleasant), 241
Liverpool Royal Institution, 292, 293
Liverpool, (2nd) Earl of. *See* Jenkinson, Robert
Liverworts. *See* Cryptogamia
Loch Lomond, 46–47
Lombe, Edward, 304
London, 3, 22, 31, 40, 44, 50, 53, 54, 55, 56, 58, 59, 60, 62, 63, 64, 66, 67, 68, 70, 85, 95, 98, 104, 109, 112, 115, 116, 117, 121, 122, 126, 128, 132, 134, 138, 144, 145, 146, 151, 169, 175, 177, 179, 181, 182, 186, 187, 192, 194, 196, 204, 206, 209, 210, 212, 214, 216, 217, 218, 220, 221, 223, 226, 229, 230, 235, 241, 242, 243, 244, 247, 249, 253, 254, 259, 270, 277, 281, 284, 287, 295, 302, 303, 307, 310
London Botanic Garden, 31
Longman, Rees & Co. (publisher), 260
Louis XVI, King (of France), 81, 197, 201
The Loves of the Plants (1791). See *The Botanic Garden* (E.Darwin)
Lowestoft, Suffolk, 144, 212, 243, 270, 280, 307
Luc, Jean André de, 106, 182, 200
Lycoperdon. See *Battarrea*
Lyncei Minus Cognitarum Stirpium et Purpura (Columna 1616), 226

Macie (later Smithson), James Lewis, 118
Macky, John, 109
Macleay, Alexander, 216, 229–230, 235, 266, 278, 287, 288, 298, 302
Madras, 145
– botanic garden, 148
Manchester, 90
Mansel, William (Master of Trinity College Cambridge and Bishop of Bristol),

276, 278, 282
Mansfield, (3rd) Earl of. *See* Stormont, Lord
Mantis religiosa (praying mantis), 89
Mantissa (botanical supplement), 294–295
Marie Antoinette, Queen (of France), 82, 199–200, 201
Markham, Richard. *See* Salisbury, Richard
Marseilles, 88, 90
Marsham, Thomas, 66, 113, 114, 115, 116, 117, 118, 127, 198, 210, 213, 217, 218, 229, 286–288
Martin, Thomas (husband to Frances Julia 'Fanny' Smith), 283
Martineau, Philip Meadows, 24
Martyn, Thomas, 6, 147–148, 173, 216, 222, 275, 276, 277, 279, 288–289, 292, 297
Matlock, 129, 181
Maton, William George, 258, 307
Maty, Paul Henry, 112
Mauritius, 135
Mead Place, Lambeth (James Sowerby's London home), 220
Medulla-cortex theory (Linnaeus), 79
Memoir and Correspondence of the Late Sir James Edward Smith (P. Smith 1832), 45, 235, 311, 312
Michelangelo, 99
Microbryum davallianum (formerly *Gymnostomum davallianum*), 226
Milan, 104, 206
Mill Hill (Middlesex), 242, 247, 252, 254
Miller, Philip, 5, 138
Miscellaneous Tracts relating to Natural History, Husbandry, and Physick (Stillingfleet 1759), 6
Monaco, 92, 94
Monandria (Linnaean class), 5
Monboddo, Lord. *See* Burnett, James
Monet, Jean-Baptiste de. *See* Lamarck, the Chevalier de
Monk, James Henry, 291–292
Monoecia (Linnaean class), 239
Monro, Alexander, 34, 36, 48
The Monthly Magazine, 263, 264, 270
The Monthly Review, 132, 136, 162, 174, 175, 239, 248
Montpellier, France, 85, 88, 89, 90
Morley, Lady. *See* Parker, Frances
Mosses. *See* Cryptogamia
Muhlenberg, Gotthilf Heinrich Ernst 'Henry', 188–191

Muralt, Béat-Louis de, 84
Murray, David William. *See* Stormont, Lord
Muscologia Hibernica (Turner 1804), 240
Museum National d'Histoire Naturelle in Paris, 239
Museum Regis Adolphi Friderici (Linnaeus 1754), 71. See also *Reflections on the Study of Nature*
Mutis, José Celestino, 69

Naples, 85, 86, 88, 99–100, 101, 184
Napoleon, 263, 273, 281
Napoleonic Wars, The, 21, 273
Naturæ discere mores (Linnean Society motto), 230
The Natural History of the Rarer Lepidopterous Insects of Georgia (Smith 1797), 213–214
Natural History Society (Edinburgh) (later the Royal Physical Society of Edinburgh), 41, 42, 46, 47, 48, 49, 67, 116, 251, 310
Natural History Society (Norwich), 25
Natural selection. *See* evolution
Natural system (of classification), 74, 75, 152, 154, 156, 157, 251, 254, 270, 297, 300
Neill, Patrick, 262
Nelumbo nucifera (formerly *Cyamus nelumbo*) (Indian lotus), 254
New Illustration of the Sexual System of Linnaeus (Thornton 1799–1807), 64, 221
New Zealand, 56
Nice, 88, 91, 92
Nîmes, 89, 90
Noailles, Louis de (4th Duke of Noailles), 82–83, 119
Nomenclator ex Historia Plantarum Indigenarum Helvetiæ (Haller 1769), 226
Non-Trinitarianism, 195
Norfolk and Norwich Museum, 299, 308
Norfolk and Norwich Triennial Music Festival, 299
North, Brownlow (Bishop of Winchester), 290
North, Lord Frederick, 33
Norwich, 3, 19, 20, 21, 22, 23, 24, 25, 27, 28, 29, 30, 31, 33, 40, 44, 50, 57, 62, 64, 68, 88, 89, 94, 109, 118, 128, 173, 181, 193, 195, 196, 204, 205, 206, 207, 210, 216, 217, 218, 220, 221, 226, 230, 235, 240, 241, 245, 247, 249, 254, 259, 269, 270, 271, 281, 282, 283, 284, 299, 309
– Castle, 3, 27
– Directory (1783), 22
Market Place, 19, 22
– textiles, 21, 105, 193

Norwich Natural History Society, 25
The Norwich Post, 22
Nymphæa alba (European white waterlily, white lotus, white water rose or white nenuphar), 255

'Observations on the British Species of Bromus, with Introductory Remarks on the Composition of a Flora Britannica' (Smith, 4th volume of Linnean *Transactions* in 1798), 237
Octagon Chapel, Colegate, 20, 22, 23, 24, 293
"On 2 new Species of Cypripedium" (Salisbury), 127
On the cultivation of the plants belonging to the natural order of Proteeæ (Knight, Hibbert 1809), 267
"On the Flora Scoticae Supplementum" (Smith 1784), 49
"On the Phenomena of Vegetable Odours" (Smith 1782), 48
'On the Proteaceae of Jussieu' (Brown 1809), 267
On the Tendency of Species to form Varieties; and on the Perpetuation of Varieties and Species by Natural Means of Selection (Darwin, Wallace 1858), 311
Oosterdijk, Professor Nicolas George, 78
Opie, John (Cornish artist), 210
Orbe, Canton de Berne, 139, 225
Orbea variegata (carrion-flower), 91
Orders (Linnaean), 4, 125, 156, 221, 237, 239, 254. *See also* Classes
Oreopanax capitatus (formerly *Aralia capitata*), 160
Oriani, Barnaba, 206
Outlines of the Natural History of Great Britain and Ireland (Berkenhout 1770), 3, 27
Oxford, 127, 128, 132, 204, 239, 243
Oxford, University of, 32, 33, 40, 61, 72, 109, 118, 131, 232, 234, 237
Padua, 104
— botanic gardens, 32
Pallas, Peter Simon, 72–73, 272
Pantheon theatre, 109, 176–177
Panton Square, London, 209
Paradise Row, Chelsea, 66, 69, 75, 104, 107, 109, 116
Paradisus Londinensis (Hooker and Salisbury 1805–1808), 254, 255, 260, 263, 264, 265
Paris, 53, 54, 62, 73, 79, 81, 82, 83, 85, 86, 87, 88, 90, 97, 107, 112, 126, 134, 136, 154, 155, 156, 157, 158, 193, 197, 239, 284
Parker, Frances (Lady Morley), 299
Parma, 104
Passiflora (passion flower), 161

— *biflora* (formerly *Passiflora lunata*) (two-flowered passion flower), 161
— *lunata* (see *Passiflora biflora*)
Pavia, 104, 105
— university, 104, 174
Pelargonium (geranium), 25
Pennant, Thomas, 47
Pennington, Sir Isaac, 276, 279, 289
Persoon, Christiaan Hendrik, 240
Pertenhall, Bedfordshire, 275
Peyrou, Place Royale du, 89
Philosophia Botanica (Linnaeus 1751), 27, 28, 215, 298. See also *Elements of Botany*
Philosophical Transactions. *See* Royal Society, The
Physospermum cornubiense (formerly *Ligusticum cornubiensis*), 162
Phytologia (E. Darwin 1800), 28
Pimelea (pimelea), 188
Pisa, 96
— botanical gardens, 32
Pistacia lentiscus (myrtle), 100
Pistil, 4, 148, 156, 162
Pitcairn, Dr David, 54–55, 60, 66, 70
Pitchford, John, 27, 29, 57, 62, 68, 70, 72, 118, 119, 128, 129, 166, 167
Pius VI, Pope, 99, 102
Plant morphology and physiology, 301
Plantago media (hoary plantain), 5
Plantarum Historia (Columna 1592), 226
Plantarum Icones Hactenus Ineditæ, Plerumque Ad Plantas In Herbario Linnaeano Conservatas Delineata (Smith 1789–1791), 134, 135, 144, 146, 152, 159, 164, 167, 173, 175, 310
— second fascicle (1790), 146, 152
— third fascicle (1791), 173
Platt, Thomas, 232, 233, 235, 236–237
Platylobium, 188
Polyandria (Linnaean class), 5
Polygamia (Linnaean class), 239
Polynomials, 5
Pompeii, 100
Ponsonby, Henrietta. *See* Bessborough, Countess of
Portland, Duchess of. *See* Bentinck, Margaret Cavendish
Portlandia, 140
— *grandiflora* (Bell flower), 160, 161

'Portrait of an eminent botanist' (Rising 1793), 185
Price, Benjamin (Secretary of the Westminster Library), 209
Priestley, Joseph, 70, 198
Prince, George, 65, 116
Preformation, 78–79
Prodromus Floræ Græcæ (Sibthorp, Smith 1806–1816), 232, 233, 235, 236, 259
Prodromus Stirpium in Horto ad Chapel Allerton Vigentium (Salisbury 1796), 251
Prosperin, Erik, 186
Pultenæa (bush peas), 188
Pulteney, Richard, 73, 120–121, 145, 151, 153, 183, 188, 214, 221

The Quarterly Review, 291–292, 293
Quercus (oak), 147
  – *cerris* (Turkey oak), 147
  – *suber* (cork oak), 147
  – *x hispanica* (Lucombe oak), 147

Raphael, 20, 98
Ray, John, 27, 125, 167, 237, 284
Reale Società Agraria (Royal Agricultural Society, Turin), 137
Reduvius personatus (formerly *Cimex personatus*) (the masked hunter insect), 114
Rees, Abraham, 261, 268
Reeve, Robert (Pleasance Smith's father), 143, 282, 286
Reflections on the Revolution in France (Burke 1790), 199
Reflections on the Study of Nature (Smith 1785, translation of Linnaeus's preface to *Museum Regis Adolphi Friderici* (1754), 71, 310
Regia Scientiarum Taurensis Academia (Royal Academy of Sciences of Turin), 137
Relhan, Richard, 134, 275, 277, 282
Reliquiæ Rudbeckianæ (Smith 1789), 132, 134, 310
Repton, Humphry, 30, 36
Rising, John, 185
Rockingham, Marchioness of (Mary Watson-Wentworth), 137, 140–141, 145, 146, 159, 160, 161, 162, 186, 194, 243
Rome, 85, 88, 97, 98, 99, 101, 102
Roscoe, William, 241, 244–248, 249, 251, 255, 278, 280, 282, 283, 290
Rose Castle, 282, 283
Rose, Hugh, 27, 28, 29
Rotterdam, 77
Roussea, 135
  – *simplex*, 135

Rousseau, Jean-Jacques, 86–88, 135, 147, 195, 196, 199, 200, 222
Roxburgh, William, 145
Royal Academy of Arts, 185, 277
Royal Infirmary, Edinburgh, 32
Royal Institution (Albermarle Street, London), 247, 259, 268, 292
Royal Medical Society, Edinburgh, 39, 47
Royal Society of Sciences (Uppsala), 185
Royal Society, The, 42, 55, 56, 65, 70, 72, 114, 115, 118, 124, 165, 185, 233, 276, 277, 284, 295
—'s *Philosophical Transactions*, 123,
Royal Swedish Academy of Sciences, 185, 186
Royen, David van, 78
Rudbeck, Olof (the elder), 131
Russelia, 135
Russell, Francis (Marquess of Tavistock), 282
Russell, John (6th Duke of Bedford), 278, 282

Saint-Fond, Barthélemy Faujas de, 239
Saint-Germain-en-Laye, 82
Salisburia adiantifolia. See *Ginkgo biloba*
Salisbury (formerly Markham), Richard, 40, 41, 117, 127, 128, 137, 144, 181, 242, 247, 251–259, 260, 262–268, 270, 292, 312
Salisbury, Bishop of. *See* Barrington, Right Reverend Shute
Salix (willow), 240, 248
San Germano, 102
Sandifort, Eduard, 78
Sanremo, 94, 95
Saussure, Horace-Bénédict de, 106
School of Botany (Paris), 158
Schultes, Josef August, 298
Scopoli, Giovanni Antonio, 104, 105, 152, 155, 237
Senebier, Jean, 138
Serra, Abbé José Correia da, 83, 97, 189
Sexual system, 4, 27, 34, 64, 75, 82, 89, 102, 114, 125, 138, 154, 156, 181, 182, 221, 254, 261, 263, 296, 297, 300, 301
Shaw, George, 166, 173, 187, 216, 230
Sheffield, 44, 195, 197
Shugborough, 283
Sibthorp, John, 61, 68, 118, 127–128, 132, 204–206, 211, 231–234, 235, 236, 237, 241, 307

–'s herbarium, 233
Siddons, Sarah, 109, 177, 247
Sidmouth, 1st Viscount. *See* Addington, Henry
Sierra Leone, 177, 178, 204
Sierra Leone Company, 177, 178
Sistine Chapel, 99
A Sketch of a Tour on the Continent, In the Years 1786 and 1787 (Smith 1793), 81, 82, 84, 101, 105, 195, 197–198, 199, 200, 203, 208, 230
Slave trade, 178, 198, 246
Smith (née Reeve), Pleasance, 7, 45, 143–144, 146, 210, 212, 216, 218, 219–220, 223, 235, 242, 243, 244, 245, 247, 261, 270, 280–281, 282, 285, 293, 295, 299, 302–303, 304, 308, 311, 312
Smith, Esther Anne (Smith's sister), 21, 104, 107, 109, 143, 207, 210
Smith, Frances (Smith's mother), 19, 20, 26, 44, 49, 104, 207, 295
Smith, Frances (Smith's sister), 21, 207
Smith, Frances Julia (Smith's sister, 'Fanny'), 21, 207, 247, 283
Smith, Francis (Smith's brother), 20, 44, 107, 109, 178, 193, 207, 283
Smith, James (Smith's father), 19–22, 23, 24, 26, 30, 32–33, 35, 37, 38–40, 44, 46, 55, 59, 60, 61, 62, 67, 68, 70, 73, 85, 86, 88, 90, 112, 129, 151, 178, 193, 194, 205, 207
Smith, John 'Warwick', 271
Smith, John Frederick (Smith's brother), 20, 32, 178, 207, 285, 287
Smith, Richard (Smith's brother), 21, 193–194
Smith, Sarah Maria (Smith's sister), 21, 207, 285
Smith, William (MP for Norwich), 281
Smithia, 138, 255, 263
– *conferta*, 138
– *sensitiva*, 137–138, 142, 185, 255, 262–263
Smithson (formerly Macie), James Lewis. *See* Macie, James Lewis
Social Contract (Rousseau 1762), 86
Société d'Histoire Naturelle de Paris, 127, 159. See also *Société Linnéenne de Paris*
– *Actes*, 159
Société des Botanophiles (Angers), 137
Société Linnéenne de Paris (later *Société d'Histoire Naturelle de Paris*; see also *Institut National des Sciences et des Arts*), 126, 127, 158, 159
Society for Effecting the Abolition of the Slave Trade, 246
Society for the Promotion of Natural History (SPNH), 65–66, 68, 78, 113, 115, 116, 117, 119, 123, 124, 174–175
Society of Arts, 65
Society of Dilettanti, 270

Soho Square, 56, 59, 69, 109, 124, 125, 144, 222, 234, 262, 264, 270, 295, 296, 297, 310
Solander, Daniel, 56, 57, 58, 137, 296
Solanum pseudocapsicum (Jerusalem cherry, [Madeira] winter cherry), 91
'Some Observations on the Irritability of Vegetables' (Smith 1788), 123, 124, 137
Some Thoughts Concerning Education (Locke 1693), 24
Somerset House, 277
Sowerby, George (son of James Sowerby), 269
Sowerby, James, 134–135, 137, 140, 144, 159–160, 161, 164–165, 167, 168–169, 170, 175, 180, 181, 187, 192, 193, 220, 230, 234–235, 236, 237, 246, 248, 249, 255, 258, 260, 272–273, 281, 286, 296, 299–300, 310
Spallanzani, Lazzaro, 74, 79, 104–105
Species Plantarum (Linnaeus 1753), 5, 62, 157, 167, 211
Species Plantarum (Linnaeus, 2nd Edition 1762–1763), 151, 176
A Specimen of the Botany of New Holland (Wilson, Smith 1794–1795), 188
Spencer, Countess (Margaret Spencer), 184
Spicilegium Botanicum. Gleanings of Botany (Smith, Sowerby 1791–1792), 169, 173, 249
St Bartholomew's Hospital, London, 54
St Margaret's Church, Lowestoft, 307
St Peter Mancroft parish (Norwich), 27, 207
St Vincent, Earl of. *See* Jervis, Sir John
St Vincent's Rocks, Bristol, 27, 30
Stamen, 4, 5, 123, 148, 156, 162
— anthers, 5, 123, 261
— filament, 5, 123
Stanley, Edward Smith (13th Earl of Derby), 283, 307
Stereum hirsutum (a bracket fungus), 31
Stillingfleet, Benjamin, 6, 28
Stirpes Novæ Aut Minus Cognitæ (L'Héritier 1785–1791), 155
Stoever, Dietrich, 63, 186
Stokes, Jonathan, 64, 66, 68
Stone, Robert, 69
Stormont, Lord (David William Murray, later third Earl of Mansfield), 181, 185
Stuart, Charles Edward (Bonnie Prince Charlie), 98–99
Stuart, John, 3rd Earl of Bute, 6, 119
Styphelia, 188
Sumner, Humphrey, 276, 278
Surrey Street, Norwich, 218, 282, 304
Swainson, Isaac, 65, 117, 118

Swartz, Olof, 173, 186, 285
Switzerland, 80, 85, 86, 105, 106, 138, 142, 184, 199, 211, 226
Syllabus of a Course of Lectures on Botany (Smith 1795), 203
A Synopsis of British Fuci (Turner 1802), 240
Synopsis Fungorum (Persoon 1801), 240
Systema Naturæ (Linnaeus 1735), 4, 29
Systema Naturæ (Linnaeus, 12th edition 1767–1768), 212
Systema Vegetabilium (Linnaeus, 14th Edition, 1784), 69

Tavistock, Marquess of. *See* Russell, Francis
Taxonomy, 5, 84, 134, 234, 265, 298, 301
Taylor, Dr John, 24
Taylor, William, 24
'Tentamen Botanicum de Filicum Generibus Dorsiferarum' *Mémoires de l'Académie Royale des Sciences de Turin* (Smith 1793), 137, 185
Test and Corporation Acts, 23
Tetandria (Linnaean class), 220
Tetratheca, 249
Thackeray, George (Cambridge University Vice-Chancellor 1814–1815), 281, 282
Thomson, William, 40, 41, 42, 66, 117
Thornton, Robert John, 64, 221–222, 264
Thouin, André, 83, 136, 239
Thouinia, 135, 136, 152
— *spectabilis* (formerly *Humbertia madagascariensis*), 136, 152, 153
Thunberg, Carl Peter, 56, 61, 174, 185–186
Tingry, Pierre-François, 115, 141
Toulon, 91
A Tour to Hafod (Smith 1810), 271
Tournefort, Joseph Pitton de, 27, 83–84, 154
—'s herbarium, 83, 84, 107, 134
Tracts Relating to Natural History (Smith 1798), 6, 29, 206
Trapp, Joseph, 63, 186
Treaty of Amiens (1802), 226
Trifolium, 174
— (Afzelius), 174
Troilius, Charles, 272
Turin, 85, 105, 106, 137
Turner, Dawson, 216, 222, 240, 241, 243, 256, 257, 259, 264, 265, 268, 269, 270, 272, 284, 285, 298, 299, 308
Turner, Joseph, 278, 282

Turrea, 152
Turton, William, 298

Uffizi gallery, Florence, 97
Ulex europæus (common gorse), 6
Unitarianism, 23, 24, 178, 198, 245, 278, 294
University of London, 301
Uppsala, 6, 60, 63, 131, 132, 185
—, University of, 3, 58, 61, 63, 73, 174, 177
— Cathedral, 131

Vaillant, Sébastien, 83, 84
Valmy, 197
Vatican, 98, 99
Vaughan, Walter, 77, 78, 129
Vauvray, Marquess of. *See* Girardin, René Louis de
Venice, 103, 104
Verona, 104
Veronica spicata (spiked speedwell), 167
Versailles, 81, 82
Vesuvius, Mount, 88, 100
Vienna, 285
—, University of, 154
A Vindication of the University of Cambridge, (Monk 1818), 291
Viola tricolor (heartsease, or love-in-idleness), 182
La Virginia (opera by Angelo Tarchi, 1785), 95
Voght, Caspar, 203
Voltaire, 195
Voyage to Jamaica (Sloane 1725), 61

Wachendorfia paniculata (red root), 161
Walker, Revd Dr John, 39, 41, 42, 43, 48
Wallich, Nathaniel, 301
Wansford, 32, 33
War of 1812, 190
Watson-Wentworth, Mary. *See* Rockingham, Marchioness of
Webb, William (Cambridge University Vice-Chancellor 1817–1818), 289
Wedgwood, Josiah, 66
Wenman, Francis, 232
Wesley, John, 24

Westminster Library, 209
Whewell, William, 292
White & Son, Benjamin (publisher), 135, 175, 239
White, John (publisher), 239
White, John (surgeon), 186, 249
Whitehurst, John, 70
Wilberforce, William, 178, 185
Wilcke, Johan Carl, 186
William Frederick, Prince (Duke of Gloucester and Edinburgh, and Chancellor of Cambridge), 244, 278
Wilson, Thomas, 187
Winchester, Bishop of. *See* North, Brownlow
Windsor Castle, 179
Withering, William, 64, 73, 148, 162, 167, 237
Woburn Abbey, 299
Women in Botany, 147–148, 181, 261
Wood, James (Cambridge University Vice-Chancellor 1816–1817), 279, 289
Wood, Revd William, 261, 268
Woodward, Thomas Jenkinson, 28, 44, 62, 69, 73, 83–84, 119, 129, 151, 162, 167, 168, 170, 174, 176, 178, 180, 183, 185, 192, 194, 200, 204, 213, 216, 232
Woodwardia radicans, 185
Worlidge, Thomas, 20
Wright, Richard, 134
The Wrongs of Africa (Roscoe 1787–1788), 246
Wyttenbach, Jacob, 138, 141

Yorke, Philip (3rd Earl of Hardwicke), 278
Yorkshire, 29, 44, 45, 90, 128, 174, 193
Younge, William, 67, 88, 90, 91, 92, 94, 95, 96, 97, 98, 99, 100, 101, 102, 103, 105, 106, 107, 117, 195, 197

Zoology and Botany of New Holland (Wilson, Shaw 1793; later *Zoology of New Holland* and *A Specimen of the Botany of New Holland*), 187
Zoology of New Holland (Wilson, Shaw 1793; constituting half of the second issue of *Zoology and Botany of New Holland* (1793)), 188
Zouch, Revd Thomas, 174